Introduction to Computer Engineering

B. S. WALKER, B.Sc. (Eng.), M.Phil., C.Eng., M.I.E.E.

Lecturer in Computer Technology, University of Reading, formerly
Lecturer in the Electrical and Control Engineering Department,
University of Surrey

HART PUBLISHING COMPANY, INC.
NEW YORK CITY

Contents

3. Analogue computers: problem solving

4. Arithmetic

5. Logic

10. Memory stores

Foreword

Automatic control has been used for many years but the rate of expansion in the use of automatic control methods is probably greater now than it has ever been. Digital methods in the recording and processing of data and in decision elements are widely used; the introduction of cheap, reliable, microcircuits is causing a rapid expansion of the use of such methods. Analogue methods are widely used in the design of automatic control systems and analogues may be incorporated in the controller, or data processor used with such systems. The increasing field of use of both analogue and digital methods calls for engineers trained in such methods: the publication of an authoritative text on computer engineering is therefore timely.

The author is well fitted to provide such a text. He has worked as a computer engineer and has taught computer engineering at both undergraduate and postgraduate levels. As even a casual reader will infer, the author is an enthusiast for his subject. His enthusiasm led to the introduction of one of the first courses in computer engineering to be offered in this country and to the design of an instructional digital computer, now being produced commercially.

Although I do not always agree with Mr Walker's views or predictions of future trends, I am pleased to have the opportunity to recommend this book.

W. F. LOVERING, M.Sc., C.Eng., F.I.E.E.
Professor of Electrical and Control Engineering,
University of Surrey.

Preface

This book is written for anyone who wishes to find out how computers work, and how they are conceived and made. Primarily it is for undergraduate engineers and technologists, but much of it should be comprehensible to anyone who is scientifically inclined. Computers play an increasing part in all aspects of our lives today; it is my belief that very many people, including those who are not directly concerned with computers would like to know – and need to know – what they are and how they work.

There is already a wealth of literature about computers; the amount of it increases so rapidly that it is virtually impossible to read all of it. The technology advances and changes continually. It might well seem an impossible task to get a grasp of the subject in a short time, or as part of an already crowded curriculum; in fact, although the technology does advance and change quickly, the fundamental principles and basic philosophy change slowly; Babbage, a century ago, postulated most of what exists today. If the principles and philosophy are mastered, the logic behind the technical advance is easier to follow, and the subject becomes a rewarding and interesting study.

Many universities and technical colleges now include computer technology in their courses and some enterprising schools are introducing it into their science and mathematics. We started a course in computer engineering as part of our Dip. Tech. course at Battersea C.A.T. in 1963, and had the problem of deciding what should be taught. This book is based on the syllabus we evolved and I believe it to be what is required. Good design, in engineering, often gets less credit than it deserves, since it seems to produce the obvious solutions to problems. What is usually overlooked is the work that goes into the analysis of the problem itself before the solution is attempted. Our approach, at Battersea, and mine in this book, is first of all to see what must be done by computers, and why, and then to evolve a logical solution as to how. Current practices are then used as examples of how problems have been solved, without prejudice as to how they may be solved in future. It is my hope that some of the readers of this book will solve these same problems by new and more ingenious means and find ways to analyse and define the future problems.

This book is not a reference book; engineers and authors of much greater skill and knowledge than I possess have already provided excellent and comprehensive books for reference and for advanced and detailed study. A number are quoted as recommended reading at the end of my chapters. My object has been to try and interest the reader, and to help to develop in the reader's mind a feeling for the philosophy of automatic computation. I have tried to outline the subject as a credible whole, without more detail than is necessary. Those whose life is to be devoted to the design, development or construction of automatic computing devices will get all the detail they need in the course of their daily experience; others whose work is more remote from it should not need the detail anyway.

This preface would not be complete without an expression of gratitude to all those who have helped me in the production of my book. My thanks, and admiration, must first go to Professor W. F. Lovering, who was Head of the Department of Electrical and Control Engineering at Battersea when this book was first conceived. I was already a devotee of computer engineering as a result of my time at the Royal Military College of Science, and my work in industry prior to joining his staff; Professor Lovering listened patiently to what I had to tell him. It was he who made me search out and try to formalise the philosophy behind computer engineering, and his energy and determination that made our course one of the first to be started; finally it was on his suggestion that I stopped being critical of the shortcomings of other people's books and wrote my own. Thanks, too, must go to my wife, who put up with me while I was writing, and to June Bonny who was able to convert my hieroglyphics into a beautifully typed manuscript.

Finally, I must record my thanks to Dr D. B. G. Edwards of Manchester University and Mr A. C. Savage of Elliott Brothers, who read my book in manuscript and helped me greatly with constructive criticism and suggestion.

Reading, 1967 — B. S. WALKER

Introduction

One of the problems of learning, or teaching, about computers, is to explain away the mystique which has grown up around them; they are complicated things; some are very large, and all are costly. They can perform great feats of calculation which means sums, and great feats of data processing which means routine office work. In their design and construction many fascinating and worthwhile problems are encountered; but to gain a general understanding of them is quite easy and the effort is rewarding.

In the 19th century Charles Babbage, who by any standards must be judged as the father of modern digital computers, made a 'computing engine'. Ada, Countess Lovelace, the daughter of the poet Byron, wrote about Babbage's 'engine' and her writing is a model of technical description. Two statements she made are of particular significance, being as true today as when they were written. The first is that the 'engine' or computer can do only what we know how to order it to do; the second is that the work of preparation of problems for entry into the computer throws new light onto the problems themselves.

Countess Lovelace did not envisage, in her writings, that computer engineering in itself would one day become an educational discipline, or she might have made the point, also, that this aspect of computing engines is valuable. The student will find that this is so, both from the standpoint of gaining a better understanding of a highly automated world, and as a mental exercise.

Calculation and computation

A convenient starting point for the study of computer engineering and automatic computing systems, is to make a distinction between the terms *calculator* and *computer*. The word 'calculator' is derived from the Latin word for the little stones or beads used in an abacus. Many of us learned to count and do simple arithmetic with a bead-frame, which is a simple abacus. The Japanese have made a refined study of the technique of calculation by abacus and use it very expertly. Most of us are familiar with adding machines, desk calculators, and slide rules, which are all calculators.

In many dictionaries little difference in definition is made between *calculate* and *compute*. For our purposes the word computer must imply more than calculator. We use calculators and calculation in computation, but the latter also implies an element of judgement or decision. An illustration of this is the solution of an equation by the method of successive approximation. The first step is to insert trial values of the unknowns and *calculate* a result, which, in general, will differ from the required result. Examination of the difference leads to an improved selection of trial values, which can then be inserted and the result is recalculated. The process is repeated as many times as is necessary to reach the desired result or a value near enough to it. This whole process might well be termed a *computation*; it is in this sense that a computer differs from a calculator, since a computer could be made to do the whole problem, making the necessary value corrections at each stage. A calculator would require human intervention at each stage to make the decisions and enter the new values.

Feedback

Consideration of this decision faculty of the computer leads to the introduction of the concept of *feedback*, basic to all automation. Feedback is a concept of such fundamental importance that it is surprising that the appreciation and study of it is so recent. The meaning of the term feedback is this: in a process to achieve a desired result, the actual result is compared with the desired one; if the discrepancy between actual and desired results is used to modify the process, then the process is a feedback controlled one. Sometimes this kind of process is called *closed-loop*.

A little thought should convince us that this is no new idea; it occurs continually in nature, it is fundamental to all trial and error methods and is the basic concept of cybernetics. Without our own built-in feedback systems we could not ride a bicycle, nor even put food into our mouth. The child daubing its face with egg while trying to find its mouth is learning to close a control loop. Some unfortunate people lose their nervous system closed-loop control, due to a disease and become 'unco-ordinated'. This kind of disease comes under the heading of 'ataxia'.

Returning to the example of the equation solution by successive approximation, we see that this is an example of a feedback system. The calculated result is compared with the desired one; the discrepancy is fed back to the decision-making element, man or machine, and the input is modified in the light of the information fed back. If we did such a problem on paper, numerically, the process would be carried out in discrete steps. In driving a car along a road we solve equations of this kind continuously; the feedback is continuous, and it is to be hoped that the correction is continuous also. We shall see that throughout this text, the terms computer and computation imply the inclusion of feedback systems, controlling calculations.

Analogue and digital computers

The technology of automatic computers has become divided under two main headings: *analogue* and *digital*. It was mentioned above that a problem might be solved continuously or in discrete steps; this means that the inserted values and corrections might be continuously changing, or might change periodically by finite increments. Analogue computers operate on continuous data and generate a continuous output or resultant. Digital computers do calculations in the same way that we solve numerical problems; they require feeding with data at discrete intervals and do calculations on it, step by step. Their output is numerical, consisting of a number or a succession of numbers.

Though the technology has grown up into these two divisions, it is important not to allow ourselves to consider the philosophy of automatic computation as being divided likewise. A numerical problem may be scaled and entered into an analogue computer, and an answer derived that can be interpreted as a number. A digital computer can be fed from continuously varying data by sampling it; the computer operates on the data samples, and its discrete output values can be interpreted as continuous, as in graph plotting.

Digital and analogue computers can be worked together in what are called *hybrid* systems; they are, in fact, complementary, and both have their place in the scheme of things. In the design or selection of a computing system, the choice of technique should be the one to do the job most satisfactorily, and not personal preference or current fashion.

In the following chapters we shall study analogue computers first, because it seems more convenient to do so. Less space is given to them than to digital computing systems simply because so much more of analogue technique falls into the realm of conventional electronics, with which this book is not primarily concerned.

Suggestions for further reading

Faster than Thought by B.V.Bowden. Pitman, 1953. This book tells
more of Babbage and his engines, and Countess Lovelace.
Chapter 1 and the appendixes are particularly interesting.
Automatic Digital Calculators by A.D. and K.H.V.Booth.
Butterworths, 1956. Chapters 2 and 3 give a resumé of the
development of computing devices, and there is a useful
bibliography.
Giant Brains by E.C.Berkeley. Wiley, 1949. This contains a very
comprehensive bibliography of reference to early computers.

1 Analogue computing: the problem

1.1 Concept of an analogue

An analogue is 'something which is like something else,' which is not a very informative definition in this context; an example will be found more helpful. Suppose we have a tank of fluid and we wish to know at any time how much fluid is in the tank; an easy way is to dip a rod into the fluid and measure the wetted length. The wetted length of the rod will correspond to the quantity of fluid in the tank and we have, then, this length as an analogue of the quantity of fluid. We should note that the analogy is restricted to the quantity of fluid; it is not analogous to the type of fluid, its temperature, or any other quality of it, and only in that tank. We can calibrate the rod and tank in suitable units, say, inches and gallons, and produce a calibration curve relating them. If the tank has a constant cross section, so that its contents vary linearly with its depth, we can evolve a 'scale factor' relating N gallons to n inches in the form of a constant which, multiplied by the wetted length, gives the contents in gallons.

It might be found more convenient to measure the tank depth another way; a float could be arranged to rest on the surface of the fluid, and as it moved, operate the armature, or 'wiper', of a potentiometer. The resistance between one end of the potentiometer and the armature would then be the analogue of the quantity of fluid in the tank. By applying a voltage between the potentiometer terminals, the voltage picked off by the armature would also be an analogue and, by choice of suitable components, could be made to have direct proportionality with the tank contents – or any other simple relationship.

Electrical components are easy to interconnect and currents and voltages are relatively easy to measure, and for this reason electrical analogues have become widely used. Consider again the tank and fluid; if we fill it from a tap, allowing a steady rate of flow, then its contents will increase linearly with time. We can simulate this with a capacitor charged from a source of constant current. The voltage appearing across the capacitor will also rise linearly with time. If we choose suitable scale factors we can make the capacitor voltage the equivalent of the filled depth, and the electric current flow the equivalent of the fluid flow. By operating an electric switch and fluid tap simultaneously, the capacitor voltage will remain the analogue of the tank contents. We have, in this way, evolved a 'real time' analogue, although rather a trivial one. We should note the following points from it:

(a) the analogue could represent a real system, or an imaginary one;
(b) all the quantities can be related by scale factors, including time;
(c) the analogue could represent any real or imaginary system, having the same mathematical relationships between its system parameters;
(d) in real time operation the analogue equivalents could be controlled by the real ones.

1.2 Analogues of simple systems

Two simple real systems are shown in Fig. 1.1

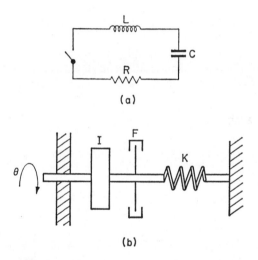

Fig. 1.1

Figure 1.1(a) shows a simple series connection of resistance, capacitance and inductance (R, C and L). Fig. 1.1(b) shows a mechanical arrangement of a flywheel having a polar moment of inertia I, with a friction device on the same shaft, having a viscous friction coefficient of F units per radian per second, and a torsion spring, having a torsional coefficient of K units per radian.

If the capacitor in Fig. 1.1(a) is charged, and then the switch is closed, the current in the circuit will be determined from the differential equation:

$$L\frac{di}{dt} + Ri + \frac{1}{C}\int idt = 0 \qquad \text{(i)}$$

In a similar way the flywheel of the mechanical arrangement of Fig. 1.1(*b*) may be rotated and released. The deflection θ of the shaft, at any instant, will be determined by the differential equation:

$$I\frac{d^2\theta}{dt^2} + F\frac{d\theta}{dt} + K\theta = 0 \qquad \text{(ii)}$$

Differentiating equation (i) to remove the integral term we get

$$L\frac{d^2i}{dt^2} + R\frac{di}{dt} + \frac{1}{C}i = 0 \qquad \text{(iii)}$$

and we can see that it is exactly analogous in form to equation (ii). By suitable scaling, each system could be used as the analogue of the other, and the observed behaviour of one could be interpreted and scaled to predict the behaviour of the other.

The solution of the differential equation will define the behaviour of any system governed by the same mathematical relationship. Consider now Fig. 1.2.

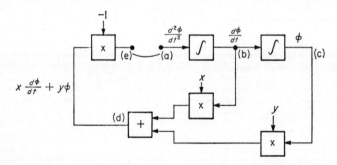

Fig. 1.2

The boxes shown in the figure have the following qualities:

The boxes marked with the integral sign integrate the quantity at their input with respect to time.

The boxes marked with multiplication signs multiply their input quantity by the number inserted at the arrow.

The box marked with a plus sign adds its inputs together to form its output.

We commence by postulating a quantity at (a) which is equal to $d^2\phi/dt^2$, whatever ϕ may be. Then at (b) there must be output from the first integrator $d\phi/dt$, being the definite integral, from 0 to t, of its input at (a). Likewise at (c) there must be the quantity ϕ, being the integral of $d\phi/dt$. The output at (b) is applied to the multiplier where it is multiplied by x; the output at (c) is likewise multiplied by y, and the multiplied values, added by the adder, emerge at (d).

We have, then, at (d):

$$x\frac{d\phi}{dt} + y\phi$$

This we multiply by -1, and we have at (e):

$$-x\frac{d\phi}{dt} - y\phi$$

When we close the link (ea); the value at (e) must become equal to the value at (a).

Hence:

$$\frac{d^2\phi}{dt^2} = -x\frac{d\phi}{dt} - y\phi$$

which must be the working condition for the arrangement of components we have connected. If we substitute the values R/L for x and $1/CL$ for y, then the arrangement is the analogue of the electrical network of Fig. 1.1(*a*), and the quantity ϕ corresponds to the current. Likewise the substitution $x = F/I$ and $y = K/I$ makes ϕ the equivalent, or analogue, of the deflection of the mechanical system flywheel, θ. In a similar way, using more integrators and multipliers it would be possible to set up and produce analogues for more complicated differential equations. If the parameters are correctly scaled, the solution of the equation will be determined by measuring ϕ as a function of time.

In the example we have studied, ϕ may be in the form of a damped oscillation; the measuring device will need therefore to be capable of making such a measurement of a changing quantity.

The reader may be left wondering why we have chosen to solve the problem with integrators and not differentiators. The first reason is a philosophical one: the solution of differential equations is by integration generally.

The second reason is a practical one and most important. It is very difficult to exclude noise from a circuit, caused by neighbouring electrical

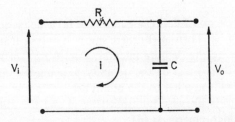

Fig. 1.3

apparatus, 'dry' joints and terminal connections, resistor noise and the like. The derivative of a noise pulse depends on its rise and fall time, rather than its amplitude. Any low-level noise in our circuit, if the differentiators were efficient, would have a severe effect. We shall be able to gauge the effect better when we study the computing elements, in more detail, in the next chapter.

An analogue device, then, of the type shown in Fig. 1.2 will serve as an analogue computer for solving differential equations – if it can be made. It remains for us to see how the 'boxes' may be filled and conveniently interconnected.

1.3 Integrating devices

An integrator is any device whose output is the time integral of its input. In the earlier part of this chapter we have already considered such a device; the current into a capacitor is proportional to a voltage. The voltage developed across a capacitor is proportional to the charge stored in it, that is, the time integral of the current into it. Since the current is, in turn, proportional to the voltage causing it, the output voltage across the capacitor must be the time integral of this voltage. This seems simple enough; let us examine it more closely. Fig. 1.3 shows the circuit.

Now, V_o = voltage across the capacitor

$$\text{and} \quad i = \frac{V_i - V_o}{R}$$

Then

$$\frac{V_i - V_o}{R} = CDV_o, \quad \text{where} \quad D = \frac{d}{dt}$$

RC has the dimensions of time; we put $RC = T$.

Then $$V_i = V_o(1 + TD), \quad \text{or} \quad V_o = \frac{V_i}{1 + TD}$$

Solving this equation and substituting initial conditions, we get:

$$V_o = V_i\left(1 - e^{-\frac{t}{T}}\right)$$

It is immediately apparent that V_o is not, in general, the time integral of the input voltage V_i. The time integral of a step function is a *ramp* function; however, the initial rise of V_o, while $t \ll CR$ can be approximated to a straight line as in Fig. 1.4.

During such a period, while $t \ll CR$, the circuit is an approximate integrator. By making R and C very large it might be possible to fill our 'boxes' with this simple network. But, $CR = T$ seconds and 1 megohm $\times$ 1 microfarad $= 1$ second, which seriously limits the scope of a computer using these integrators, with reasonable working values of C and R.

If we are familiar with the phenomenon known as Miller capacitance, or with the Miller integrator, we should readily make the next advance. It is apparent that, if we amplify the output voltage very greatly, we need only use the portion of the time scale where $t \ll CR$. Fig. 1.5 shows a CR circuit with a high gain amplifier.

The amplifier is represented by the triangular 'box' and it reverses the polarity of any signal applied to its input. We will define the amplifier voltage gain:

$$\text{gain} = \frac{V_o}{V_i} = -A, \quad \text{where } A \text{ is a large number.}$$

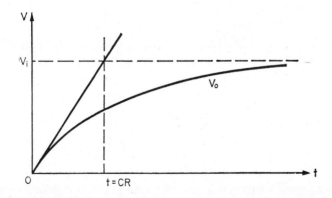

Fig. 1.4

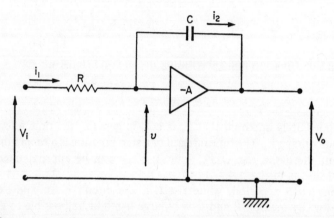

Fig. 1.5

We assume that the amplifier has an infinitely high input impedance, that is, it draws no input current. In this case i_1, the current through the resistance, R, is equal to i_2, the current through the capacitor, C. We have then:

$$V_i - v = CD(v - V_o) \quad \text{and} \quad -\frac{V_o}{A} = v$$

Then

$$V_i + \frac{V_o}{A} = -CRD\left(\frac{V_o}{A} + V_o\right)$$

Put $RC = T$; we now get:

$$-AV_i = V_o + TDV_o + TDAV_o$$

$$= V_o\,[1 + TD(A + 1)]$$

Whence

$$V_o = \frac{-A}{T(A + 1).}\frac{V_i}{\left\{D + \dfrac{1}{T(A + 1)}\right\}}$$

Now, if A is very large

$$V_o = -\frac{1}{T}\left(\frac{1}{D}\right)V_i \simeq -\frac{1}{T}\int_0^t V_i\,dt$$

A more precise solution will be worked out in the next chapter in which we shall be interested in the degree of error of this approximation. For the time being we will assume $A \to \infty$ and we have a perfect integrator. A typical three-stage valve amplifier circuit can have a gain, at very low frequencies, of more than 10^7; the term $1/A$, which we neglected in our approximation, is very small. The assumption we made earlier as to the non-existence of input current is also quite reasonable for amplifiers of this kind. It appears, then, that we have an adequate integrating device for our integrating boxes.

1.4 Multipliers and summing devices

In the examples we considered, multiplication by a preset constant was required; but the solution of some equations calls for multiplication by a variable relating to the problem. We need, then, two kinds of multiplier.

1.5 The virtual earth principle

If we consider once more the high gain amplifier used for integration, we can make a simplifying assumption. If the gain, $-A$, is very large, then so long as the output voltage of the amplifier is a reasonable finite value, its input terminal at v must be at a negligibly small voltage, relative to ground, i.e. it is relatively at earth potential compared with the magnitudes of V_o and V_i; we can say $v \simeq 0$. Consider then Fig. 1.6.

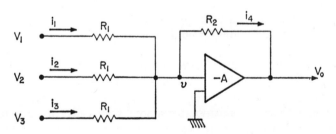

Fig. 1.6

Making the assumption of no input current, we have:

$$i_1 = \frac{V_1}{R_1}; \quad i_2 = \frac{V_2}{R_1}; \quad i_3 = \frac{V_3}{R_1} \quad \text{and} \quad i_4 = i_1 + i_2 + i_3$$

$$V_o = -i_4 R_2 = -R_2\left(\frac{V_1}{R_1} + \frac{V_2}{R_1} + \frac{V_3}{R_1}\right)$$

that is:

$$V_o = -\frac{R_2}{R_1}(V_1 + V_2 + V_3)$$

which is the sum of the voltages at the input, if $R_2 = R_1$, with a sign reversal. Consider now the case where there is only one input, say V_1. Then:

$$V_o = -\frac{R_2}{R_1}V_i$$

It is clear that by arranging the ratio of values of R_2 and R_1, we can achieve multiplication by a constant by this means.

In order to multiply by a variable, we can arrange for the value of R_2 to change with the value of the variable: this can be done by a servomotor device, for example. In this chapter we are examining analogue computation from the point of view of what needs to be done, and what can be done, in order to survey the problem as a whole. In the following chapter we shall be concerned with how we achieve the desired result.

Summarising, we have so far seen how a simple differential equation could be set up for solution and we have examined the feasibility of making electronic integrators, summing devices, sign reversers and multipliers. We will continue this chapter by examining more complicated problems and see what more requirements come to light.

1.6 More complicated computing problems

The present advanced state of development of analogue computing technique is to a considerable extent attributable to the war-time effort applied to fire-control instrument design; fire control instruments were used for gun direction, and notable among them were the anti-aircraft predictors. It is worthwhile spending a little time on the study of these instruments; the type of problem they were used to solve exemplifies the requirement for real time computation, and many of the devices used in them are now common analogue computing components.

The predictor was designed to direct guns at moving aircraft, with some hope of hitting them. In the early stages of the 1939–45 war this was a hope and little else; but, in spite of the great increases in aircraft performance during the war period, by the end, predicted fire had become precise enough to be really effective. On robot targets such as 'Buzz-bombs' having predictable behaviour, directed fire became nearly 100 per cent effective. The gun has now been superseded by the guided missile, but the guidance system of this has inherited much from the predictor. The crux of the problem of hitting a moving target with a gun is the time of flight of the shell. At extreme range, targets were engaged so that the shell took as much as forty seconds to reach its target; in this time an aircraft, even a propellor-driven one, could fly many hundreds of feet. The assumption had to be made that the aircraft flew a straight course, which was not too unrealistic, since it could only aim its bombs accurately by doing so. The type of shell used had a time fuze mechanism* which was set before firing; the fuze caused the shell to burst after the time set. The purpose of the predictor was to work out, continuously, from present target data, where the target and shell could meet, and the shell should burst, allowing for target speed and time of flight. The predictor directed the gun in elevation and bearing and set the fuze-time of the shell, automatically. Fig. 1.7 shows the geometry of the problem.

The gun and radar are positioned at 0, and the present target position is shown at A. The radar measures the 'slant range' to the target OA, the target bearing NÔC, and the target elevation, AÔC. The aircraft is flying on course AB. In order to hit the target, the gun must be fired on the bearing NÔD, with elevation BÔD, allowing an additional element for the shell trajectory OSB. The fuze must be set for time T, where T is the time taken for both the shell and the aircraft to reach B. With the aid of a set of trigonometrical and ballistic tables, an artilleryman could solve this problem in a few minutes; but by this time the aircraft would be only a memory. This is a typical problem demanding a machine solution, since it is in real time.

The predictor solved the problem in this way: first the radar data was resolved from Polar to Cartesian co-ordinates with reference to the gun position. This resolution, performed continuously, gave the relative co-ordinates of Eastings, Northings, and Height, which we will call E, N and H. Since the target was moving, the values of these co-ordinates were continuously changing; on the assumption of straight flight, the time derivatives, $\dot{E}$, $\dot{N}$, $\dot{H}$, would be constant. If the time of flight, T, could be known, then the position after time T was calculable from the present data; it would be given by:

$$E + T\dot{E}; \quad N + T\dot{N}; \quad H + T\dot{H}$$

The problem remained of determining T.

---

* There is a military convention that shell fuzes are spelt with a 'z'.

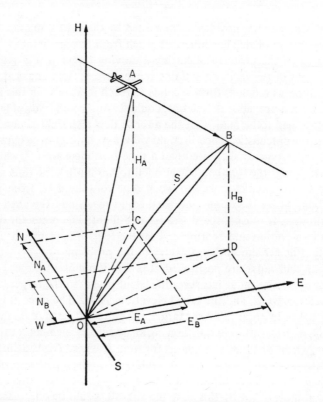

Fig. 1.7

In another part of the predictor the actual gun bearing and elevation and fuze-setting (time) were resolved, giving other values of E, N and H, appropriate to the shell burst at those settings. By matching the future position co-ordinate values with the gun-setting values an 'error' was determinable in each co-ordinate; this error was used to cause servo-systems to vary the gun settings (and, of course, the gun) so as to decrease the error. This process, in effect, was the closing of the control loop; when the error in each co-ordinate, and in T, had all been reduced simultaneously to a minimum, the gun was on target and, if fired, caused the shell to burst close to the aircraft. In addition to the trigonometrical conversions, the predictor had to take into account the ballistic behaviour of the shell, barometric and wind conditions, and other corrections called for in precise gunnery. It then solved four simultaneous differential equations in real time.

The predictor was a special purpose analogue computer; its mechanisms and method of operation were forerunners of those used in present day computing systems.

1.7 Simulators

A nuclear pile or reactor can be used to generate heat by converting fission energy into heat energy. The generated heat energy can be led away to a power-station to transform water into superheated steam which, in its turn, drives turbo-alternators and generates electricity. The control of such a complicated system as this is not easy. When the reactor is allowed to 'go critical' a very great deal of heat is released and the rate at which it is released depends on several factors; the pile temperature rises until a heat balance is achieved of heat generated equalling heat extracted. Heat conduction is dependent on time, and there will be temperature gradients and temperature time-lags at each stage. The rate at which the heat is extracted will depend on the quantity of fluid or gas passed through the pile and into the boiler system.

The boiler temperature will depend on the heat in, the water in, and the steam output to the turbines; the steam output will need to be regulated so that the turbines generate the desired amount of electric power. It is easily seen that the required electrical power output must decree the control settings of the reactor, continuously. Strict watch must be kept on all parts of the system so that temperature, pressure, and radio-activity limits are not exceeded, and corrective actions are continually required to make everything operate within limits and at maximum efficiency.

A system such as the one described is enormously expensive and if mistakes are made it can be dangerous. Skilled operators and subtle and complicated control devices must be employed to achieve safety and economy; these skills must be learned and the controls devised and made to work – a trial and error attack on this problem, with an operating reactor, would not be satisfactory. To get over this problem a *reactor simulator* is used; this is an analogue of the real reactor which is made to generate voltages corresponding to all the control parameters of the system – temperatures, pressures, and nuclear fission parameters. The relationships between the parameters are also simulated and in this way a voltage analogue model of the system is built up. On this analogue the operators try out and accustom themselves to the controls, exploring safety limits and determining most efficient conditions. The automatic controllers are also tested using the simulator.

The behaviour of the reactor generating system is all expressible in various forms of differential equations; we have seen that differential equations can be simulated and solved using integrating and summing amplifiers and the like. A reactor system, though very complicated, and demanding a very great number of components, can likewise be simulated.

We should note the use of the word 'simulator'. Simulators and analogue computers consist largely of the same kind of elements and, organically, are much alike. An analogue computer is set up to solve a problem, usually expressed in mathematical terms, and an answer is desired which is also reducible to mathematical terms. A simulator, on the other hand, simulates the behaviour of a system, causing output variations in the correct relationship to input variations; the output variations may be used directly or measured, but the mathematical interpretation of them may not be immediately important. Generally analogue computers are general purpose equipment which may be set up, at will, to work on a variety of problems; they may even be set up as simulators. Simulators are generally tailored to do a particular job or represent a particular actual system.

One further example of a simulator will be mentioned since it is in common use, and that is the aircraft flight simulator. In the same way that reactors are expensive, so are aircraft. Air liners, and modern airforce equipment, are very complicated and it is common to build simulators on which to train pilots. The pilot operates a control and the reaction of the aircraft is simulated on his instruments, and, sometimes, on the position of his simulated control cabin. This is a typical simulation since the pilot is not likely to interest himself in the actual differential equations governing the good behaviour, or otherwise, of his aircraft when he is flying it. On the other hand, aircraft designers, like reactor designers, have to solve many dynamic problems involving differential equations. They make extensive use of analogue computers for this, and for the design and development of the simulators.

The reader should now have gained an idea of the kind of large problem for which analogue computers and simulators are used; we will interest ourselves in the following sections in somewhat simpler applications, and in the units and sub-units from which such systems, large and small, are built.

Suggestions for further reading

An Introduction to Electronic Analogue Computers by M.G.Hartley. Methuen, 1962.

2 Analogue computer elements

Analogue computers are generally electronic and usually use voltages to represent problem variables. In the flywheel problem we considered in Section 1.2 the variable in which we were interested was θ, the angular deflection of the flywheel; we might be interested in liquid level, or temperature, or pressure or some similar parameter; in order to set the problem up on an analogue computer we scale the values of the parameter to within a voltage range. For instance, if our analogue computer has a working range lying between $-100V$ and $+100V$, and if θ were limited to two radians in each direction, then we could conveniently take $50V$ to be the analogue of one radian. If we set up the analogue of the flywheel problem by interconnecting amplifiers as integrators and summing devices, and if we start the computer with $\theta = 0$, and its analogue, $V = 0$, nothing is likely to happen since $d\theta/dt$ and $d^2\theta/dt^2$ will be equal to zero also, and the system, should remain still. To start the flywheel oscillating we apply a deflection to it, of, say, one radian, and then release it; the electrical analogue can be started in a similar way, by holding the point of the circuit corresponding to θ at $50V$ and then removing the voltage suddenly. This could be the starting condition, too, for the LCR circuit: the initial condition could be that the voltage across the charged capacitor is $50V$.

In order to set up our problem, therefore, we need to be able to establish voltages within the working range. We need also, in solving the problem, to multiply voltages by constants. Both these needs are met by the use of resistance potentiometers.

2.1 Resistance potentiometers

Fig. 2.1(a) shows a resistance potentiometer, with its resistive element terminated at H and L. A sliding contact to the resistive element is brought out at A. The sliding contact is termed the *armature* or *wiper* and is made to be movable to any point on the resistive element, or *winding*. Normally the winding is wound round a flexible card of insulating material which is bent round into a circle, as shown in Fig. 2.1(b), and the position of the sliding contact is varied by turning the armature shaft.

If H is connected to $+100V$, say, and L to $0V$, then the point A will

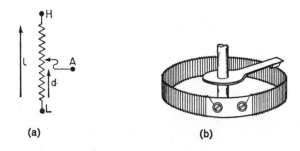

Fig. 2.1   (a)   (b)

assume any voltage within the range $0 < A < +100V$ according to the angular position of the armature shaft. The voltage at A will be given by the expression:

$$V_A = 100 \frac{d}{l} \text{Volt}$$

It is particularly important to remember that this relationship will only be true so long as no current is drawn from the point A, that is, the point A has negligible loading. If any current does flow, there will be an error, and the error is only negligible if the current drawn is small enough.

The ends of the potentiometer may be connected across any voltage source, and the voltage at A may then be adjusted to any fraction of the applied voltage, dV/l. The fraction can take any value less than unity and this, therefore, permits the voltage V to be multiplied by a constant (fraction).

The potentiometer can also be used as a variable resistor, by connecting only H and A or L and A.

The requirements of a resistance potentiometer, or more briefly a 'pot', for analogue computer use are most stringent. Normally a good computer should have an accuracy of one part in one thousand, and all components within it should be better than this. This entails, in the case of a pot, that it must not only give this accuracy of setting but it must maintain it over the permissible working temperature range of the computer, and while carrying its permitted maximum current. There must be a negligible contact potential and contact resistance between the armature and the winding and the transition of the armature across the turns of the winding must be smooth. Naturally, as the armature contact moves from one turn of the winding to the next there will be a small step of voltage or resistance; this step must be small compared with the overall accuracy figure specified the magnitude of these steps defines the *resolution* of the potentiometer

Another important specification for a computer pot is that of linearity. This requires that the winding resistance exactly maintains the d/l ratio, defined by the armature shaft position; it should be noted too that the control of armature shaft position, and its indication, to one part in one thousand, demands a high degree of mechanical precision.

These requirements are met in the following way. The potentiometer card is wound with very many turns of fine resistance wire; the wire itself is most carefully gauged to ensure that its diameter and resistivity are maintained constant to within fine limits. The wire is wound on to the card ensuring even spacing and even tension. The overall resistance value is made high; for computers having a range of $-100V$ to $+100V$, the potentiometers generally are of the order of 30KΩ to 50KΩ; this keeps the current to a low value and, as a result, little heat is generated in the winding. The edge along which the sliding contact moves is finely polished, and the contact surface itself is of specially developed material, chosen for compatibility with the material of the resistance wire.

Due to the angular accuracy called for in setting, it is common practice to use a helical winding; the resistance card is curved round not in a single turn but in a spiral of, say, ten turns. It thus requires ten turns of the armature shaft to sweep the whole length of the winding. The setting precision of one part in a thousand overall can then be met to an angular precision of one part in one hundred, which is a fairly easy scale division.

To ensure linearity and accuracy, the precautions mentioned above require to be observed most strictly, and this is expensive. On small, fairly simple computers, it is normal practice to have one very high-grade linear potentiometer as a 'master', carefully calibrated and corrected. The remaining potentiometers have a lower specification, as regards accuracy and linearity, though their resolution must be of the same order. When an accurate setting is called for, or when a resistance value has to be determined accurately, the potentiometer is switched into a 'bridge' circuit and compared with the master. A meter is provided, with a sensitivity control; the master and the measured resistor are compared by a 'null' method, with a high degree of precision if the meter is sensitive. The value of the setting is read off the scale of the master.

A more elaborate method of pot setting is used on more sophisticated machines where great accuracy is called for; the master pot is replaced by a high precision, switched attenuator, or by an accurate digital voltmeter. The digital voltmeter method is expensive but quick and easy to use; the reference voltage is applied across the potentiometer, and the armature is adjusted until the voltmeter indicates the required setting. The working of digital voltmeters is discussed in the section on analogue-digital conversion, later in this book. We shall see that the digital voltmeter method is analogous to the switched null method, in fact.

2.2 Function potentiometers

There is a further type of potentiometer which finds extensive use in analogue computers and simulators; this is the function pot, which generates voltages at its armature which are a special function of its shaft setting. Typical are trigonometrical, logarithmic, and square law potentiometers.

We have hitherto considered the card on which the winding is wound to be rectangular, that is, a strip of even depth along its length; thus every turn of resistance wire is of the same length and resistance. Suppose now we take a card whose shape is made to conform to the graph of a function, for instance $y = \cos x$. Then each turn of the resistance wire winding corresponds to the length of one vertical ordinate; n turns will have a resistance equivalent to the sum of the length of n vertical ordinates. Remembering how we learned integration, we see that, so long as the winding is evenly spaced and the wire is homogenous, the resistance of the winding between any two points will be the analogue of the integral of the function defining the card shape, between the same two points, and with respect to the horizontal ordinate.

If the potentiometer is connected across a voltage source, the voltage dropped across any length is proportional to the resistance of that length, and thus the potentiometer will generate output voltages that are required functions of the shaft rotation. A particularly useful form of these potentiometers is as resolvers; the card is wound on a $\cos x$ former, giving an output of $\int_0^x \cos x \, dx = \sin x$. The card is made to occupy an exact 90° quadrant; the shaft rotation then generates, at the potentiometer output, a voltage which is $V \sin x$, where V is the applied voltage and x the angular shaft position.

A point that was stressed earlier, is that the accuracy of the potentiometer output depends on its being negligibly loaded. Since the potentiometer needs to have a high resistance, this is of particular importance; however the potentiometer is almost invariably followed by a summing or integrating amplifier which has a high input impedance.

For very accurate work it may be necessary to have a buffer amplifier at the output of a potentiometer; this adds considerably to cost and is not incorporated unless the demand is very stringent.

A more economical method is to design the computer so that the pots are set under loaded conditions. The input resistors to all amplifiers are made to be a fixed value, say, one megohm. When pot setting is performed, a one megohm load is switched across the pot output in this case.

2.3 Operational amplifiers

These elements are the principal organs of the analogue computer and simulator, being the 'active elements' used for summing, integrating, multiplication, and as buffers and inverters. We shall first examine the way in which they are externally connected to perform these functions; from this we shall be able to establish the characteristics which are desirable for the amplifiers, and then study how these characteristics can be achieved.

2.4 The summing amplifier

Fig. 2.2 shows the schematic diagram of an inverting amplifier having a gain $V_o/v = -A$ where A is a large number, and the negative sign indicates that the output polarity is the opposite of the input.

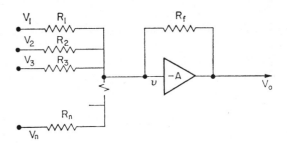

Fig. 2.2

We assume that the amplifier input draws no grid current from the external circuit:

$$\frac{V_1 - v}{R_1} + \frac{V_2 - v}{R_2} + \cdots \frac{V_n - v}{R_n} = \frac{v - V_o}{R_f} \qquad \text{(i)}$$

$$V_o = -Av \qquad \text{(ii)}$$

This gives, after substitution for v from (ii)

$$V_1 \frac{R_f}{R_1} + V_2 \frac{R_f}{R_2} + \ldots + V_n \frac{R_f}{R_n} = -V_o - \frac{V_o}{A}\left[1 + \frac{R_f}{R_1} + \frac{R_f}{R_2} + \ldots + \frac{R_f}{R_n}\right]$$

(iii)

Now, ideally:

$$-V_o = \frac{V_1 R_f}{R_1} + \frac{V_2 R_f}{R_2} + \ldots \frac{V_n R_f}{R_n}$$

(iv)

For example, putting $R_f = R_1 = R_2 = R_n = R \ldots$

$$-V_o = V_1 + V_2 + \ldots + V_n$$

The error in (iii) must be

$$\frac{V_o}{A}\left[1 + \frac{R_f}{R_1} + \frac{R_f}{R_2} + \ldots \frac{R_f}{R_n}\right]$$

(v)

Expressing this as a percentage, we get

$$\text{Error per cent} = \frac{100}{A}\left[1 + \frac{R_f}{R_1} + \frac{R_f}{R_2} + \ldots \frac{R_f}{R_n}\right] \text{per cent}$$

(vi)

We can see that the greater the gain, A, the smaller the error; if the gain is finite or not very great, then the smaller the number of input branches the less will be the error. The error seems also reducible by increasing the values of input resistor with respect to the feedback resistor; this leads naturally to a scaling down of the output to a smaller absolute value. Since the measuring errors and similar circumstantial errors are proportionately increased, the apparent gain in accuracy by this means is illusory.

2.5 Multiplication by a constant

From Fig. 2.3, making the same assumptions as before, we get:

$$\frac{V_i - v}{R_1} = \frac{v - V_o}{R_f}$$

(vii)

Substituting for v, as before, from (ii)

$$V_i \frac{R_f}{R_1} = -V_o - \frac{V_o}{A}\left[1 + \frac{R_f}{R_n}\right]$$

(viii)

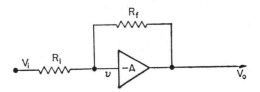

Fig. 2.3

Ideally:

$$V_o = -V_i \frac{R_f}{R_1}$$

The ratio R_f/R_1 is arranged to be the value of the multiplier constant. The error is:

$$\frac{V_o}{A}\left[1 + \frac{R_f}{R_1}\right] \quad \text{or} \quad \frac{100}{A}\left[1 + \frac{R_f}{R_1}\right] \text{ per cent} \qquad \text{(ix)}$$

Once more, if the gain is high enough the error is reducible to a neglible value. For a gain that is finite, or not very great, the error increases as the ratio R_f/R_1, that is, as the magnitude of the multiplier increases.

2.6 The servo-multiplier

Fig. 2.4 shows the arrangement of a servo-multiplier. An operational amplifier controls a power amplifier which drives the servo-motor. The servo-motor drives, through a reduction gear box, the armature of a resistance potentiometer. The ends of this potentiometer are connected to the positive and negative reference voltage lines; thus any position of the armature will pick off a definite voltage, and this is fed back to one input of the operational amplifier. The other input of the operational amplifier is from the variable which is to be the multiplier. If the feedback voltage and the variable voltage are exactly equal and opposite, there will be no current supplied to the motor and it will not turn. If there is a difference, then this will be amplified and cause a current to the motor which will turn, and move the potentiometer armature. We arrange the polarities so that the motor turns in the direction to decrease the original difference voltage.

If the gain of the amplifier system is high, a very small difference will be sufficient to drive the motor; the armature of the potentiometer will then follow the input voltage within close limits. The shaft, which carries

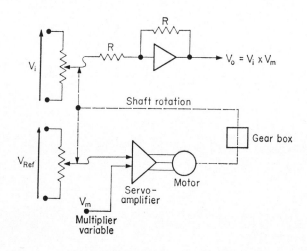

$V_o = V_i \times V_m$

Fig. 2.4

the potentiometer armature used for the position control, carries, as a rule, several other potentiometer armatures. If the variable to be multiplied is applied across one of these, the output from its driven armature will be the product of this and the multiplier.

If several potentiometers are fitted, then several variables may be multiplied simultaneously by the multiplier. Commonly, at least one of the driven potentiometers is a function pot, say, a logarithmic or trigonometrical one; the output from this will be that function of the input multiplier variable. There are a number of useful artifices that can be performed using servo-multipliers of this type; a typical example is to generate x^2 or x^3 from the variable x. All that is required is to apply the x voltage, not only to the input, but to one of the 'slave' potentiometers, for x^2, and the output of this to a second slave, to give x^3.

The construction of servo-multipliers demands engineering of the highest standard. In order to follow rapid variations of the input voltage the servo must be very fast and very sensitive. On the other hand, it must be completely stable, and should have no 'overshoot'. It should have the minimum possible static error. Those whose interests include control engineering will realise that this specification demands an excellent motor, highly precise gear box and mechanical construction and electronic design of the highest standard for the amplifiers and position control system. Whatever our interests we should be aware that devices of this kind can never be cheap.

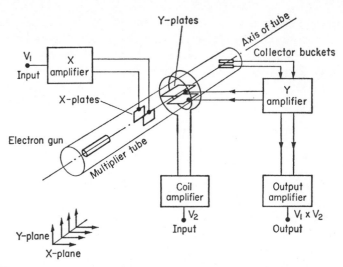

Fig. 2.5

2.7 The crossed-field multiplier

Fig. 2.5 shows the arrangement of the multiplier. The basic element is a special cathode ray tube which does not need to have a fluorescent screen, although a small one may be included as an aid to focussing. The electron-gun and associated focussing system directs a thin beam of electrons up the tube as in a conventional cathode ray tube. One of the variables, which is to be multiplied, is applied to the X-plates and causes the beam to be deflected in the X-plane. The second variable for multiplication is applied through an amplifier to the coil, which generates a magnetic field which is exactly aligned with the axis of the tube. Thus an undeflected beam will not interact with the magnetic field since it has no component of velocity transverse to it; but, if the beam is deflected by the X-plates, there will be a velocity component in the X-direction proportional to the X-deflection voltage. This component is transverse to the magnetic field and interacts with it, according to the well-known relationship, $F = Bev$; the electron beam will, as a result, be deflected in the Y-direction, but an amount also proportional to the coil current. The deflection in the Y-direction causes the electron beam to move away from the centre line of the collector cups or buckets, and they assume different potentials. The cups are connected to the input of a sensitive difference amplifier; the output of this amplifier is fed to the Y-plates in such a way as to cancel the Y-deflection, and it also provides the output voltage, since, when the Y-deflection is completely cancelled, the voltage on the Y-plates must be exactly proportional to the original deflection, and this is proportional to the product of the input variable voltages.

2.8 The quarter-squares multiplier

The principle of this device is summed up in the relationship:

$$\tfrac{1}{4}[(a + b)^2 - (a - b)^2] = ab$$

We have seen earlier how addition and subtraction of two voltages can be reliably performed, to generate $(a + b)$ and $(a - b)$. A function generating circuit can be made to perform the squaring operation to any degree of accuracy. The arrangement of the complete unit is as in Fig. 2.6.

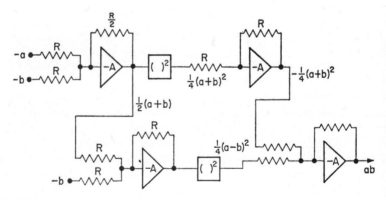

Fig. 2.6

2.9 The logarithmic multiplier

This is probably, in concept, the simplest of all the multipliers, depending on the relationship:

$$\log xy = \log x + \log y$$

The two log functions are generated by means of a function generator and added by a virtual earth amplifier.

2.10 The mark-space ratio multiplier

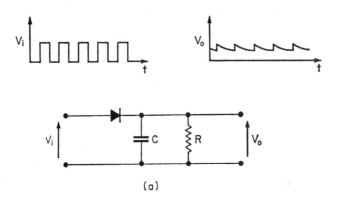

(a)

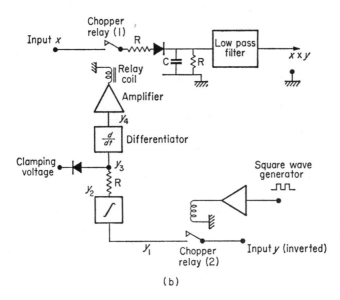

(b)

Fig. 2.7

The principle of this device lies in the operation of the circuit shown in
Fig. 2.7(a). The input provided to the circuit is a 'square wave' of voltage,
V_i. Each pulse of voltage causes a pulse of current into the capacitor

charging it; at the same time the resistance R is discharging the capacitor. The capacitor will be in an equilibrium condition when the total current in equals the total current out. The voltage waveform at the output of the network will amount to a steady d.c. equilibrium value, on which is superimposed a small sawtooth waveform, having a fundamental frequency equal to that of the input square wave.

The d.c. voltage will be dependent on the square wave parameters in two ways:

(a) on the amplitude of the square wave (for constant mark-space ratio);
(b) on the mark-space ratio (for constant amplitude).

If we can arrange for the amplitude to be linearly dependent on one variable, while the mark-space ratio is linearly dependent on the other, the output voltage will be linearly dependent on the product.

The first requirement is easily met; we apply the voltage corresponding to the first variable to the circuit of Fig. 2.7(b) through a *chopper*, that is, we interrupt the circuit connection repeatedly with a switch of some sort; for the time being, we can consider this as being achieved by using a relay. The output voltage from the chopper will have an amplitude equal to the circuit input voltage, and a mark-space ratio dependent on the circuit controlling the relay coil. It now remains to control the chopper by means of the second input; we can do this by a commonly used artifice for generating pulses of controlled, variable, length. The time integral of a square wave is a *ramp*, as shown in Fig. 2.8. If we apply a train of square pulses to an integrating circuit we shall get, at the output, a voltage waveform of a succession of ramps, and the slope will depend on the amplitude of the square wave going in.

This waveform is 'clamped' using a diode; the time taken to reach the clamping voltage will be inversely dependent on the amplitude of the input square wave; the truncated ramp, so formed, is applied to a differentiating circuit, which produces pulses of width equal to the duration of the sloping part of the truncated ramp. These pulses provide the relay current to the multiplier chopper relay. The pulse 'on-time' is inversely proportional to the amplitude of the applied voltage; we therefore invert the waveform, before applying it to the circuit which produces pulses of relay current. The duration of these pulses, which hold the relay closed, are then also proportional to the input variable.

The final d.c. output of the multiplier is passed through a filter circuit which smoothes out the sawtooth ripple.

In the figure, for simplicity, we have shown waveforms for the multipli-

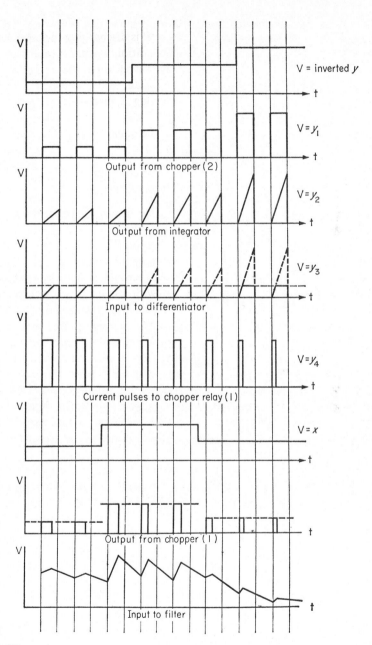

Fig. 2.8

cation of two voltages having 'step' changes; the chopper frequency would be many times the basic frequency of either input variable waveform, if accuracy and linearity are to be obtained.

2.11 The Hall Effect multiplier

The *Hall Effect* is an important aspect of the behaviour of semi-conductor materials; it provides a useful basis for a multiplier.

Suppose we have a block of doped semi-conductor material such as is used in transistors. Either *n* or *p*-type material can be used; we will choose *p*-type, which is rich in holes which act as the current carriers in the conduction mechanism of the material, analagously to electrons but of opposite charge. Fig. 2.9 shows a greatly enlarged block of semiconductor arranged to exhibit the Hall Effect.

If a positive potential is applied at O, then a current flows through the block from O to P, in the form of a stream of drifting holes. We apply a magnetic field of flux density B, from top to bottom of the block, as indicated; the moving holes or positive charges, interact with the magnetic field since they are moving transversely to it. Each experiences a force given by the relationship $F = Bev$, where F is the force, B the flux density, v the velocity, and e is the charge on the electron. This force acts in the direction xy and thus the holes move in that direction. This results in the y surface developing a positive potential with respect to the x surface, and this potential is proportional to B, and to the number of holes, that is, the current in the direction OP. We therefore make the flux density, and the current through the semi-conductor proportional to the variables we wish to multiply, and the voltage xy is proportional to the product.

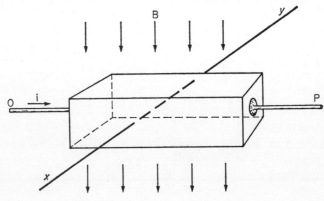

Fig. 2.9

2.12 Multipliers reviewed

We have examined a range of possible multiplication techniques, in principle. The choice of which one to use in any particular circumstance depends on the requirements and, as ever, on economics. Although the principles are simple, a good deal of engineering design is required in each system to make it work. A considerable amount of precision hardware is required in each to make it accurate and reliable; some of the systems are inherently fast, that is they react quickly, giving an output which is virtually instantaneously the required product, whereas some have stringent limits on operating speed. We shall review them once more in the light of these considerations.

The servo-multiplier depends on a motor driving a potentiometer shaft: it is therefore limited in speed of operation by its mechanical limitations. Good servo-multipliers are quite fast and can cope with input signals that vary with frequencies up to about 80 c/s for fairly small amplitudes; for larger amplitudes they tend to have a considerably reduced performance, say 3 or 4 c/s. A servo-multiplier of this kind, however, is very costly and suffers from the added disadvantage that its moving parts suffer from wear. The static accuracy of a servo-multiplier depends mostly on the quality of the potentiometer used and, of course, on the amplifier sensitivity. These can be at least commensurate with the accuracy of the rest of the system in which it is embodied. It has the advantage of being able to multiply several variables at once, and can be used as a function generator.

The cross-fields multiplier can be made very fast indeed – as fast as an oscilloscope, in fact. It is highly complicated since it needs cathode ray tube supplies, a current deflection amplifier, and voltage amplifiers that need to be as linear as possible to achieve accuracy. It has the further disadvantage of mechanical size; with its power supplies it needs to be of the same order of size as a precision oscilloscope. It is also of the same order of cost.

The quarter-squares and logarithmic multipliers are the most economical and can be quite small units if high accuracy is not required. They can be arranged to borrow operational amplifiers from the system in which they operate; but if high precision is required, each may well have to be a self-contained system with three or more high-grade operational amplifiers, and complicated and expensive diode-resistance networks to get a close approximation to a true log or square law. They are inherently fast since they are entirely electronic.

The variable mark-space ratio system, though simple enough in principle, needs quite complicated electronic circuitry in practice. The main complications are due to the requirements for linearity, and stability. It can be made quite fast since it is purely electronic, but the maximum frequency of input signal it can reasonably handle must be much less than the chopping frequency, or pulse repetition frequency, of its basic pulse train. If only approximate results are required a multiplier of this kind can be quite simply made and is not very expensive. The demand for high precision and stability increases cost and complexity, as with all the others.

The Hall Effect multiplier is fairly new, but considerable development has already been done on it to make it reliable, and accurate. Apart from the semi-conductor itself, its expense depends largely on linearisation of the current through the transistor, and on the production of the magnetic field, which needs either a very large number of turns on the field coil or a high current. The field circuit is naturally highly inductive and this limits the speed of operation. In terms of most analogue computer applications, however, it could be considered as a fast system. Mechanically, also, it is very small, and has no moving parts. We should note that mechanical size is of considerable importance throughout computer engineering; a computer system, analogue or digital, may contain hundreds or even thousands of units of various kinds. Apart from the cost of the space it takes up, a spatially large computing system may incur for its designers many awkward problems due to the length of lines required to interconnect its various parts.

2.13 Diode function generators

The simplest of these, used in many applications of electronics, is the *square law* rectifier; many diode rectifiers of the metal oxide type have a voltage-current relationship which approximates closely to $I = KV^2$.

Where high accuracy is not demanded these may be used in simple networks to generate an output voltage which is the square of an input voltage. The more usual configuration for diode function generators is as shown in Fig. 2.10 (*a*).

The circuit works in this way: the diode bias resistors R_B are connected to negative biasing potentials. On applying a gradually increasing voltage V_i, the diode D_1 will only conduct when its input point rises to a positive potential, which depends on the ratio of R_1, R_{B1}, and V_{B1}. Once it starts to conduct, the output voltage becomes $V_1\dfrac{R_f}{R_4}$. The output then rises linearly

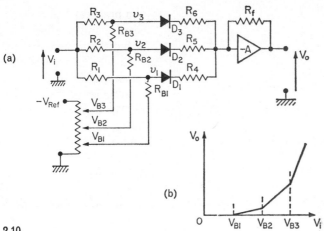

Fig. 2.10

with a slope equal to R_f/R_4, until V_i rises far enough to cause V_2 also to become positive; then the diode D_2 conducts bringing R_5 into the circuit. This causes an increase of slope equal to R_f/R_5, and the combined slope of the output voltage curve becomes $\dfrac{R_o}{R_4} + \dfrac{R_f}{R_5}$. As V_i is increased further R_6 is also brought into circuit, further increasing the slope. The form of the output-input relationship is shown on the curve of Fig. 2.10(*b*); it is a straight-line, segmental approximation to a curve, and by careful choice of resistor values can be made to fit the curve to as small a degree of approximation as may be required. It is possible to apply the diodes connected in the opposite polarity, with positive bias voltages, and the input voltage V_i may then go negative and generate a negative output characteristic.

It leads to a quicker understanding of the system if we consider the diodes to be merely voltage controlled switches which cause the gain of the summing amplifier to vary so that it generates the correct slope of the output curve. At first sight the system seems complicated, but it is possible to approximate to many curves quite accurately with a small number of break points. The diode network can be incorporated, instead, in the feedback network to allow curves of other shapes to be generated, such as those with decreasing slopes. This is a technique that allows scope for much ingenuity and a high degree of accuracy and flexibility; the more virtues we demand from it, however, the more complicated it must become and the more it costs.

2.14 The integrator

We now examine the integrating amplifier circuit in rather more detail so that we can appreciate how accurately, or otherwise, it integrates, and determine the limits of its operation. Many users of analogue computers, and control engineers in particular, use the technique of the Laplace transform in their problem solutions; it is customary to express the behaviour of circuits and devices which have time-dependent behaviour, in terms of the Laplace operator s. Those who intend to work in this field should learn the technique in detail, since it is a powerful one; it permits the formulation of differential equations into polynomials in s, where s represents the operation d/dt, analogous to the operator D, but its use implies the inclusion of all initial conditions in the setting up of the equations. In this analysis we shall use the operator s; we can, in this context, merely regard it as d/dt, so long as we assume all initial conditions to be zero. We also introduce the term *transfer function*, in the form used by control engineers, that is: $\frac{\theta_o}{\theta_i}(s)$. This expresses the relationship of the output, θ_o, to the input, θ_i, as a function of the operator s. As a simple example, consider once again the integrating RC network of Fig. 1.3 which we examined earlier; we found that the relationship connecting the output V_o to the input V_i was given by:

$$V_o = V_i - RC\frac{dV_o}{dt}$$

Substituting s for d/dt we get:

$$V_o(s) = V_i(s) - sRCV_o$$

or,

$$V_o(1 + sRC) = V_i(s)$$

This gives the transfer function for the network:

$$\frac{V_o}{V_i}(s) = \frac{1}{1 + sRC} \quad \text{or} \quad \frac{1}{1 + sT}$$

where $T = RC$

Fig. 2.11 shows the connection of a high gain, sign-reversing, amplifier arranged as an integrator.

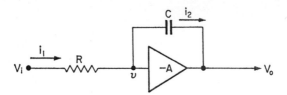

Fig. 2.11

We have, assuming that no grid current flows in the input of the amplifier:

$$\frac{V_i - v}{R} = \frac{(v - V_o)}{\dfrac{1}{sC}}$$

We have also:

$$\frac{V_o}{v} = -A$$

Whence, eliminating v, and rearranging, we get:

$$V_o(s) = \frac{-A}{RC(A + 1)} \cdot \frac{V_i}{\left\{s + \dfrac{1}{RC(A + 1)}\right\}}$$

This gives the transfer function:

$$\frac{V_o}{V_i}(s) = \frac{-A}{T(A + 1)} \cdot \frac{1}{\left\{s + \dfrac{1}{T(A + 1)}\right\}}$$

where $T = RC$, the integrator time constant.

Suppose we apply a step function of amplitude V; the Laplace transform for this is V/s

We have then:

$$V_o(s) = \frac{-A}{T(A + 1)} \cdot \frac{V}{s\left\{s + \dfrac{1}{T(A + 1)}\right\}}$$

Now this is of the form $\dfrac{1}{s(s + \alpha)}$, which is the Laplace transform of

$$\frac{1}{\alpha}\left[1 - \exp\left(-\alpha t\right)\right]$$

Expressing V_o as a function of time:

$$V_o = \frac{-A}{T(A + 1)} \cdot T(A + 1)\left[1 - \exp\left(-\frac{t}{T(A + 1)}\right)\right]$$

or simply,

$$V_o = -A\left[1 - \exp\left(-\frac{t}{T(A + 1)}\right)\right]V$$

If we now compare this with the simple RC integrating circuit, which we examined earlier, we see that V_o is of exactly the same form, but scaled up in amplitude by the factor, A, and the time constant is also scaled up by the factor, $(A + 1)$. Since we are only interested in values of V_o of about the same order of magnitude as V, we are thus restricting ourselves to the very small portion of the curve of Fig. 1.4 which would be called substantially linear. If $(A + 1)$ is a large number, say 10^7, then the time constant will be $10^7 T$, or for $CR = 1$ second, 10^7 seconds. Integrating over a period of a few minutes will again ensure that we only operate in the linear region of the curve.

To determine the error, such as it is, we expand the expression for V_o. This gives

$$V_o = -A\left[1 - \left(1 - \frac{t}{T(A + 1)} + \frac{t^2}{2T^2(A + 1)^2} - \frac{t^3}{6T^3(A + 1)^3} + \text{etc.}\right]V\right.$$

Now, if $A \gg 1$: $\dfrac{-AtV}{T(A + 1)}$ tends to: $\dfrac{-t}{T}V$

which is the true time integral of a *step function*, that is, a *ramp function*. The error is represented by the remaining terms of the series.

Consider only the first error term: this gives a percentage error of:

$$\frac{100t}{2T(A + 1)} \text{ per cent after } t \text{ seconds.}$$

For an integrator having $T = 1$ second, and $A = 10^7$ we have, after 1 000 seconds:

$$\text{error per cent} = \frac{10^5}{2 \times 10^7} = 0 \cdot 005 \text{ per cent.}$$

2.15 Summary of computing elements

In our survey of techniques in this chapter we have seen how the following operations can be performed, to any required accuracy:

(*a*) addition and subtraction;
(*b*) multiplication by a constant;
(*c*) multiplication by a variable;
(*d*) function generation;
(*e*) integration.

We may consider division as multiplication by a reciprocal, which we can generate with a function generator, or by logarithmic subtraction. Likewise differentiation is possible in exactly the same way as integration, with only the resistor and capacitor transposed. Pure differentiation is rarely carried out since differentiators are inherently susceptible to noise interference. Since the equations are solved, in general, by closing a loop, it usually is possible to arrange the circuit to avoid differentiation and division.

In all our studies so far, we have assumed that amplifiers can be made with the following qualities:

(*a*) very high gain;
(*b*) the capability of amplifying very low frequencies and d.c. levels,
(*c*) high input impedance;
(*d*) low output impedance rendering them unsusceptible to loading;
(*e*) high stability;
(*f*) no grid current or leakage current at the input.

We shall need to go into electronic considerations to see how these requirements can be met.

2.16 Buffer amplifiers

It is often necessary to use an amplifier to provide a 'buffer' between one circuit and the next in order to prevent undesirable interaction between them. In particular, we may require to prevent the loading of the output of a stage by its successor, or unwanted signal feedback. A typical example would be the provision of an amplifier having a fixed, high input impedance, following a potentiometer, to prevent the wiper output from being loaded by the following stage. It is desirable that circuits in an analogue computing system can be connected together at the patch-board without

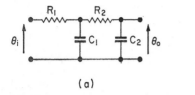
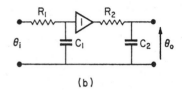

(a)   (b)

Fig. 2.12

the operator having to consider problems of impedance-matching and loading. If units can be considered as isolated and autonomous, the transfer function of a cascade of units is then merely the product of the individual transfer functions. A simple example is shown in Fig. 2.12. The two single *lag* circuits, when directly connected, require a more complicated analysis than when they are buffered and the transfer functions, though of the same form, are different in detail.

The patching requirement can be made most easily if all circuits or units have an infinite input impedance and a zero output impedance. In this ideal case, no output could be loaded, however many other circuit inputs were attached to it. Like 'ideals' in engineering, generally, such an arrangement is impractible: we must make do with real circuits, and units, having input impedances as high, and output impedances as low as we can reasonably make them. In practice, in a good computer system, this approximation to the ideal is good enough for most purposes. Buffer amplifiers provide the means; they range from simple single valve or transistor stages to quite complicated multi-stage arrangements.

2.17 Followers and long tailed pairs

There are many applications in computer and simulator design for circuits of the cathode follower, or emitter follower type. This configuration, illustrated in Fig. 2.13, has the following characteristics:

(a) a gain close to unity;
(b) a very high input impedance;
(c) a very low output impedance;
(d) a wide frequency response.

The analysis of this type of circuit is amply covered in books on general electronics and will not be dealt with here. We should note, however, that in computer applications the circuit configuration has a *long tail*, that is, the cathode or emitter resistor is taken down to a negative HT supply,

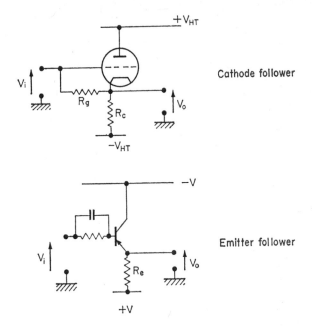

Fig. 2.13

which is well negative of any signal voltages permitted by the operating range. With a valve, the grid bias resistor is commonly of the order of a megohm, which gives the apparent possibility of an input resistance value of twenty to fifty megohms. In practical conditions this is rarely achieved, but a well-designed circuit may have an input resistance of ten megohms or more, which for purposes of analogue computing, can reasonably be considered as infinite. Recently developed high voltage, high gain transistors, especially the *field effect* type give comparable values.

The output resistance can be made quite low, especially in the case of the transistor:

$$r_{out} = r_e + \frac{r_b}{\beta + 1} \simeq 25 + 1\Omega$$

for a standing current of one milliamp which is fairly typical. In comparison with the order of input resistances of circuit units, this is a fair enough approximation to the zero 'ideal' output impedance.

It should be remembered that the follower circuit is not a phase or polarity reversing amplifier; the output voltage changes in phase with

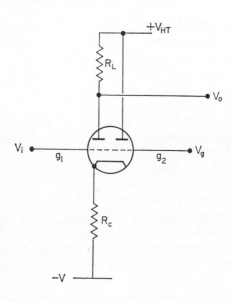

Fig. 2.14

input voltage changes. Using the long tail configuration, the circuit gain can be made very nearly unity: a well designed circuit can approximate closely to an ideal buffer.

The long tail follower is often found as part of a long tail pair circuit, which has a number of computing applications. Fig. 2.14 shows the circuit arrangement. Generally a double valve is used having a common cathode; similar, matched, transistor configurations are also available. The analysis of this type of circuit will be found in works on electronics; we shall study one particular application of the circuit in the next section.

Circuits having very high input impedances are susceptible to noise pick-up on their input leads, which must be kept short or screened. Buffer amplifiers, of the follower type, require careful design and use; normally they are not constructed as separate units, in analogue computer practice, but are built in to function units and amplifiers as input and output circuits.

2.18 Operational amplifiers: d.c. type

These are the amplifiers used throughout as summers and integrators. Since they require to be sign-reversing, they need to have an odd number of gain stages. Pentode valve amplifier circuits can have voltage gains, per stage, of several hundred, and it is practicable to have a d.c. gain of 10^7 over three stages (falling to rather less than 10^4 for low frequency a.c.). Transistors generally produce lower stage voltage gains than this, and more stages are required to achieve the same sort of figure for overall gain, which makes the transistor version a little more complicated than the valve type; it is generally much more compact and has simpler power supply requirements, on the other hand.

Since these amplifiers are required to amplify stationary, or slowly-moving voltages levels they must be d.c. coupled throughout; that is, the stages cannot be isolated from each other by coupling capacitors. This entails that the anode or collector of each stage must be directly coupled to the grid or base of the succeeding stage; it is easily seen that this complicates the power supply requirements to the stages. It is customary in analogue computing systems to use HT supplies of both polarities, so the provision of suitable supply levels to the individual stages poses no insurmountable difficulties; however this kind of circuit requires a good deal of initial adjustment and tends to need continual re-adjustment as valve or transistor parameters vary with age or ambient conditions. Stabilisation of multi-stage circuits of this kind is a severe problem, and re-adjustment after component replacements can be tedious and tricky.

2.19 Chopper stabilised amplifiers

Nowadays d.c. coupled amplifiers are not much used. A far better technique is to use a chopper, in the input circuit. In this way the applied voltage level is interrupted or modulated at the chopper frequency, and this produces a pulse train of amplitude depending on the applied voltage. This pulse train approximates to an alternating voltage at the input of the amplifier; amplifier stages can then be designed as high-gain a.c. stages with capacitor coupling between them. Each stage can be directly supplied from the main HT supplies. At the output, the a.c. waveform is demodulated by another chopper, operating exactly in phase with the first; the demodulated output is smoothed to remove chopper-frequency ripple, and fed to an output buffer stage, for any necessary power amplification.

Although much of the difficulty of making a stable d.c. amplifier is overcome by the chopping technique, it does not eliminate *drift*. By drift we mean the tendency for there to be slow, internally generated, voltage variations, between grid and cathode in valves, and between base and emitter in transistors. These slow changes are interpreted by the amplifier as signals and amplified accordingly, causing gross error, and instability.

This drift, in valves, is mainly caused by random thermal emmission variations at the cathode, and by heater voltage variation. In transistors it comes mainly from the vagaries and variations of I_{co} due to thermal changes, internally or externally generated, in the transistor base material. Overall negative feedback does nothing to reduce it, since, from the amplifier's point of view, the input level variations due to drift are indistinguishable from level variations due to the wanted signal.

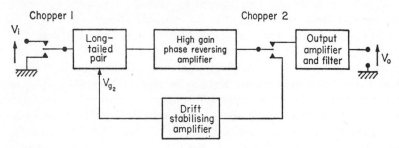

Fig. 2.15

Drift correction can be achieved very satisfactorily by an extension of the chopping technique. Fig. 2.15 shows a typical arrangement, embodying a long tail pair circuit as the input stage; the input signal is taken to g_1, and the first stage output, V_o, is taken from the anode at the same side. The second anode is taken directly to HT+, with the result that the second half-valve is effectively a cathode follower. The mean potential of the cathode is therefore held by the voltage Vg_2, applied at g_2: if a drift potential occurs between g_1 and the cathode, and if it can be detected, then the appropriate equal and opposite correcting voltage, applied at g_2 can be made to neutralise it. The two chopper armatures now move between two pairs of contacts; the upper position connects the input voltage, V_1, to the amplifier, the first stage of which consists of half the long tail pair. After amplification, the signal is fed out through the second chopper, demodulated and smoothed.

In the lower position the first chopper connects *signal ground* to the amplifier input. If there is no drift, then there should be no signal at the output; the second chopper samples the output and applies it to the stabiliser amplifier.

If an output voltage does exist, then, since the input is grounded, this is due to a drift error of some kind; the stabilising amplifier generates a correcting voltage which is supplied to the grid of the cathode follower part of the long tailed pair. Drift voltages change slowly in comparison with the chopper frequency, and to the correcting voltage is smoothed before application to the stabilising grid. In this way, any tendency of the amplifier to drift, for any reason, is immediately detected and the drift is cancelled out. The system is most effective; for instance, a one per cent change in heater volts to an unstabilised amplifier may give many millivolts apparent input drift; in spite of changes of this kind the stabilisation system will generally hold a good amplifier to within ± 2 microvolts over a period of several hours.

We should note that the drift is quoted as 'apparent at the input'; it is generally measured as an output variation, which is divided by the gain, to put it into terms of input volts. It may not, in fact, occur at the input, but at some other point in the circuit. It is, however, corrected by adjustment at the input, and the neutralisation of apparent input drift is a good measure of the performance of the stabiliser.

There are several variations of this drift stabilisation technique, though the principle is the same, that is, of sampling the output and injecting a correction by means of a long tailed pair.

We have shown choppers hitherto as relays. Very precisely built, high frequency relays are commonly used, but solid state switches have achieved popularity in some applications. A transistor is said to be saturated, when the base has brought the emitter into full conduction, and there is an abundance of current carriers; in this state it conducts easily. When the base potential is set to a value that cuts off the emitter, the transistor is virtually an open circuit. A transistor may be used as a chopper, the chopper control voltage being applied at the base to switch the transistor off and on. Much work has been done on transistor choppers and some very good circuits have been evolved; they have the advantage that they are small, need little power to switch them, and can operate at high frequencies. Relay choppers are often preferred, since they are robust and simple, and having several sets of contacts lend themselves to applications like the drift stabiliser. A considerable advantage of the relay over the transistor, is that the signal path is separate from the switch control circuit.

Transistorised operational amplifiers are stabilised against drift by the chopping technique and are in most respects similar to valve types. They usually require more stages to achieve the high gain called for, and like any multi-stage amplifier this calls for careful design. In order to assist the stabilisation, it is common practice to provide a thermal stability control; this usually consists of mounting all the transistors in an aluminium block, together with one power transistor. The heat dissipation from the power transistor, or from a small resistive heating element driven by it, heats up the block to a predetermined working temperature. Current to the power transistor is controlled by a thermistor temperature measuring device. This system maintains the temperature of all the amplifier transistors between close temperature limits, a few degrees above the maximum permitted ambient temperature.

2.20 Range and precision

One of the problems that has beset the transistor circuit designer, in search of good analogue computer circuits, is that of achieving adequate range, that is, the voltage scale in which the system is operated. Valve computers have generally been equipped with HT supplies of the order of 300 volts plus and minus of 'computing earth'. The operating range is, generally, between plus and minus 100 volts. Until recently it has not been practicable to operate transistors over such a large range, and transistorised equipment usually works in the range between plus and minus 10 volts. The precision of each system is the same; quantities for computation on a transistorised equipment are merely scaled down to the smaller range, and this occasions no difficulty.

We must remember, however, that analogue computers, and simulators, are frequently used in connection with other equipment, such as servo-motors, signal generators and the like, and external connections are made to measuring instruments and recorders. Today, many of these are also transistorised and operate over comparable ranges to the transistorised computer. The main problems which are occasioned by the smaller operating or computing range, are that measuring instruments etc., have to be ten times as sensitive, as when using the ± 100 volts range. But more important than this, the whole system is about ten times as sensitive to external electrical noise, which may be picked-up by the peripheral apparatus and in the leads connecting it to the computer. In ideal conditions such as should be found in a computing laboratory, such noise should be minimal. However, analogue computers, and especially simulators, are not always run in ideal environments. The laboratories in which they are used are commonly filled with other apparatus of a kind that generates electrical noise, and operating a computer with a small operating range often has its difficulties. Most users prefer a range of at least 100 volts overall, or ± 100 volts, for fairly trouble-free operation. This range requirement is still a major problem in the design of transistorised computing circuits.

2.21 Conclusion

Having surveyed a range of computing elements of the kind used in analogue computing, it now remains for us to see how these can be interconnected to solve problems. A general purpose analogue computer needs to contain an adequate number of each kind of computing element for the problems it is intended to solve; it needs also to have them arranged in such a way that they can be easily interconnected by the operator, and so that their outputs can be measured and recorded. Other facilities the operator needs are those for testing each element to check its performance, and for setting up the initial conditions of the problem. Finally the interconnection should be arranged so that the best precision and accuracy can be obtained from each element of the system, and from the overall system.

Clearly if all these requirements are to be met, the system must be carefully thought out by the designer and carefully and correctly operated by the user; like all computing machines an analogue computer forms a link between the designer and user, making them collaborators or members of the same team, having a common object. The designer must keep in mind the user's needs; the user, to get the best results, needs to appreciate the designer's intentions and the design limitations of the system. It is particularly important, when assessing the value of experimental results, that the user understands the terms and conditions in which the accuracy and precision of the computing elements are defined, so that he can reliably assess the limits of error in his results.

Although computers often take a lot of the labour out of mathematics the intelligent use of them entails mathematical skill and a thorough knowledge of how they work.

In the next chapter we shall examine some typical, fairly simple, problem solutions; from these we should be able to formulate ideas as to how a complete system should be put together to be a useful mathematical or engineering tool.

Suggestions for further reading

Computer Handbook by H.D.Huskey and G.A.Korn. McGraw-Hill, 1962.
This is a most comprehensive reference book, and will be found useful as a starting point for many enquiries in the field of computer engineering.

3 Analogue computers: problem solving

In this chapter we see how some typical problems may be set up in analogue form for solution. From these can be adduced some of the requirements of a complete computer or simulator.

3.1 Analysis and simulation of a servo-system

The type of system we shall study is called a *d.c. position-controlled system*; it is of particular interest to us since it is embodied in servo-multipliers, as the potentiometer driving element. It has many other useful applications and provides an illustrative example of the use of analogue computation in the study of the dynamic behaviour of a real, or envisaged, electromechanical system. The schematic is shown in Fig. 3.1.

The motor used is a special kind, much used in servo-systems. The armature is supplied with a constant current, I_A; the field winding is split into two halves, and the field current is used to control the motor. On the same shaft is a tachogenerator, which is a small generator designed to give

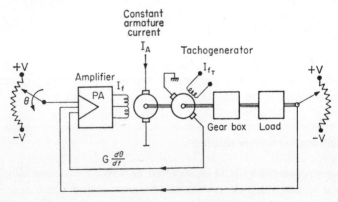

Fig. 3.1

an output voltage, linearly proportional to the speed. The field current, I_{ft}, to the tachogenerator is adjustable and controls the constant of proportionality between voltage output and speed, rated in volts per rev/sec per amp. It is common practice for the motor and generator to be made as one unit; considerable design effort goes into these machines to give truly linear relationships in both motor and tachogenerator, between field current and speed, and speed and ouput voltage and to give as little *cogging* as possible. The motor shaft drives into a gear-box having a step-down ratio of n:1, that is, n turns of the motor shaft drives the gear-box output shaft one turn. The gear-box output shaft carries the load, of which we require to control the position. To the load is attached the armature of a potentiometer, so that the position of the load is always represented by a voltage, which is its analogue. The load may be anything having inertia and offering frictional resistance; in the case of the servo-multiplier, the load is the armatures of all the 'slave' potentiometers.

The field current to the servo-motor is provided by the power amplifier, PA, having a *push-pull* output arrangement; by this means the effective field of the servo-motor may be applied in a positive or negative sense. When the current flows from the HT supply equally through both halves of the coil, the resultant field is zero. Increasing the current on one side, with an accompanying decrease on the other, allows a resultant field due to the current difference. Since the system is symmetrical the difference may be in either sense, giving either polarity and, therefore, either direction of armature torque and rotation.

The power amplifier is driven by a summing amplifier, which algebraically sums:

a) the voltage analogue of the load position;

b) the voltage analogue of the speed, from the tachogenerator;

c) the voltage analogue of the desired position; in the diagram, this is provided by a potentiometer.

In a servo-multiplier, this voltage would represent the problem variable which we wish to be the multiplier.

The operation of the servo-system is like this: suppose the *desired* position is not the same as the *actual* position; we arrange that the voltages representing desired and actual positions are of opposite polarity. The summing amplifier will add these voltages algebraically, producing their difference as an 'error' voltage which is applied to the power amplifier. The field currents become unbalanced in such a way as to cause the motor to drive the load in the direction which decreases the error. When the actual and desired positions coincide, the field currents will again be balanced, there will be no motor torque and therefore no motion.

The tachogenerator is included for this reason: viscous friction depends linearly on the speed of the shaft, and there will be a term, $f\dfrac{d\theta}{dt}$, in the differential equation governing the movement of the load and motor shaft. The voltage from the tachogenerator is of the form $G\dfrac{d\theta}{dt}$, since it is also linearly dependent on shaft speed. The polarity of the tacho voltage and the value of G are controlled by the direction and magnitude of the field current I_{ft}. It is possible to inject into the servo-amplifier, the voltage equivalent to $G\dfrac{d\theta}{dt}$ in such a sense that the value of G modifies the value of the friction coefficient, f, by being subtracted from it. The actual physical effect of this is to increase the value of control voltage applied to the amplifier and, therefore, increase the torque of the motor as the friction increases with speed. We cannot, of course, reduce the actual friction by this means; what we do is to increase the effective gain of the system proportionately with the speed. If the gain were to be increased by the same amount, at low speeds, the damping might well be insufficient, and the system might oscillate. Introducing tacho feedback in this way allows the damping of the system to be adjusted to its most effective value over the whole range of speed of the servo system. The implication of damping may be understood if we appreciate that an underdamped system will be subject to 'overshoot' errors and oscillation, whereas an overdamped system will be sluggish.

Properly, the behaviour of servo-systems and the like are in the province of control or servo-engineering, rather than computer engineering; but the analysis of such systems, in order to determine optimum damping values and similar quantities, is a typical analogue computer task; it is also of importance to the understanding of servo-multipliers and their performance limitations.

There are two basic approaches to setting up the servo-system in analogue: first, we may derive the equations of motion of the load, and the torque coefficients of the motor, and set up the analogue computer as a *differential analyser*, or, we may derive the transfer function of each element of the system and set up the computer as a simulator. Fig. 3.2 shows the connection of the analogue computer as a differential analyser to study the position servo-system.

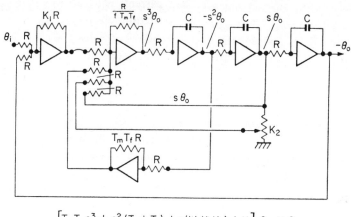

$$\left[T_m T_f\, s^3 + s^2\,(T_m + T_f) + s\,(1 + K_1 K_2) + K_1\right]\theta_o = K_1\,\theta_i$$

T_m = motor and load time constant = $\frac{J}{f}$

T_f = field time constant = $\frac{L}{R}$

$\left.\begin{array}{l} K_1 \\ K_2 \end{array}\right\}$ scaling coefficients

Fig. 3.2

3.2 Simulation of transfer functions

In setting up a simulation on an analogue computer we require to construct simulations of the various transfer functions. These are generally set up using an operational amplifier in conjunction with passive networks, using the relationship:

$$\frac{V_o}{V_i} = \frac{-Z_f}{Z_i}$$

where Z_f and Z_i are the impedances of the feedback loop, and input network respectively. For instance, let us consider the simulation of the servo-motor and power amplifier which supplies its field current. The characteristic of the amplifier, which we will suppose to be linear will be, say amperes output per volt input. The field circuit, into which the amplifier drives, is an 'iron circuit' and has a quite large inductance, L; since it normally has many turns on the coils in order to reduce the current requirement, it will have a considerable resistance R. The inductance will oppose sudden changes in field current, and we will have as a result, a lag in the way the current and field values follow the input. The lag can be expressed in terms of the time constant, L/R, by solving a simple differential equation. If we now express the relationship of *current out* to *voltage in* as a transfer function in terms of the Laplace operator s we get

$$\frac{I_o}{V_i}(s) = \frac{K_i}{1 + sT}$$

where K, is a coefficient expressed in ampere per volt input, and $T = L/R$. We can therefore set up an amplifier to simulate this by arranging for it to have the same transfer function. Consider now the arrangement of Fig. 3.3.

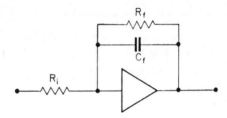

Fig. 3.3

In this case:

$$Z_f = \frac{\dfrac{R_f}{C_f s}}{R_f + C_f s} \quad \text{and} \quad Z_i = R_i$$

whence:

$$Z_f = \frac{R_f}{s R_f C_f + 1} = \frac{R_f}{1 + sT}$$

Then

$$\frac{V_o}{V_i}(s) = -\frac{R_f}{R_i} \cdot \frac{1}{1 + sT}$$

This network then, can be arranged so that $R_f/R_i = K_i$, and $T = L/$ and it will correspond to the amplifier and field coil part of the ser system, if we arrange the signs correctly.

Likewise, the motor has a linear speed output with input current, s K_2 rev/sec per ampere of field current. In terms of shaft deflection, thi $K_2 2\pi \dfrac{\omega t}{I_f}$, where ω is the angular velocity, and I_f the field current.

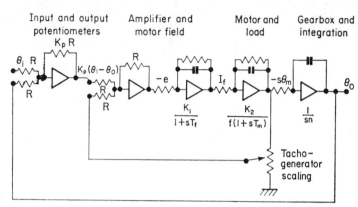

Fig. 3.4

angular deflection, θ, of the shaft, is the time integral of the velocity and, therefore, of the field current, and we can write:

$$\theta = K \int_o^t I_f \, dt \quad \text{or} \quad \frac{\theta_o}{\theta_i}(s) = \frac{K}{s}$$

or the transfer function. The transfer function of the gear-box is merely $'n$, and this constant can be embodied in the K for the motor, if we wish. Thus the motor, amplifier and field time constants, can all be represented by two operational amplifiers and associated resistors and capacitors.

In general, the motor will have friction and inertia associated with it. These can be considered as part of the load, or their time constant can be absorbed in the T value for the motor field, according to how they are measured, or for convenience.

Fig. 3.4 shows the complete interconnection of the simulated system, with each element represented by the analogue of its transfer function.

Further representative examples

s worthwhile to examine some other analogue computer problem set- since they illustrate further points of interest.

Consider the simple equations

$$\frac{x}{t} - y = \sin kt \qquad\qquad \frac{dy}{dt} + x = 0$$

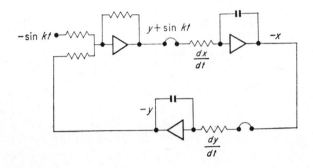

Fig. 3.5

We rewrite the equations:

$$\frac{dx}{dt} = \sin kt + y \qquad\qquad \frac{dy}{dt} = -x$$

The equations can then be set up as shown in Fig. 3.5, and the circuit behaviour will be according to the equations. In the general case, using the Laplace notation we can write:

$$F(s)x + G(s)y = A(t) \qquad\qquad\text{(i)}$$

and

$$f(s)x + g(s)y = a(t) \qquad\qquad\text{(ii)}$$

where $F(s)$, $f(s)$, $G(s)$, $g(s)$ are functions of s; $A(t)$ and $a(t)$ are the applied forcing functions. Rewriting the equations:

$$F(s)x = A(t) - G(s)y \qquad\qquad\text{(iii)}$$

$$g(s)y = a(t) - f(s)x \qquad\qquad\text{(iv)}$$

Following the procedure of the simple example, we solve equation (iii) for x as a function of t, and (iv) for y, likewise. We cross connect the two systems and thereby solve them simultaneously. In like manner, we can expand the system to solve more complicated equations, of any number of variables, up to the limit imposed by the number of amplifiers available.

Sometimes we require to introduce a forcing function of the type $A\sin(\omega t + \phi)$ where ϕ is a phase angle. At very slow speeds of operation it would be possible to produce $A\sin \omega t$ from a signal generator or oscillator, and switch it into circuit at the point in the cycle corresponding

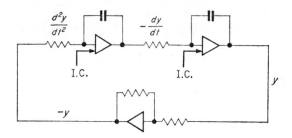

Fig. 3.6

the phase angle ϕ, at time zero. Generally it is better to produce functions of this kind on the computer itself. The differential equation:

$$\frac{d^2y}{dt^2} + y = 0$$

gives a sinusoidal solution: Fig. 3.6 shows the arrangement. If we set in the calculated initial condition values corresponding to the amplitude A and phase angle ϕ, the circuit will oscillate commencing at the right point of the cycle; this arrangement then forms part of the problem set-up and starts up with the rest, on switching to 'compute'.

3.4 Time scaling

The servo problem we have studied brings out a particular point that we should note, that of *time scaling*. It is possible to have quite a wide range of time constants in the analogue set-up; we may have to alter them to achieve accuracy, or make the *read out* suitable for recording. We can scale time in the same way as any other parameter, but it must be remembered that the derivatives of variables will also be subject to scale factors. *Real time* computation is equivalent to using a time scale factor of unity; but, if we express time scaling, $t = m_t T$, where T is physical, that is, real time, and t is the problem independent variable time, and m_t is the scale factor, then a derivative, s, will become

$$\frac{1}{m_t}\frac{d}{dt} = \frac{1}{m_t}s,$$

and s/m_t is the analogue derivative. Likewise the second derivative in the analogue will be s^2/m_t^2.

The servo-system we have simulated or analysed might be a servo-multiplier or, for instance, a swing bridge of great size and inertia, having the same form of mathematical relationships between its parameters; in the former case the response time would be necessarily very short, measurable in milliseconds; in the latter it would be long, measurable in minutes. Both systems could be represented by the same analogue by suitable time scaling.

If we work in real time, using the simulator system, we have the advantage that any element of the loop can likewise be real, that is, by use of suitable transducers we can introduce, and test, a real component, such as an aeroplane aileron, or a servo-motor, or part of whatever it is that we are simulating. This has great advantages when we have difficulty in determining the actual transfer function of a part of a system, or if, for any reason, we are unable adequately to represent it in analogue. For instance, a human operator in the control loop is most difficult to represent due to human non-linearities and inconsistencies.

On the other hand, real time operation may have drawbacks; in a process control study, parameter variations and lags may be of hours' duration, while the behaviour of a fast servo may be difficult to measure or record owing to its speed.

Inaccuracies due to integrator approximations and the like, are reduced as the time scale is reduced and this again may be a good reason for speeding up the time scale. Likewise, with a fast acting analogue we can view the outputs on an oscilloscope. If the forcing function, or input control signal is repetitive and fairly fast, this presents no particular difficulty but for problems in which the initial conditions have to be set for each study, we have the following very important requirement.

3.5 Repetitive mode operation

Normally in a problem solution we set up the circuit and set up the initial conditions all through it, and then allow computation to take place. T repeat the process we need to set up again all the initial conditions. typical facility that has been developed for use on analogue computer is the *repetitive mode*, in which we set up the initial conditions throug relay contacts: the computer is then arranged to open the relay contac right through the system, to allow computation, and then after a adjustable period, to close the contacts again, once more setting up th initial conditions; after a further period it computes again, and so o This allows a 'single shot' operation to be viewed as a continuous opera tion on a CRO.

3.6 Initial condition setting

If we think back to our original analogues of the flywheel and spring, and *LCR* circuit, we should remember that they had no dynamic behaviour, unless stimulated by imposing an initial deflection of the angular position, or by charging the capacitor. A regulator system should normally be at rest unless a disturbance is created, and then we are interested in how soon the system can overcome the disturbance and settle down again. We therefore need a convenient system by which we can set in the initial conditions of any differential equation we are studying, or a desired amount of deflection of some kind in a simulated system. We likewise want the system to remain at rest while we are setting up these conditions. The most important clue to solving this problem lies in the flywheel and capacitor example; in charging the capacitor or deflecting the flywheel, we store energy in the system. On releasing the system from constraint, this energy is also released and we can study the dynamic behaviour. In the analogue system the only elements which can store energy are the capacitors. We therefore set up initial conditions on the integrators, using a circuit arrangement of the type shown in Fig. 3.7. When the relay contact is in the upper position, the integrator is switched out of the computing circuit

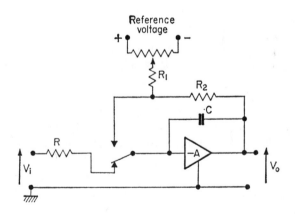

Fig. 3.7

and connected for setting. The two resistors R_1 and R_2 are equal, with the result that the output of the integrator, which is now connected merely as a sign reverser, is equal and opposite to the voltage set in by the setting potentiometer; the capacitor is charged to this voltage. When the relay armature is switched to the lower position, the integrator is put back into the computing circuit, with the capacitor in the charged state, and the output voltage is at the set voltage, corresponding to the desired initial condition.

We should consider, now, what happens during the period during which the relay armature is between the upper and lower contacts. No capacitor has yet been made perfect; there is always some leakage of charge, albeit small, and there will tend to be a voltage drop due to this. But since the capacitor is connected back to the input of the very high-gain virtual-earth amplifier, a small variation of voltage at the output will induce a corresponding signal at the amplifier input, in such a sense as to neutralise the output variation. We saw, in our study of the integrator, that the effect of the amplifier gain is to increase the time constant of the CR combination. In this arrangement the CR time constant approximates to the capacitor leakage time constant, and this is long, anyway. The advantage that accrues from this is not only that the initial condition voltage is held substantially constant during the period of relay changeover, but that we can add another useful computing facility merely by maintaining the relay contact in the intermediate or open-circuit state.

3.7 The 'hold' facility

If during the computation we wish to examine the conditions in the circuit at any point, the computer may be switched to *hold*. This disconnects all the integrator inputs, and the voltage conditions will remain stationary throughout the circuit.

Due to the action of the amplifier-capacitor combinations discussed above, the voltage conditions will hold for a considerable period with no detectable variation; furthermore, if a measuring instrument, such as a meter or CRO, is connected to any integrator output point, provided that it does not load the circuit unduly, the capacitor voltage remains substantially unchanged; the amplifier supplies such current as is drawn by the measuring device.

A typical circuit arrangement for an operational amplifier is shown in Fig. 3.8. The circuit allows for the amplifier to be connected as a summer or integrator, with two preset values of integrator time constant; terminals are usually included so that other capacitors or resistors can be connected when required. The relay arrangement allows for *hold, set initial condition* and *compute*.

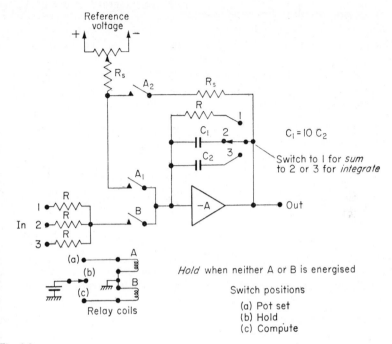

Fig. 3.8

3.8 The arrangement of an analogue computer

We have studied the kind of problem analogue computers can be used to solve, and the kind of sub-units which are used in the solution. A computer made with a particular application in view, or a simulator for a system of which the characteristics are known, can be made on an *ad hoc* basis with a number of amplifiers and other components pre-determined by the requirement. A general purpose computer for laboratory use poses, as a first and major consideration, the problem of what components and what numbers to provide. Naturally, the money available will always establish an upper limit. The decisions that have to be made are what precision and accuracy are necessary or desirable, what sort of multipliers, and how many of each, and how many amplifiers and passive elements may be required.

Amplifiers are the basic elements of any analogue computer system and the complexity of a problem that can be handled by any system must always be limited by the number of amplifiers available.

Precision, in all engineering systems, is a costly quality. What must be aimed at by a computer designer – or purchaser – is to ensure that no item is more precise than it needs to be, or than the rest of the system calls for, and that the components provided are used to the best advantage.

In the previous chapter a circuit was shown of an amplifier arranged so that it could be used either as a summer or integrator; this is fairly standard practice in analogue computer design, but the cost of precision capacitors is considerable and, for economy, systems are often put together with some amplifiers arranged as summers, some as integrators, and some as both.

In a laboratory such as in a college, university, or research department, there may be several people, or teams, requiring to use the computer. A very effective economy, in this case, is to use a *patch-panel* system. All the interconnecting points, inputs and outputs to amplifiers and the like, are brought to a central point on the operating console, to which is attached a removable patch-panel; the operator plugs up the problem on the patch-panel, remote from the machine, and when it is ready the patch-panel is attached to the machine, automatically making all the necessary machine connections. Plate 1 (facing page 64) shows a patch-panel used on a typical computer installation. The panel can be removed, in its plugged-up, or patched state, while another operator uses the machine with a similar panel. Each problem under investigation can, in this way, remain patched even though the machine is in use for something else. As each panel is attached the potentiometer settings have to be set up, but panel-patching is normally the job which takes most time.

Very large installations sometimes incorporate automatic potentiometer settings, set up by a punched-tape or punched-card input system; naturally any time saved on a large system is valuable. In general, large computers are hard to use to best advantage since, for any but large problems, many of their facilities will not be used. The computer shown in Plate 2 (facing page 65) is made in two parts, each with its own patch-panel. The two parts may be used separately, sharing only the measuring facilities, or they can be used as one large integrated system. For work not requiring the highest precision it is often a good economy to have several small computers that are compatible with each other: they can then be brought into use together whenever a problem calls for more facilities than can be provided by any single one.

The use of patch-panels causes a number of engineering problems. Every interconnecting line has to be quite long, and inter-wiring capacity has to be avoided by careful layout. Currents are generally not high in computers, but even small voltage drops have to be avoided over long runs of wire or cabling. This frequently entails the use of buffer amplifiers on cables connecting different cabinets in large installations. Finally, any input current in integrators causes inaccuracies due to charge leakage from the integrating capacitor; likewise, cable insulation and insulation in the patch-panels, is necessarily of the best, if integration errors are to be avoided; a patch panel must be compact, which makes for short leakage paths along its surface. The material of which it is made must be carefully chosen to prevent insulation loss by tracking, or moisture condensing on its surface.

The patch-panel shown in Plate 1 has several hundred connections and each must make a perfect contact each time the panel is inserted. The mating parts of each connection are made to slide together when the panel is pushed into position, and each contact is maintained by spring pressure. The design of such a contact is not difficult, but it does require a considerable degree of mechanical precision if all are to work faultlessly every time. The contacts must be plated with material which does not corrode and which should be highly polished. What is most important is that each and every removable panel mates perfectly with the fixed receptacle which is part of the main computer. In the costing of a computer installation, the patch-panel often seems a very expensive item: experience shows that it is unwise to attempt any false economies in this part of the assembly.

The relative number of amplifiers, passive elements, multipliers and additional facilities such as non-linear networks, that should be included within the cost limits, is difficult to decide, and it can only be done by careful consideration of the type of problem for which the computer can be used. A fairly simple second order system can be simulated or analysed with about ten amplifiers; third and higher order systems call for many more. For instructional purposes, usually, the kind of problem in which we are interested is of the second order of complexity since the principles can easily be seen, and calculations performed on the computer can be fairly easily confirmed by algebraic methods. Thus the commercial range of analogue computers designed for schools and colleges commonly include ten or a dozen amplifiers, a selection of potentiometers and high grade capacitors, with some provision for attaching simple non-linear networks of diodes, resistances, and the like. A patch-panel arrangement for this kind of computer is particularly valuable, to give the maximum access to the computer facilities.

A computer based on ten or twelve amplifiers is of little scientific or mathematical use. Quite interesting and difficult problems can be set up and solved with an assemblage of, say, twenty-five amplifiers, and two or three multipliers, but a computer even of this size is of little use for research purposes, for instance, for the simulation or analysis of complicated non-linear systems, or simultaneous partial differential equations with several variables. Plate 2 (facing page 65) shows a medium-sized computer installation, which we shall take as an example and consider in some detail since it is typical. This installation was chosen after very careful consideration, and the value of each facility provided was carefully examined. The requirement was about as general as could be: the installation was to be used for instructional purposes, and for research; the kinds of problems it was required to cope with were not restricted to any particular branch of engineering, mathematics, or science. We should not consider the provision of facilities within the computer to be in accordance with, or define, any golden rules or magic numbers; experience has shown that the choice of facilities was a good one, but other equally good choices might have been made.

3.9 An example of a working analogue computer: Solartron 247

This analogue computer provides a good illustration of medium-sized general purpose equipment. (See Plate 2.) It is installed in the computer laboratory of the Electrical and Control Engineering Department of the University of Surrey. The major part of its employment is on problems of control engineering but is by no means limited to these; it serves both for research and for instruction, and is used daily by several people, or groups.

There are several design features that we should note. The first is that it is designed on a *modular* basis. There are two major modules: the installation is essentially a pair of twin analogue computers, each having its own patch-panel and half the total complement of amplifiers and potentiometers. The halves can be used separately and independently; multipliers and non-linear function units can be borrowed from the central cabinet for use with either half, merely by patching. The major modules, and parts of the machine common to both, are also constructed of modules. Each cabinet is fitted with standard racks, and each rack can carry a quota of smaller modules, that is, amplifiers, multipliers etc. Power supply modules are housed in the lower racks.

The patch-panels each contain 816 sockets, and are removable from the machine. Each gives access to its own quota of amplifiers and potentiometers and has a group of sockets available for connecting it across to the other panel.

For the solution of problems which entail more facilities than either of the halves can offer, the computer operates as one system; one operating position becomes the master; the other is the slave.

The potentiometers are housed within the desk; the lids slide back to allow access to the knobs, for setting. There are forty-eight potentiometers attached to each half, about one-third of which are 'free', that is, not permanently connected to anything except the patch-panel, from which connections go to both ends of the potentiometer winding, and the wiper. The remainder are connected to amplifiers and have one end grounded, to *computer ground*; this is the main zero volts connection as a computing reference; it is specially wired as a continuous circuit with heavy gauge conductors; for computing purposes normal frame and chassis ground connections are inadequate.

A digital voltmeter is provided and is used for all measurement and setting up. The potentiometers are not calibrated; each has ten switched attenuator positions and a fine adjustment. Potentiometer setting is done in the circuit, under working conditions, and all are set against the same reference potentiometer using the voltmeter as a comparator; or if a high absolute accuracy is not demanded, they may be set directly against the voltage reading. Beside each potentiometer knob is an indicator light; the potentiometer to be adjusted is selected by a coded set of push buttons, near to the voltmeter digital display. The selected potentiometer is indicated by its light.

There are some seventy-two operational amplifiers, with multipliers and non-linear function units. For economic and functional reasons these units have different performance specifications within each type. For instance, about half the amplifiers are capable of accepting up to five inputs; more are capable of accepting three, while some are pure inverters. Half the total number of amplifiers can be used as integrators or summers; the rest are summers only, that is, they have resistive, but not capacitive feedback connections.

Two of the multipliers are servo-multipliers, having six potentiometers on shaft, that is, they can multiply five variables by one, or be used as resolvers. Single-variable multiplication is performed using the more compact and economical quarter-squares type. Mark-space multipliers are also provided, and for convenience and economy these are modular. Each is made up of a mark-space unit which generates a carrier wave, mark-space modulated by one variable; this may be fed into up to five height units, which modulate the height in accordance with the variable applied to them. In this way a five-by-one multiplication can be achieve by these units also.

The system has the normal control functions of *potentiometer settin* or *set initial conditions* and *hold* and *compute*. It provides also *problem check* in both static and dynamic modes. In the dynamic mode, all inte grators are switched out of the computing circuit and run for a predeter mined period; their outputs are examined at the end of this time, whic gives an accurate assessment of their dynamic performance.

For problems which have a very short duration, the system can be ru in a repetitive manner, that is, initial conditions are set, the system com putes for a definite period, and then the initial conditions are reset, and s on.

With a large and expensive installation, computing time is valuable what may at first seem a luxurious provision may, in fact, turn out to b an economy. For instance, on this computer, very rapid selection c monitor points is possible by the push button-system, and this gives rap dity in setting-up and problem checking. Further speed is gained by th provision of a *print-out* facility: the printer can be seen at the left-hand en of the computer. This is used in the following way: any point to be mon tored is set up by push-button. If the printer is enabled, the push-butto address and voltage value are printed out onto a paper record. In the auto matic mode, up to ten monitor points may be preselected; the compute is set to *sample and hold*, that is, after preset periods it switches the syster to *hold* and measures the value at each of the selected points. These ar then printed out on the record.

By the provision of detachable patch-panels, quick setting arrange ments, and automatic print-out, the minimum machine time is used o any problem, and several users can have the benefit of it, more or less, a once. We shall see in later chapters how computer designers and users are always preoccupied with questions of *machine time*; computers, bot analogue and digital cost a good deal and date quickly. Computer tim must be used economically if they are to justify their cost.

3.10 A non-electronic analogue device: the three-term controller

Automatic controllers are used extensively in industrial process-control t regulate the operation of chemical apparatus, steam boilers and simila plant. Very briefly, such an arrangement corresponds to the closed-loo

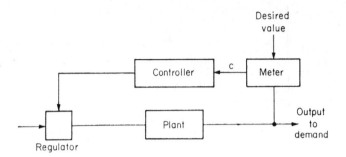

Fig. 3.9

diagram of Fig. 3.9. A desired value is set, corresponding to a steam pressure or some similar output parameter. The task of the controller is to control an input parameter, for example, boiler fuel, in such a way that the output *set-point* value remains constant in spite of *demand* or load changes.

In proportional control, the deviation of the actual output value from the set-point value is measured and amplified to form the *correction* signal – the inverse of the error in the servo-system.

The correction is then applied to the controlled input parameter so that the applied correction is directly proportional to the error. At first sight this might seem to be a satisfactory arrangement: Fig. 3.10 shows a typical plant response to a sudden demand change, using proportional control. We see immediately that the demand change is not completely accommodated by this simple system. First, there is the lag due to the plant time constants, which may be of many forms, for instance inertial or thermal, or of the type known as *transport* lags. These occur, for example, when an increase in boiler fuel is called for by a controller, and a finite

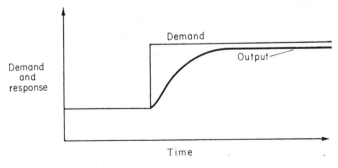

Fig. 3.10

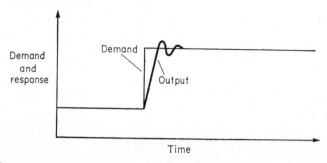

Fig. 3.11

invariant delay occurs while the fuel travels along a conveyor to the fur-
nace. The second inadequacy of the system is important philosophically;
it lies in the fact that the controller needs an error to operate it: if there is
to be operation, there must be error. In a static regulator system this
can be overcome by setting the set-point a little above the actual desired
value, so that the actual output does correspond to the required value;
the amount of permanent error required is called the *off-set*. Now, the
control correction is proportional to the error, and thus for a larger steady
control action, a larger off-set is required, and while the system may act
correctly at the normal set value, it will be in error at all other values.

The object of the so called *three-term controller* is to overcome these
deficiencies. The second term in the correction equation, (the proportional
being the first) is the *integral* term; by this, we mean that the error value
is integrated with respect to time, and this also is applied as a correction
to the controlling parameter. It is easily seen that so long as an error exists,
the integration continues to generate a correction; in theory this eliminates
the requirement of an off-set. The third term is the derivative term, by
which we mean that the rate of change of error is measured, and the
amount of correction is made proportional also to this. A typical plant
response, as a result of three-term control, is shown in Fig. 3.11. The
differential equation corresponding to a three-term controller is of the
form:

$$A \frac{d\theta}{dt} + B\theta + C \int \theta \, dt = \theta_o$$

where θ is the error and A, B, C, are the coefficients corresponding to the
amount of each kind of control applied, B being the *proportional gain*. The
behaviour of systems under three-term control, and the optimum values
of A, B, C, are typical of analogue computer studies of control engineers.

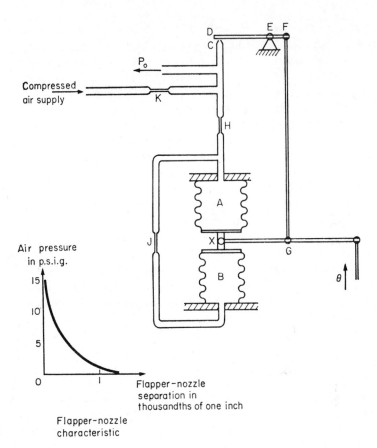

Fig. 3.12

3.11 Operation of the three-term controller

We have cited the above example for another reason; although electronic three-term controllers exist, the great majority of controllers in use at this time are pneumatic. Fig. 3.12 shows an arrangement of a *flapper-nozzle* pneumatic amplifier, arranged to give an output pressure to a regulator with three-term control.

The system is simple and effective. The flapper-nozzle characteristic is shown also on the diagram. The nozzle and flapper are shown as C and D. Compressed air from the supply enters the nozzle system through the restrictor, K, which is a capillary tube; the pressure at the nozzle is fed through the *derivative restrictor*, H, into the bellows, A. When the flapper is closing the nozzle aperture, the pressure builds up in the nozzle-pipe and bellows almost to the main-supply pressure; when the flapper moves from the nozzle a fraction of a thousandth of an inch, air escapes at the nozzle and pressure is dropped across the restrictor, K, and the pressure in the bellows, A, decreases likewise allowing the bellows to contract. Let us for the moment neglect the bellows, B; the flapper-nozzle characteristic is far from linear, but we require the output pressure, P_o, to the regulator, to be a linear function of the error movement, θ. The linkage, EFG, acts as a feedback system; if θ is a small movement in the direction of the arrow, the flapper moves towards the nozzle, causing the pressure in the bellows, A, to rise. The bellows expands, and the point X moves downwards, thereby opening up the nozzle again. Now the movements of X and θ are very much greater than the total nozzle movement – perhaps a quarter of an inch, compared with a length of a thousandth of an inch; the movement of θ is almost exactly offset by the movement of X; this in turn can be made truly proportional to the pressure, P_o, if the rate of the bellows spring conforms to Hooke's Law. Thus the feedback linkage achieves linearisation of the awkward flapper-nozzle characteristic.

Now consider the effect of the restrictor, H; in the steady state, no air flows through it and there is no pressure drop across it. In the event of a change in θ, that is, an error change, the immediate effect will not all be felt by the bellows, A, owing to the pressure drop across the restrictor, H. The feedback is rendered less effective and the overall gain is increased temporarily, thus causing a more rapid variation of P_o, the correction, and making the response more rapid. The flow through the restrictor is taken to conform to the equation:

$$q = (P_o - P_A)t$$

where P_o is the output pressure and P_A the bellows pressure. But $\int q\,dt$ is proportional to the total quantity of the air transferred into the bellows, A, and therefore to the pressure, and the movement of X. Over a short period, assuming linearity, X depends on P_o and $d\theta/dt$, giving the system transfer-function of the form:

$$P_o = K_1(1 + sT_D)\theta$$

where K_1 is the proportional gain and T_D the time constant due to the restrictor and bellows, A.

We can now consider the effect of the bellows, B, known as the *integral bellows*. In the steady state, that is, when there has been no change in θ

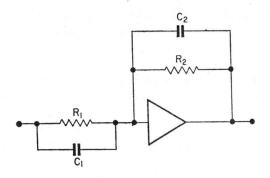

Fig. 3.13

for some time, the pressures in bellows A and B will be equal, and equal to P_o; now the pressure in bellows B will be proportional to the time integral of the flow through the restrictor, J. We have:

$$\int K(P_A - P_B)\, dt = P_B$$

where K is a constant of proportionality; in terms of the operator s

$$\frac{KP_A}{s} - \frac{KP_B}{s} = P_B$$

which yields a transfer-function:

$$\frac{P_B}{P_A} = \frac{1}{Ks + 1}$$

which is analogous to the approximate integrator expression $\dfrac{1}{1 + sT}$, with which we are already familiar. There is thus a contribution to the movement of X due to the bellows pressure P_B which is proportional to the integral of the error, θ. The transfer-function of the whole system becomes:

$$\frac{P_o}{\theta}(s) = K_c \frac{(1 + sT_D)}{(1 + sT_I)}$$

where T_I is the time constant of the B-bellows and J-restrictor combination, and K_c the proportional gain equivalent. This embodies the control terms, though not exactly as in the original differential equation. This transfer-function can be simulated electronically by the arrangement shown in Fig. 3.13. We should note from the form of the transfer-function that if we can, in an ideal case, make our time constants T_I and T_D equal, the response, P_o, will be truly proportional to the error θ, and the correction will be perfect. Alas, for the ideal; we rarely encounter it in engineering.

The three-term controller exemplifies an analogue computation performed by a non-electronic means. We would do well to remember that automatic computation, whether digital or analogue, does not depend on electronics; sometimes mechanical techniques are more convenient, but the philosophy of computation is just the same, the difference is only in the means or technique. Quite extensive pneumatic and mechanical analogue computers and differential analysers have been built. The R.A.E. Tridac, is an example of a truly great mechanical differential analyser.

Suggestions for further reading

General:
Analogue Computation by A.S.Jackson. McGraw-Hill, 1960.
Analogue Computer Techniques by C.L.Johnson. McGraw-Hill, 1963.

Three-term controllers:
Introduction to Process Control S. tems Design by A.J.Young. Instrument
  Publishing Co. Inc., 1955.

4 Arithmetic

4.1 The decimal system

We have learned to perform arithmetic operations using a decimal system, most probably because we have ten fingers – a simple abacus literally at our finger tips. In the early development of our arithmetic faculty we learned first to count and then to add and subtract, as a continuation of counting. Although counting is itself a progressive addition of unity, we first had to learn words for the numbers and the addition process was taken for granted; then, if we had not already grasped the idea of addition of numbers other than ones, we were shown how; we did it by successive counts. Thus, to add three to five we counted to three, and then, starting on our fourth finger, we counted to five, and then counted through from one again, up to the eighth finger – the one we had remembered – and then we had performed the required addition. To the adult this seems pretty simple; the reason for the detailed description of this simple process is to show that, though it is in fact simple, there are several steps to the process. If we are to design a machine to perform such a process, every step must be mechanised. A machine or piece of electronic circuitry, however complex, cannot know anything as we know things and cannot be taught anything as we are taught. Any process we require to be carried out must be reduced to its simplest terms and every single, simple step must be contrived.

Reverting to the arithmetic of our simple sum; the first step is to identify each of the first three fingers with a remembered number in a remembered sequence. There is an abstraction, even here, since the finger called 'three' is only one finger but represents, in itself, the magnitude of the number of fingers counted up to it. We need to beware of abstractions in mechanising processes, since machines are material things and abstractions can be difficult to mechanise. The next step is to remember what the other number was that we wished to add; then to count up to it; to remember the final finger we had reached; then count through from one to that finger. Finally we call out the answer or write it down. A machine to repeat this process would do as follows, using more computer-oriented terms: first call from memory, or *read in*, the first number and then count to it. Next the machine must call from memory, or read in, the second number and count to it, from the end of the previous count. The digit reached must be marked, or its position stored in memory, or otherwise *registered*, and then the final count made, placed in store, or *printed out*.

We soon learned that we did not need our fingers to do these additions. We came to know, by trial and error, that $3 + 5 = 8$ and all the other combinations of two digits. That this became progressively a memory process should be apparent if we think back on the mistakes we used to make doing this kind of sum when we were small. When we had determined all the combinations of pairs of numbers in the range zero to nine, this information was stored in our memory in some kind of order; we had in fact built up our first table, the addition table.

This can be made out as shown:

0	1	2	3	4	5	6	7	8	9	0
1	2	3	4	5	6	7	8	9	0	1
2	3	4	5	6	7	8	9	0	1	2
3	4	5	6	7	8	9	0	1	2	3
4	5	6	7	8	9	0	1	2	3	4
5	6	7	8	9	0	1	2	3	4	5
6	7	8	9	0	1	2	3	4	5	6
7	8	9	0	1	2	3	4	5	6	7
8	9	0	1	2	3	4	5	6	7	8
9	0	1	2	3	4	5	6	7	8	9
0	1	2	3	4	5	6	7	8	9	0

The table is probably not used by any child remembering the additions, but it is a good way, and a suitable way, of storing the information for mechanisation. It has also some interesting features; each row or column is a count, that is an addition of unity to the previous row or column. There is also a diagonal line of zeros. Any sum occurring on or below this diagonal entails a 'carry' figure to the next addition, when we have progressed to doing sums having more than one digit in the answer. This process requires memory storage since this digit must be held somewhere while the next sum is being done.

Addition by table can well be described as using *table look-up* procedure. When we come to multiplication, we have many tables and most of us did not enjoy memorising them. Our multiplication processes are done by table look-up, though, at first, we also did these by progressive counts. Table look-up is not a difficult arrangement to mechanise.

We should now look at the structure of a decimal number. Consider for example, the number 347; this is the sum of the three numbers: 300 + 40 + 7. These numbers expressed to the decimal radix, that is 10, are:

$$3 \times 10^2 + 4 \times 10^1 + 7 \times 10^0$$

The radix index is implied by the position of the digit with reference to the radix point. Here we have shown no radix point; we could write 347·0 and this would fix the significance unambiguously. Numbers to the right of the radix point are fractions; the sequence of indices continues:

$$347·15 = 3 \times 10^2 + 4 \times 10^1 + 7 \times 10^0 + 1 \times 10^{-1} + 5 \times 10^{-2}$$

and so on.

The position of the radix point is most important. The five digits 34715 represent a very different magnitude of number according to whether the radix point is to the left or right. The number is in fact *scaled* by the position of the point. When addition is performed, the radix points of the numbers to be added have to be aligned, that is the numbers put into the correct scale relative to each other. In multiplication the numbers do not require the same kind of alignment, though, in performing a long multiplication, many of us do align the radix points. If we do not, we none the less count the index positions to scale the answer. We shall meet the word 'scale' again later in connection with digital computers; we have already met it in connection with analogue computers.

Let us examine a quite simple multiplication process, by means of an example; suppose we wish to multiply 237 by 154. We write this sum down and carry it out as follows:

$$
\begin{array}{rl}
237 & \\
154 & \\
\hline
948 & (\times\ 4) \\
11850 & (\times\ 5 \times 10) \\
23700 & (\times\ 1 \times 10^2) \\
\hline
\end{array}
$$

Answer 36498

In detail, we commence by registering, that is, writing down the numbers. The word 'register' is used frequently in computer work to mean a device in which a number can be written, or held, or stored.

The next step is selecting the digit of lowest significance and doing a mental table look-up for 7 × 4. We register the 8, and mentally register the 2, which we must carry to the next stage. A machine to do this must also register both these figures. Now we do a table look-up of 4 × 3, and add the carried 2 to it and register the resultant digit 4 on paper, together with the carried 1 in our memory. Finally we look up 4 × 2, add the carried 1, and register the result. Next we commence with the 5, bearing in mind that it is in fact 5 × 10 = 50 and that the scaling of the partial total has to align it with the previous partial total. Finally we multiply by the one, representing 100. Note that the multiplication by one calls only for writing the number down, without any other process than alignment. Now a final addition gives the answer. This 'simple' process has entailed, *inter alia*, nine multiplication table look-ups, several stored carries and additions, two alignments and an addition sum in which several addition table look-ups have been called for in each digit position. To mechanise this process, all these steps have to be mechanised. None would be difficult but there are many of them.

4.2 Arithmetic to other radices

We work to radix ten because we are accustomed to doing so; it is not necessary, though, that we stick to ten. Consider for example the number to radix seven:

$$346_7 = 6 \times 7^0 + 4 \times 7^1 + 3 \times 7^2$$

This number corresponds to 181, radix ten. There is a corresponding number in every radix to every number in every other radix system. The smaller the radix chosen, the longer the number of the same magnitude, but otherwise each system is as good as every other. It is worthwhile to familiarise ourselves with working in other radices. Digital computers for reasons of convenience commonly work in numbers to radices two, eight and occasionally three. Circumstances might decree any other radix, though it does not seem likely at this time.

4.3 Conversion from one radix system to another

To convert from a system having a larger radix, to that of a smaller, is a fairly simple process, and there is a convenient drill for doing it. For instance, let us convert the number 181, radix ten, to a number, radix seven. We write the number as for normal division and divide by the radix to which we wish to convert, writing the remainder after each division on the right:

$$7)181 \quad 6 \text{ (remainder)}$$
$$7)\underline{\ 25} \quad 4 \qquad \text{,,}$$
$$\overline{\ \ \ 3}$$

When the number to be divided becomes too small, it is itself a remainder. We now read off the remainders in order, commencing from the last, giving 346, which is what we might have expected from the previous example.

Now let us take the same decimal number 181 and convert to radix two and then to radix eight using the same process:

radix 2:

2	181	1
2	90	0
2	45	1
2	22	0
2	11	1
2	5	1
2	2	0
	1	

radix 8:

8	181	5
8	22	6
	2	

Answer   10110101   Answer   265

If we now convert the digits 2, 6, 5 of the second sum also to radix two we get:

$$2 = 2^1 \qquad\quad = 10$$
$$6 = 2^2 + 2^1 = 110$$
$$5 = 2^2 + 2^0 = 101$$

Writing these sequentially we get 10110101, as we have for the answer to the radix two calculation by the direct method. A quick way of doing transformations to radix two is to do them to radix eight and write down the remainders in radix two form.

The student should try some examples of this method of conversion and think out the system carefully.

Conversion to the larger radix is not so convenient. The simplest way is to write the number as the sum of the digits to their various index powers. Again, when converting binary to decimal, which is the commonest mode, using the digits in threes and converting from eight is easiest.

For example:

$$10110101 = 2^0 = 1$$
$$2^2 = 4$$
$$2^4 = 16$$
$$2^5 = 32$$
$$2^7 = 128$$
$$\text{Answer} \quad \overline{181}$$

or

$$10110101: \quad 101 = 5 \times 8^0 = 5$$
$$110 = 6 \times 8^1 = 48$$
$$010 = 2 \times 8^2 = \overline{128}$$
$$\overline{181}$$

A look-up table for powers of 2 is useful.

4.4 Some binary arithmetic

Numbers expressed to the radix two are called *binary numbers* and the radix point is referred to as the *binary point* in the same way as we familiarly refer to the decimal point. Binary arithmetic using numbers expressed in this mode is the most common form of arithmetic used in present day digital computers. We shall examine the reasons for the choice in a later chapter; meanwhile it is advantageous to become familiar with arithmetic processes done in binary form. It is easiest to start at the beginning, as we did as children for decimal arithmetic. We have the advantage of understanding the meaning of indices or powers already, so we may speed up the process considerably.

Binary numbers have the same structure as any other numbers in that each digit represents an index significance, or power of the radix, multiplied by the digit value. Since the radix is two, the digit value can only be 0 or 1, which simplifies things. For example:

$$10110101 = 2^0 \times 1 + 2^1 \times 0 + 2^2 \times 1 + 2^3 \times 0 + 2^4 \times 1 + 2^5$$
$$\times 1 + 2^6 \times 0 + 2^7 \times 1$$

In counting the sequence is as follows:

$$0 = 0$$
$$1 = 1$$
$$10 = 2$$
$$11 = 3$$
$$100 = 4$$
$$101 = 5$$
$$110 = 6$$
$$111 = 7$$
$$1000 = 8$$

As in decimal counting we add one to the previous count and then carry one when we have a number equalling the radix.

The regularity of the pattern should be noticed: the last digit alternates between 0 and 1 at every step, the second digit gives two zeros and two ones alternately, the third digit, four zeros and four ones, and so on. This allows the table to be written very quickly when we need it.

Now we will try addition: again the process is simple, since the addition table is simple, viz:

	0	1
0	0	1
1	1	0

The sum requiring a 'carry' is, as before, on or below the diagonal of zeros and, in this case, there is only one such sum. Writing down two numbers to be added, and then adding, by table, gives, for example:

```
  101101101
  100110111
 ──────────
 1010100100   sum
  101111111   carry
```

It is a useful exercise to construct an addition table which includes carrys. There can only be eight combinations of three variables, each limited to two values, hence, calling the numbers a, b, c, where c is the carry from the previous stage of addition:

a	b	c	sum	carry
0	0	0	0	0
1	0	0	1	0
0	1	0	1	0
1	1	0	0	1
0	0	1	1	0
1	0	1	0	1
0	1	1	0	1
1	1	1	1	1

A similar table for subtraction can be made; here we subtract b from a, and subtract also any borrow c due to the previous stage of subtraction; algebraically we can write $a - (b + c)$. The table is as follows:

a	b	c	difference	borrow
0	0	0	0	0
1	0	0	1	0
0	1	0	1	1
1	1	0	0	0
0	0	1	1	1
1	0	1	0	0
0	1	1	0	1
1	1	1	1	1

Comparison of the answer columns (*sum* and *difference* in the two tables) may at first cause surprise since they are identical. We shall see later that this is a bonus for using binary arithmetic when we come to mechanising the process. Tables of the form we have been discussing will be referred to in the next chapter on logic as *truth tables*.

So far we have dealt with integral numbers. There is no difficulty in dealing with the arithmetic of fractions in the same way as we have already been doing integral arithmetic, so long as we align the binary point. We note that whereas in the decimal system a fraction $0\cdot125 = \frac{1}{10} + \frac{2}{100} +$

$\frac{5}{1000}$, the binary fraction $0 \cdot 1101 = \frac{1}{2} + \frac{1}{4} + \frac{1}{16}$; carpenters and similar craftsmen have long been in the habit of subdividing their measurements in a form of binary system. It depends on what *precision* is required for a measurement; we shall study the term 'precision' later on.

Turning now to multiplication; the multiplication table is again, rather simple:

$$1 \times 0 = 0$$
$$1 \times 1 = 1$$

Although the length of binary numbers makes them somewhat more unwieldy than decimal, the binary system might well have appealed to us as children, had we had the choice.

The drill for binary multiplication is the same as that for decimal; for example 1001011×11011 can be executed:

```
      1001011
        11011
      1001011
     1001011
    1001011
   1001011
  11111101001
```

The student will find it advantageous to convert these sums into decimal form and prove the results.

The following points are noteworthy when we analyse the process we have performed. First, when we have a one in the multiplier, we merely write down the multiplicand, unchanged, except in significance or alignment. For every significance, or digit position, the alignment means a shift of the number to the left by one place. The addition of the partial totals is complicated; it can be made more easy doing it piecemeal, using an addition table and working to a simple programme as follows:

(*a*) examine the least significant digit of the multiplier and if a one, write down the multiplicand; if a zero, do nothing;

(*b*) examine the next least significant digit of the multiplier and do as in (*a*) but if a one write down the multiplicand followed by a zero, that is, shifted one place to the left;

(*c*) examine the third least significant digit of the multiplier and do as before, but if a one the multiplicand should be shifted two places.

Each step will be seen to be the same. Now if a one occurs and the number is written down, the total so far should be added up at each stage and a cumulative total maintained. Then each addition of partial totals is an addition of two numbers only, with their appropriate carrys. Using the foregoing example:

(*a*) least significant digit is a one; write down the multiplicand;
(*b*) next least digit is a one; write down the multiplicand, shifted left one place, and add to the accumulated total:

$$\begin{array}{r} 1001011 \text{ from } (a) \\ 10010110 \text{ from } (b) \\ \hline \text{giving } 11100001 \end{array}$$

(*c*) the third digit is a zero; do nothing;
(*d*) and (*e*) the fourth and fifth digits are ones:

$$\begin{array}{r} 11100001 \quad \text{(previous partial total)} \\ \text{Add } 1001011000 \text{ from } (d) \\ \hline 1100111001 \\ \text{Add } 10010110000 \text{ from } (e) \\ \hline 11111101001 \end{array}$$

This gives the same answer as before, and we have used only the simplest of processes, i.e.:

determine if one or zero;
add according to addition table;
shift one place to the left.

The advantages of the binary system from the point of view of ease of mechanisation are very apparent from this example.

Mixed numbers and fractional numbers follow the same rules, but with fractional numbers, in order to maintain the scale, care has to be taken over the shifting process. The product of two fractions is a smaller fraction. The simplest way of doing this on paper is to scale up the numbers to integral numbers by the appropriate number of left shifts. The answer then requires to be shifted to the right the same number of shifts as the total of left shifts for the two numbers.

Division of binary numbers is done in the same way as division of decimal numbers, by what we familiarly call long division. It is not easy to mechanise in this form, but there is an artifice which makes it practicable. We need, however, to study the *signing* of numbers, first.

4.5 Positive and negative numbers

So far we have considered all numbers as positive, or rather, we have not considered the possibility of them being anything else. Arithmetic of this kind is said to be in the *unsigned mode*. Much of the work that computers do, especially in the field of data processing, can be in the unsigned mode. Extracting information from ledgers or files, sorting cards or keeping track of actual stocks of real commodities can be done without use of negative numbers. In this kind of work, when negative numbers do occur, it is usually possible for the programmer to arrange to keep track of negative values. In banking for instance, it is to be hoped that most accounts stay positive; the few that do not will normally be carefully scrutinized, whether by the machine or not. But in scientific and mathematical work there is the need for a system which can store, register and manipulate negative numbers according to mathematical laws. It will not normally be easy for the programmer to keep track of negative numbers that occur during the course of a calculation. Thus the machine must also be able to tell a negative number from a positive one and act accordingly. It is not in the nature of machines to recognise abstractions like negative numbers, and so this must be contrived by the designer.

The following mathematical statements indicate the nature of the problem: if a and b are two numbers and $a > b > 0$, then:

(a) $a + (-b) = a - b$ = subtract b from a;
(b) $a - (-b) = a + b$ = add b to a;
(c) $-a - b \quad = -(a + b)$; addition of negatives;
(d) $b - a \quad\quad = -(a - b)$; subtraction and change sign;
(e) $-a + b \quad = -(a - b)$; subtraction and change sign.

And in multiplication and division for example:

$f)\ -a \times -b = ab$;

$g)\ -a \div -b = \dfrac{-a}{-b} = \dfrac{a}{b}$

$h)\ -a \div b \quad = -\dfrac{a}{b}$; $b \div -a = -\dfrac{b}{a}$; and so on.

The machine must be arranged to recognise the sign and modify its processes according to the effect of the sign.

There are only the two signs, $+$ and $-$, and therefore the presence of a digit or its absence, attached to the beginning or end of a number would suffice as a suitable indicator of its sign. So long as this digit accompanied the number wherever it was stored or manipulated, then there need be no ambiguity. If we make the absence of the sign digit denote a positive number, this removes the need for the sign to be written before any number unless it is necessary to make it negative; this is our normal procedure in arithmetic anyway. The consideration which must now occur is, at which end do we write the sign, or hold the sign digit? Human mathematicians write it first; and scan the number from the most significant digit down to the least; then we commence arithmetic processes from the least significant end – unless it is for division. The computer does not worry about scanning the number first; it goes right into the arithmetic from the least significant end. It would appear therefore that the best position for the sign digit would be at the least significant end also, so that the computer could obey the sign instruction first. We shall see, later, that the sign digit or indicator is usually placed at the most significant end in spite of this, and we shall see why.

If we do use our indicator digit as suggested it is not difficult to arrange that the machine obeys the rules of arithmetic and modifies its arithmetic processes according to the sign. The main difficulty that has to be overcome is that of the example (*d*) above, that is, the subtraction of two positive numbers giving a negative answer, since here the machine must decide to generate a sign digit itself, after comparing the magnitudes of the two positive numbers. In all the other examples the machine merely follows a sequence of rules; in this one it has to make a decision as well, based on the recognition that a number has become negative; but we are here discussing only the arithmetic and not its mechanisation. The examples shown should give the reader an idea of the nature of the problem. It is worthwhile, though, to examine one technique of arithmetic working that is commonly used. Since it goes a long way to affording a simple solution to the problem of sign representation, the reason for its preference is apparent.

4.6 Arithmetic to 'modulo 2' with '2's complement' negative representation

Suppose we scale all our numbers within the range $-1 \leqslant n < 1$, that is, scale all our numbers to be fractions and we work in the binary mode. Suppose also, we make the rule that negative numbers are represented by their complement *modulo 2*, that is, complement with respect to two.

The binary number for 2 is 10. We write negative numbers as their complements, i.e. having subtracted them from 10. Remember that our working range is restricted to fractions. Then, for example, the binary fraction 0·11011, if negative will be transformed thus:

$$\begin{array}{r} 10\cdot00000 \\ \cdot11011 \\ \hline 1\cdot00101 \end{array}$$

It now has a one to the left of the binary point, which acts as a sign digit, and since it is outside the defined range it should make no other difference. We must of course make provision in every register, or store, in the computer to accommodate the digit to the left of the binary point.

The implication of the expression modulo 2 is that of working to radix two, or within the range limited by two. If a number exceeds two by a quantity a, then $2 + a = a$ since the excess two is out of range. Consider the binary fraction above, limited to the specified range; then 10 (binary) + ·11011 = 10·11011 and the leading one has gone out of range. In the machine register, we design only to accommodate one digit to the left of the binary point. We are at liberty then to consider all numbers virtually as two plus a fraction, or two minus a fraction. Some simple examples will show that this works. For a first example, the trivial one of adding −·11011 to +·11011.

Now,
$$\begin{array}{r} -\cdot11011 = 1\cdot00101 \\ +\cdot11011 = 10\cdot11011 \\ \hline 100\cdot00000 \end{array}$$

Notice that the answer comes, as we should expect, to zero, and the resultant one is out of range and we can neglect it.

A second example: subtract 0·625 from 0·78125, by complementation and addition.

·625 = ·101 and complementing gives 10 − ·101 = 1·011; ·78125 = ·11001

Adding, we get
$$\begin{array}{r} 1\cdot011 \\ 10\cdot11001 \\ \hline \text{Answer } 100\cdot00101 \end{array}$$

The leading one is out of range, whence the answer is positive and equals ·15625, as it should.

Now the difficult case can be tried, i.e. subtract ·78125 from ·625:

·78125 = ·11001 and complementing gives:

$$10 - ·11001 = 1·00111 = -·78125$$
$$\text{Add} \quad 10·101 \quad = \quad ·625$$
$$\overline{11·11011 = -·15625}$$

The leading one is 'borrowed from nowhere' and is out of range. The next one indicates a negative answer; it is therefore a complement Subtracting it from 10 we get:

$$\begin{array}{r} 10·00000 \\ 1·11011 \\ \hline 0·00101 \end{array}$$

which is positive and equals 0·15625. The result of this subtraction is the −·15625 which is correct.

A few similar exercises should be worked by the reader for practice Rather a useful bonus will be found when complementing, since th complement of a number modulo 2 can be written down by the followin, rule: change every zero to a one, and every one to a zero except the leas significant. It is also a useful exercise to work out why this is so.

We could write the above down more briefly, and generally, in algebrai notation. We would have the numbers a and b as binary fractions an $a > b$. Then the first example can be written $(2 + a) + (2 - a) =$ $4 + a - a = 0$; since the four is out of range, the answer is zero.

The second example:

$$2 + a + 2 - b = 4 + a - b = a - b;$$

and the third:

$$2 - a + 2 + b = 4 + (b - a);$$

but $a > b$ and we get $-(a - b)$ which is again the correct answer.

So far we have experimented with subtraction by complementation a addition. We need also to look at the subtraction of a negative numbe Algebraically we have $2 + a - (2 - b) = 0 + a + b$, which seems to l right.

Let us try it with our original fractions:

$$a = \quad ·78125 = \quad ·11001$$
$$-b = \quad -·625 \quad = 1·011 \quad \text{after complementing}$$

Subtracting, we have 1·01101, which is the wrong answer. The reason for this is very important; we have defined our working range so that all numbers lie between −1 and +1, and this must also include the numbers resulting from our calculation. The sum of the two fractions here exceeds one and has gone out of range. In an arithmetic unit in a computer, this may happen and it is up to the programmer to prevent it; he may require, however, to be informed of the event, so the machine designer will have another consideration to take care of, that is, some means of indicating when a number has gone out of range.

Returning to the example, let us scale the problem so that it does not go out of range, by dividing each number by two before we commence and then scaling back afterwards. This division, in binary, is merely a right shift of one place:

$$a = ·11001; \qquad \text{rescaled } a/2 = ·011001$$
$$b = ·101; \qquad \text{rescaled } b/2 = ·0101$$

$-\dfrac{b}{2}$ is given by $10 - ·0101 = 1·1011$

Then $\dfrac{a}{2} - \dfrac{(-b)}{2} =$

```
            ·011001
          1·1011
         _____
       (1)0·101101
```

The leading one is a borrow from nowhere, but is out of range anyway. The remaining number when left shifted one place to restore it to the original magnitude is 1·01101. Note that this leading one is not a sign digit. Now 1·01101 = 1·40625 which is, at last, correct.

The explanation and examples shown should have given the reader enough insight into this mode of arithmetic to be able to make up and work out problems demonstrating that it works in all the circumstances of addition and subtraction. It should be noted that if the system is mechanised, or employed in a computer arithmetic unit, the machine has to do nothing except follow the laid down rules for addition and subtraction. The numbers themselves do the rest. The machine is not forced to recognise the sign of any number, whether in store, or generated within the calculation; this shows yet another bonus for the binary mode. It is to be regretted, however, that the simplicity found in addition and subtraction is largely lost in multiplication and division. For algebraically, we can see:

$$(2 + a) \times (2 + b) = 4 + 2a + 2b + ab$$

$$\text{and} \quad (2 + a) \times (2 - b) = 4 + 2a - 2b - ab$$

The last term is the required answer; the four is out of range, but the $2a$ and $2b$ terms are not necessarily so. To make the system work for multiplication a small sub-programme has to be performed so that we get: $(2 + a) \times (2 + b) = 4 + 2a + 2b + ab - 2a - 2b$, and the two ancillary subtractions follow the multiplication as a correction. Even this is not too forbidding, since $2a$ and $2b$ are only the original numbers, left shifted once. Several of the older machines used, and still use, this sub-programme for multiplication.

4.7 Binary division

We shall consider in this section only divisions of the form $[a \div b; b > a]$, that is, in which the quotient is a fraction. It is a common limitation on computer arithmetic; study of the process, and of its implementation, later in this book should convince the reader of why this is so.

Consider the following division:

$$10001111 \div 10110000 = a \div b$$

Using the familiar methods of ordinary long division, we have:

```
 ·1101        = quotient
 ┌─────────
 │10001111·0
 │1011000·0
 └─────────
   110111·0
   1011
  ─────────
   001011
   1011
  ─────────
   0000
```

Looking at the process, as we have at the other arithmetical processes, we see that we have done several mental processes which we have not recorded. In the first place we made a trial subtraction to establish: $b > a$. We then wrote down b, shifted right one place, that is, divided by two. The subtraction then gave a positive remainder; we wrote down $b/4$, and subtracted; this gave a positive remainder. In each case the quotient was one; by inspection, we saw that the next remainder, due to subtracting $b/8$ was going to lead to a negative remainder. We wrote the quotient digit as zero and subtracted, instead, $b/16$. The quotient in this case gave a one since the subtraction did not leave a negative remainder.

For a division machine, each step must be mechanised; inspection is not possible, so we have to try each subtraction, and if the remainder is negative restore the dividend to what it was before the trial. Let us take the same example, using the *restoring* method, and scaling into fractions:

0·10001111	$= a$
0·10110000	(trial subtraction)
1·11011111	(negative remainder)
0·10110000	(add, to restore)
0·10001111	$(= a)$
0·01011000	$(= b/2)$
0·00110111	(R > 0); quotient = 0·1
0·00101100	$(= b/4)$
0·00001011	(R > 0); quotient = 0·11
0·00010110	$(= b/8)$
1·11110101	(R < 0); quotient = 0·110
0·00010110	(restore $b/8$)
0·00001011	
0·00001011	$(= b/16)$
0·00000000	(R = 0); quotient = 0·1101

If the process is continued, a series of negative remainders will occur. A machine will have to have some means provided for stopping the process when the necessary number of significant figures is reached.

The restoring technique is manifestly clumsy and time-wasting due to the restorations. An artifice exists for eliminating the unwanted steps.

.8 Non-restoring binary division

Consider the numbers a and b as before; $b > a$. Now,

$$a - b + \frac{b}{2} = a - \frac{b}{2}$$

The expression $a - \frac{b}{2}$ corresponds to the second, that is, the first *success-ful*, subtraction, in the earlier example; we reached it by restoring only half the original subtractor. The principle of the system is apparent if we consider the meaning of the binary fraction which forms the quotient:

$$Q = \frac{q_1}{2} + \frac{q_2}{4} + \frac{q_3}{8} + \frac{q_4}{16}, \ldots$$

where $q_1, q_2, q_3, q_4, \ldots$ are each equal to one or zero, according as $b/2$, $b/4$ etc., were smaller or larger than the remainder of a.

Dividing, thus, gives:

```
        0·10001111
       -0·10110000      (= b)
        ----------
        1·11011111      (R < 0) Q = 0
       +0·01011000      (= b/2)
        ----------
        0·00110111      (R > 0) Q = 0·1
       -0·00101100      (= b/4)
        ----------
        0·00001011      (R > 0) Q = 0·11
       -0·00010110      (= b/8)
        ----------
        1·11110101      (R < 0) Q = 0·110
       +0·00001011      (= b/16)
        ----------
        0·00000000      (R = 0) Q = 0·1101
```

To mechanise this process will be more simple and elegant than the mechanisation of the restoring method. The procedure that must be followed can be summarised:

(a) subtract b from a;
(b) test for negative remainder;
(c) if remainder is negative, add $b/2$;
    if remainder is positive subtract $b/2$;
(d) test for negative remainder;   and so on.

Every time we have a positive remainder, set a one in the quotient and after every negative remainder, set a zero.

We shall see later, that this process can be fairly simply implemented in an arithmetic unit.

4.9 Range and precision

We have already mentioned the terms scale and range. It is important to appreciate fully the meaning of range that is, the working range into which all numbers occurring in a calculation have to be scaled. This is also called the *natural range*.

For instance, in systems working in fractions, the natural range is between zero and one, or in signed fractions, between -1 and $+1$. Whatever the problem may be, scientific or data processing, all numbers used or occurring in the calculation must be between these limits. There is no insurmountable difficulty in working under this restriction. The load falls on the programmer and he is generally quite happy to bear it since the computer can give him so many other advantages, those of speed and accuracy, for instance. The range of a machine is governed by the mode of arithmetic used; this is immediately apparent in the case of arithmetic using complement modulo 2.

The precision of the calculation, or of the arithmetic unit that does the calculation, is a very different consideration, and depends on the number of digits to which any number used is to be defined. For instance, four decimal digits give a precision, that is, a number definition to one in 10 000. Four binary digits give a precision of one in sixteen. The use of the term is exactly analogous to its use in metrology. A measurement to an accuracy of one ten-thousandth of an inch requires four significant figures to express it. In binary, a carpenters' rule needs to be divided into sixteenths to measure to a sixteenth, i.e. the fourth binary significance. If a calculation has to be performed to a particular accuracy, that accuracy specifies the precision required in registering the numbers in the calculation. Once again, note the difference between scale and precision; a computer having registration facilities for thirty-two digits to a number has its precision defined by these thirty-two digit positions in its registers. The significance of the digits may be arbitrary or depending on the range, which is dictated by the mode of operation.

.10 Floating point working

Before concluding this brief survey of arithmetic there is one more very important mode of arithmetic that should be examined; this is called *floating point* arithmetic. In all the arithmetic we have discussed so far, the binary point has been assumed as fixed arbitrarily at some point in the scale, and at some point in the corresponding computer register. Then, given this fixed position, the scale of numbers within the working range is also fixed. For some scientific problems the scale called for is very large, and scaling problems are such that they seriously impede the progress of calculation.

In order to increase the range of a computer's calculating powers, floating point operation is used, though generally, only in the larger and more sophisticated computers can this be provided by hardware. In this method of arithmetic a number is registered in two parts, commonly called the *fraction* and the *exponent*; the form of representation is analogous to logarithms. The fraction expresses the number, and its precision depends, as always, on the number of digits used to express it or register it. It usually also carries a sign indicator. The exponent is a number which defines the position of the radix point, and therefore the scale of the number or magnitude of the number. For example a number could appear registered as:

0010	+	2345678

The left-hand box holds the exponent, the middle box the sign, and the right-hand box the fraction. The left-hand box contains the number 10 which indicates that the decimal point is ten places from the right-hand end of the natural range of the computer. The decimal point is normally taken to be at the left-hand end of the fraction, that is, immediately preceding the most significant digit. The computer range is still arbitrary. Suppose for instance it is designed so that the range lies between 10^{100} and 10^{-100}, as it could with the arrangement shown, then the number 1·0 would appear as ·1 in the fraction box and 99 in the exponent box. The number shown above would be 0·000 234 567 8. This system gives an enormous range, even in binary operation, where four digits of exponent would only imply a natural range of sixteen binary places or 2^{16}, that is, 65 536; to hold this number of significant digits would require sixteen register positions. Large computers using this system permit (literally) astronomical calculations to be done without much scaling being called for. Like all advantages, there is an accompanying price to be paid. The arithmetic becomes more complicated.

For addition or subtraction in floating point operation, the numbers must first be aligned in magnitude. This entails examining the exponents and shifting one or other of the numbers, the number of places or shifts being defined by the difference between their exponents. Multiplication and division can be done with the fractions in any alignment, and here the exponents are added or subtracted to give the resultant exponent. Signs still need to be regarded, and arrangements have to be made to realign numbers which advance over the radix point position, either through the agency of the programmer or by mechanisms in the machine itself.

4.11 Summary

We have rather briefly scanned the typical processes of arithmetic of the kind one might expect a computer to cope with. The important points which have come to light are:

(*a*) even 'simple' arithmetic processes can be difficult, or at least, complicated, when they have to be mechanised;

(*b*) the actual meaning of numbers is immaterial to a machine, and the mechanisation of a problem must be so that the numbers are manipulated correctly, to give the desired answers, though the process may not be truly arithmetic;

(*c*) numbers may be signed or unsigned and the machine needs to be contrived to operate accordingly;

(*d*) the range and precision of numbers in a calculation define the requirements for a machine to do the calculation. The range can be dealt with by scaling, but the precision required defines register length, and hence complexity. The mode of arithmetic used defines the natural range of the machine;

(*e*) the use of floating point techniques offers advantages of great range, but with added complexity.

Suggestions for further reading

Planning a Computer System – Project Stretch by W. Bucholz. McGraw-Hill, 1962. Portions of this book which are of particular interest are Chapter 5 pp. 42–58 and Chapter 8 pp. 92–104.

5 Logic

5.1 Logic and the computer

In an examination of arithmetic processes in Chapter 4 we saw that numbers expressed in binary form could be added and multiplied by using the simplest of tables. The symbols used in each table were restricted to the values one and zero. The process of addition, for instance, could be accomplished like this, for two numbers a and b:

if a and b are both zero: answer is zero;
if a or b is one (but not both): answer is one;
if a and b are ones: answer is zero.

Likewise simple multiplication, $a \times b$, could be accomplished like this:

if either a or b is zero: answer is zero;
if neither a nor b is zero: answer is one.

We saw also that a table of eight sets of values could accomplish the more complicated addition process of $a + b + c$ where c is the carry figure from the previous addition.

Now consider these statements. 'The course is open to male students. Joan is a female: Joan cannot enter the course' or 'sons are male; daughters are female. John is male; Joan is female: John is a son; Joan is a daughter.' These are examples of logical statements in that they contain conclusions drawn as consequences of the given propositions. In the same way the statements about addition and multiplication of a and b above are also logical statements.

Propositional logic deals with logical deductions from propositions; the essence of the subject is to reduce statements to their simplest form and to make deductions that are unambiguous and correct. The 'truth table' summaries we have already examined are deductions based on simple unambiguous propositions and can be said, therefore, to be logically deduced. Thus we see that we can reduce the arithmetic processes of addition and multiplication to simple applications of logic. This is not to suggest, of course, that mathematical or arithmetical processes are in general logical: we merely remark that we have achieved a process arithmetic without using arithmetic, that is, without using numbers except the symbols 1 and 0, and these need not have any numerical significance.

Since computers cannot understand or appreciate numbers, it is by logical means that they are made to carry out mathematical processes. For instance, we may agree on a convention that 10 volts represents a one and 0 volts a zero; to perform a binary addition process we need to construct a circuit having two inputs and one output, such that the output/input relationship conforms to the rules:

for 0 volts on each input: output is 0 volts;
for 0 volts on one input and 10 volts on the other: output is 10 volts;
for 10 volts on both inputs: output is 0 volts.

Interpreting the output condition according to the voltage convention we have agreed, we have performed addition electrically and logically, though not numerically.

The parts of computing systems which perform arithmetic and other functions, based on logical rules, have come to be called *logic units* or, simply, the *logic* of the computer. In the early days of computer development most of these devices were designed by trial and error and sheer ingenuity. As the requirements have become increasingly complicated this method of design has become less effective and designs have often been inefficient and uneconomical; engineers and logic designers have developed techniques to help solve problems of machine logic – the techniques of *combinational* and *sequential logic*. The first of these is culled directly from the mathematicians' work on symbolic logic; the second is still in the state of evolution and a good deal of work remains to be done on it, to render it a convenient tool. It is of considerable advantage for a computer engineer to have a thorough understanding of combinational logic and at least an acquaintance with the scope of sequential logic.

The time has already arrived when problems of computer design are being solved on computers: symbolic logic techniques are amenable to programming and some computers are now built with facilities for the solution of logic problems.

Historical background

Aristotle was the first logician of note to be chronicled: his work entitles him to be remembered as the father or founder of formal logic. He did so much that little was added to the science for several centuries. For several hundred years prior to the Renaissance wise men were preoccupied with problems such as the number of angels that could be accommodated in the eye of a needle, which did not lend themselves to mathematical logic.

After the Renaissance, the concept of scientific thought grew rapidly. Leibniz, who also evolved the infinitesimal calculus, set in motion symbolic logic, the formal logic of the mathematician. There was little of particular interest to the computer engineer, however, until in 1854 George Boole wrote a paper entitled 'An Investigation of the Laws of Thought'. Among other things, Boole suggested that propositions could be labelled with symbols in the form of an algebra, and that the symbols could be manipulated according to a set of algebraic rules. The expressions resulting from the algebra could then be used to make logical deductions immediately and unambiguously. The exact nature of the propositions was unimportant; once transformed to algebra, the process of deducing truth or falsity of a statement was merely a matter of the use of symbols and following the rules. The resulting deductions could then be drawn from reconsidering the original propositions when substituted for the symbols. A very simple illustration of this technique is as follows: a proposition can be true or false and we can take true and false to have the analogues one and zero. Then a true statement can be seen to be cancelled by a false one, for $1 \times 0 = 0$; two false statements do not make a truth, for $0 \times 0 = 0$, but two truths give only truth, for $1 \times 1 = 1$. Boole's work was considerably more advanced than the study we shall pursue. He evolved the series of algebras, now known as *Boolean algebras*, and contributed a great deal to set theory and similar studies. The basis of the engineers' combinational logic is one form of Boolean algebra.

After Boole, several other mathematicians and philosophers advanced the study of symbolic logic, notably Pierce, Russell, De Morgan, Stamm and Sheffer. Most of these names will become familiar to the student since processes and theorems have been called after them. If students of engineering ever have any leisure, it is rewarding to spend some of it in looking up the work of these men. Engineering design depends a great deal on logical thought and these men were preoccupied with making logic useful, and thought as precise as possible.

Just as in the calculating machine field there was little development after Babbage's death until 1938, when Aiken commenced his relay computer, likewise, engineering interest in symbolic logic was slight until Claude E Shannon published his paper 'A Symbolic Analysis of Relay and Switching Circuits', also in 1938.

Since then, the studies of combinational and sequential logic have grown up alongside the growth of computers and the techniques are becoming well established.

5.3 Symbolic logic: introduction to sets, Venn diagrams and De Morgan's Theorem

A fundamental concept of symbolic logic is classification: by dividing things, whether real objects or statements or propositions into classes, or sets, they can be defined to any degree of precision. We have already met the term precision, and its meaning here is analogous to its meaning in the context of number definition.

We may, for instance, take the class of living beings and we can sub-divide this in many ways: male or female, human or animal or vegetable, into species, genera, racial groups, age groups, by temperament, or even by name and address. This last classification should define uniquely a single person out of all the class of living beings; he is the unique member of a class of one. All other beings are non-members of that class.

By classifying we make each thing a member of a class, or classes, and a non-member of other classes: to the question 'Is the thing a member of this or that class?' the answer is simply yes or no.

The statement that a thing is a member of a certain class is either true or false. If we define anything in terms of the classes to which it belongs, or does not belong, then to whatever precision we want the definition, it can always be reduced to a series of binary statements, that is, yes or no, or true or false types of propositions. Note again that the word 'thing' is used here in its widest possible sense, and can mean abstractions as well as realities.

Suppose we denote classes by symbols, say letters, then we could allot the symbols as follows to form a classification:

$$living = L$$
$$human = H$$
$$male = M$$
$$English = E$$
$$student = S$$

A member of all these classes would be classified LHMES, live *and* human *and* male *and* English *and* student. An English girl student could not have the same classification: she is a non-member of the class of males. We denote maleness M and it is customary in symbolic logic to denote non-membership by the symbol for the class with a bar over it e.g. $\overline{M}$, or by a prime e.g. M'. We will, here, use the barred symbol. Then a male is classified M and a non-male $\overline{M}$; our female student will be classified LH$\overline{M}$ES.

We can advance the technique further by giving the numerical value 1 (one) to a class and to membership of the class, and 0 (zero) to non-membership. M = 1, $\overline{M}$ = 0, for instance. Substituting the permitted values for the variables (symbols) we get:

LHMES = $1 \times 1 \times 1 \times 1 \times 1 = 1$ for the male student;

and

LH$\overline{M}$ES = $1 \times 1 \times 0 \times 1 \times 1 = 0$ for the female.

Anything completely fulfilling the classification requirement will have the value one. All other things will have the value zero. If we denote the class of English male students as X, then all other things are $\overline{X}$. It should be noted that some classes imply others – if we assume students all to be alive and human, in this exercise we can omit L and H without reducing our precision.

This kind of symbolic logic can be studied using an ingenious and very simple diagram, the Venn diagram. Fig. 5.1 shows the conditions for X and $\overline{X}$ on a Venn diagram.

The whole class of things, that is, the *universal class* is represented by

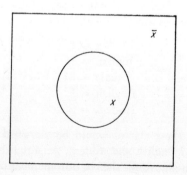

Fig. 5.1

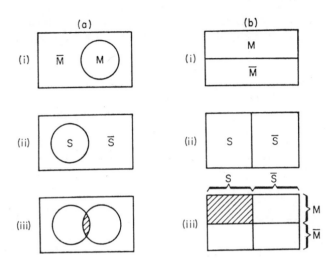

Fig. 5.2

the rectangle. The ringed area denotes all things of the class x; everything in the rectangle, but not in x, is in $\bar{x}$. We note that $x + \bar{x} = \text{universe} = 1$; also $x = 1$ thus $\bar{x} = 0$. This Venn diagram is rather trivial; but now consider the case, where the universal class, that is the rectangle, denotes all human beings. We allot areas M for all males and S for all students. The classical Venn diagram is shown in Fig. 5.2(a); it is sometimes easier, though not so general, to make our divisions or classifications as in Fig. 5.2(b).

Combining the diagrams (i) and (ii), the males and the students, gives (iii), where the shaded area denotes the class of male students, that is, all the people who are male *and* student. The larger area, made up of M or S, includes all people who are male or student, or both. The area outside is all human beings who are neither male nor student.

Working from this set of diagrams we can introduce some definitions: the shaded area is called the area of *intersection*, and the formal symbolic logic symbol for the process of intersection is $\wedge$ or $\cap$. The shaded area is thus denoted by the symbols $M \wedge S$ or $M \cap S$. The total area included in the rings is called the area of *union* and the symbol for union is $\vee$ or $\cup$: the area is thus $M \vee S$ or $M \cup S$.

In combinational logic we go a stage further towards the mathematics with which we are familiar and use the symbols . and +. The symbol .

denotes logical multiplication or AND; the symbol + denotes logical addition or OR. We can describe the diagram as follows using these symbols:

Male students, that is, the class of male and student, are denoted by M.S or simply MS;
the whole ringed area covers the class of humans who are males or students, that is M + S.

We introduce here another symbol to denote the classification of males or students who are not both that is, non-student males and female students. These occupy the areas within the rings but exclude the area of intersection. We denote this class $M \oplus S$, where the ringed plus sign $\oplus$ is called *exclusive OR*, that is, 'M or S, but not both.'

We can progress further using the Venn diagram. How do we denote the class of people who are not in either ring? Or the class not in the area of intersection? The area of intersection we denote MS; then the people outside it, whether male, student, or neither, must be $\overline{MS}$. Likewise the people outside both rings, (the lower right-hand section in b (iii)), must be $\overline{M + S}$. The bar here is extended to cover the whole expression for:

If P = MS then NOT P = $\overline{P}$ = $\overline{MS}$ and if Q = M + S then NOT Q = $\overline{Q}$ = $\overline{M + S}$.

The people who are not male, $\overline{M}$, and those who are not students, $\overline{S}$, are all the people outside the shaded area; they are the class $\overline{M} + \overline{S}$. But the shaded area = MS; therefore $\overline{MS}$ = $\overline{M} + \overline{S}$.

The people who are outside both rings are not the class $\overline{M} + \overline{S}$; they are the class of both $\overline{M}$ *and* $\overline{S}$ that is $\overline{M}.\overline{S}$. We have therefore the equalities.

$$\overline{MS} = \overline{M} + \overline{S} \quad \text{and} \quad \overline{M}\,\overline{S} = \overline{M + S}$$

where $\overline{M + S}$ is the class of people who are not either male or student.

These equalities may be proved by *perfect induction* which means 'suck it and see', a little more elegantly. We write down the expression and put in all possible values of the variables, and tabulate the results. The possible values are one and zero. For instance:

(a)	(b)	(c)	(d)	(e)	(f)	(g)	(h)	(i)	(j)
M	S	MS	$\overline{MS}$	M + S	$\overline{M+S}$	$\overline{M}$	$\overline{S}$	$\overline{M}\,\overline{S}$	$\overline{M}+\overline{S}$
0	0	0	1	0	1	1	1	1	1
1	0	0	1	1	0	0	1	0	1
0	1	0	1	1	0	1	0	0	1
1	1	1	0	1	0	0	0	0	0

Note that in column (e), M + S = 1, for M = 1 and S = 1. A whole class, for instance, the universal class = 1; thus if we add one and one we gain nothing; the answer is one and only one. This is the essential difference between logical addition and arithmetical addition. The explanation emerges if we consider the significance of the one: it has the significance of 100 per cent, that is, full membership, while zero has the significance of 0 per cent, or non-membership. Unity is here a quality not a quantity.

We see from the table that $\overline{M+S} = \overline{M}\,\overline{S}$ and $\overline{MS} = \overline{M}+\overline{S}$, for all M, S, but there are no other complete equalities for all values of the variables.

The tabular form shown is called a truth table, where the one denotes true, and the zero denotes false; it is used in formal logic to test the equivalence of statements. When two expressions or statements correspond exactly, for all values of the input variables or propositions, then they are equivalent, and equating them gives an *identity*.

The two identities we have shown here are known as De Morgan's Theorems after the first Professor of Mathematics of the University of London, who propounded them. They will be found useful later in the simplification of networks of gates and switches.

This introduction may seem very remote from the design of digital computers, but the tables we examined earlier, for the addition of numbers, are truth tables. Gates and switches having two states can be represented by variables having the values 0 and 1, and can be combined in a logical manner to give a desired result. Then, using the algebraic expressions for gate and switch arrangements, they can be manipulated by means of theorems like De Morgan's and reduced to the most suitable or convenient form.

5.4 Combinational logic

5.4.1 Complementation

Let x be a two-valued variable, taking the values one and zero: if y is dependent on x and is restricted, likewise, to the values one and zero, then we can write a table of values for $y = f(x)$, as follows:

x	$f(x)$			
	$y = 1$	$y = 0$	$y = x$	$y = \bar{x}$
0	1	0	0.	1
1	1	0	1	0

The first two functions, $y = 1$, $y = 0$, are trivial; the third function, $y = x$, is called the identity function and requires no explanation. The fourth function $y = \bar{x}$ is called the complement of x and is seen to take the value zero when x is one, and one when x is zero. We call the symbol $\bar{x}$ 'x bar', and we refer to the variable x in this form as *complemented*.

Using the binary substitution we see that:

$$\bar{1} = 0$$
$$\bar{0} = 1$$

It follows, too, that $(\bar{\bar{x}}) = x$, or the complement of $\bar{x}$ is x.

A logic element realising the function $f(x)$ may be denoted on a diagram as in Fig. 5.3.

Since the variables are two-valued, the operation of complementation

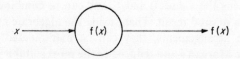

Fig. 5.3

is also that of *inversion*, when the function is practically implemented. For, if we allot, in a practical circuit, x volts for one and y volts for zero, then, for x volts input to the circuit, we must get y volts out, and vice versa. This process is performed by an *inverter*.

Since the variables are two-valued, then the function $y = \bar{x}$ can also be referred to as NOT x; the symbol corresponding to NOT x, in formal symbolic logic is $\neg\, x$.

5.4.2 The binary operations AND, OR and exclusive OR

If x and y are variables each able to take the values one and zero, we can define three functions $f(x,y)$, $g(x,y)$, $h(x,y)$ by means of a truth table:

		$f(x,y)$	$g(x,y)$	$h(x,y)$
x	y	xy	$x + y$	$x \oplus y$
0	0	0	0	0
1	0	0	1	1
0	1	0	1	1
1	1	1	1	0

The function $f(x,y) = xy$ we call *logical multiplication*.
The function $g(x,y) = x + y$ we call *logical addition*.
The function $h(x,y) = x \oplus y$ we call *sum modulo* 2 *addition*.

We have previously seen that:

$xy = x$ AND y
$x + y = x$ OR y
$x \oplus y = x$ or y, but not both, that is, exclusive OR. Since $\overline{xy}$ is NOT xy, that is NOT (x AND y), we see that the *word statement* for $x \oplus y$, x OR y, but not both, could be written in symbols as $(x + y)$ AND NOT xy which is $(x + y)\, \overline{xy}$

We have already seen, from De Morgan's Theorem that $\overline{xy} = \bar{x} + \bar{y}$, whence, using simple algebra, we get:

$$x \oplus y = (x + y)\, \overline{xy} = (x + y)\, (\bar{x} + \bar{y})$$

Whence,

$$x \oplus y = x\bar{x} + y\bar{y} + \bar{x}y + \bar{y}x$$

Now, when $x = 0$, $\bar{x} = 1$, when $y = 0$, $\bar{y} = 1$, and when $x = 1$, $\bar{x} = 0$; $y = 1$, $\bar{y} = 0$; then $x\bar{x}$ and $y\bar{y}$ must always be zero and: $x \oplus y = x\bar{y} + \bar{x}y$.

This is a useful identity which we call *anticoincidence* since it takes the value one so long as x and y are not coincident in value. The *coincidence* function given by $xy + \bar{x}\bar{y}$ is also used in computer circuit design. It is written, symbolically, as $x \equiv y$.

5.4.3 Operations and connectives

The simple example above shows how algebra can be used to transform one logical expression into another. It also demonstrates the use of the symbols and words for AND, OR and NOT. The manipulation of the variable x, y, to form the expressions, x AND y, x OR y, that is, xy and $x + y$, is called a *logical operation*. The word AND together with the symbols ., $\wedge$, $\cap$, to which it is equivalent, is called a *logical connective* since it is used to connect two propositions. In the same way OR is a connective, together with its symbols $+$, $\vee$ and $\cup$.

NOT is an operation, but we shall meet later the special connectives NOT OR and NOT AND.

5.4.4 Connectives

There are sixteen ways in which two variables x, y, each having two values, can be combined, or connected. The truth table opposite is the complete table of values which defines the operations and their associated connectives. The combinational logic and symbolic logic symbols are shown against each function, where they exist.

We have already examined f2, the AND function, and f8, the OR function. We can also recognise f7 and f10, the exclusive OR and coincidence functions; the latter is also called the *identity function* or *match*.

The functions f1 and f16 are trivial; the functions f3, f4, f5, f6, f11, f13, f14, are of no particular interest and can be ignored. The implication function we shall meet again in simplification procedures, but it is otherwise of no interest to us. Reverting to conventional arithmetic, we have dismissed ten functions as of no interest, we have identified four more and examined them; we are left with two, therefore, and these two are of particular interest. They are f9, the NOT OR or NOR function, called

x	0	0	1	1	logic symbol	combin-ational logic form	common name
y	0	1	0	1			
f_1	0	0	0	0	0	0	
f_2	0	0	0	1	$x \wedge y$	xy	AND
f_2	0	0	1	0	$x \wedge \neg y$	$x\bar{y}$	
f_4	0	0	1	1	x	x	
f_5	0	1	0	0	$\neg x \wedge y$	$\bar{x}y$	
f_6	0	1	0	1	y	y	
f_7	0	1	1	0	$x \not\vee y$	$x \oplus y$	exclusive OR
f_8	0	1	1	1	$x \vee y$	$x + y$	OR
f_9	1	0	0	0	$x \downarrow y$	$\overline{x + y}$	NOR
f_{10}	1	0	0	1	$x \equiv y$	$xy + \bar{x}\bar{y}$	coincidence
f_{11}	1	0	1	0	$\neg y$	$\bar{y}$	
f_{12}	1	0	1	1	$x + \neg y$	$x + \bar{y}$	implication
f_{13}	1	1	0	0	$\neg x$	$\bar{x}$	
f_{14}	1	1	0	1	$\neg x + y$	$\bar{x} + y$	implication
f_{15}	1	1	1	0	x/y	$\overline{xy}$	NOT AND or NAND
f_{16}	1	1	1	1	1	1	

also the *dagger function* or *Pierce function*, after its originator, and the NOT AND or NAND function, called also the *stroke* or *Sheffer function*, also after its originator. We have met both these functions before in connection with De Morgan's Theorem. We can verify the expressions NOR $= \overline{x + y}$ and NAND $= \overline{xy}$, from the truth table.

5.4.5 Universal functions

We have already postulated that all logical processes can be achieved with the trio AND, OR and NOT; intuitively, we find these the easiest connectives and operations to use. In the electrical or electronic implementation of logic, we must design and provide three different types of elements: AND gates, OR gates, and INVERTERS.

The power of the Pierce and Sheffer functions lies in the fact that they are each *universal functions*, that is, all logical processes can be carried out, using either one of these functions exclusively. A logic element which meets the requirement of one or the other can be used to provide for all required logical processes: only one standard unit need be designed and provided for the whole system. That these connectives and the logic elements derived from them are universal, can easily be seen from the following diagrams.

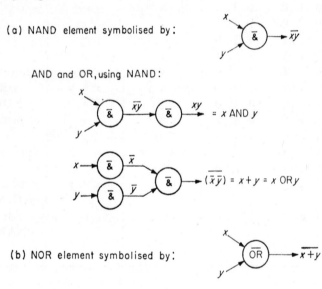

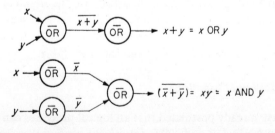

Fig. 5.4

It is to be noted that these elements are also inverters: if all inputs are made x, the output is $\bar{x}$. The design of elements to perform NAND and NOR functions using transistors and conventional electronic components is convenient and economical. For this reason many logic systems are engineered exclusively from these elements.

5.4.6 Gates

We have considered logic elements so far as having one or two inputs, and we have mentioned the word *gate*. In computer engineering usage, a logic element is referred to as a gate. In general, a gate may have any number of inputs. Customarily, the number of inputs is restricted to three or four for engineering reasons.

The term 'gate' arises from the gating action of a logic unit. Consider the AND unit: The gate has two inputs x and y; we may use y as the control, and then if y is 'down', that is zero, then the output is zero, whatever the value of x. If we now make y equal one, that is,

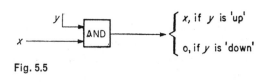

Fig. 5.5

set y 'up', then the output will conform to x, or x will be passed by the gate.

5.4.7 Symbolic representation of gates and logic elements

There are many notations in well established use to represent logic elements, gates, inverters etc., in logic diagrams. The important requirement is that the diagram shall be as simple and self-explanatory as possible. In this book we shall use the following convention:

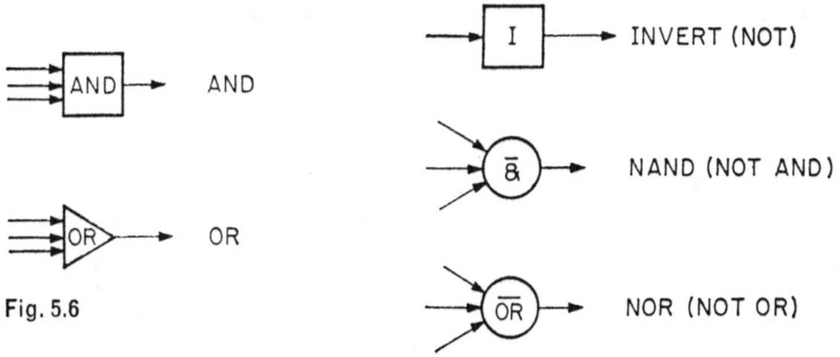

AND   AND

OR   OR

Fig. 5.6

I   INVERT (NOT)

$\bar{a}$ NAND (NOT AND)

$\overline{OR}$ NOR (NOT OR)

5.5 The evolution of logic networks

Let us consider the problem of designing a network of logic elements to achieve a binary addition; in the first instance, we will confine ourselves to the simplest form, the logic required to add x to y, where x and y can take the values one and zero. We are already familiar with the truth table:

x	y	sum
0	0	0
1	0	1
0	1	1
1	1	0

This is the truth table for sum modulo 2 addition, so we shall also be designing an anticoincidence unit. It is apparent that the right answer will be given by a simple OR unit for the first three of the four input combinations, viz: $0 + 0 = 0$, $0 + 1 = 1$ and $1 + 0 = 1$. The OR unit, however, gives a one output, also, for $1 + 1$, whereas we need a zero output. We need, therefore, to inhibit the output of the OR unit, or invert it, for the condition of $x = y = 1$, that is, when x *and* y are one. The need for an AND element is indicated, when x and y are both one, which will give a one output. If this is inverted, we shall have a zero for $x = y = 1$ and this can be used to inhibit the OR gate output. The arrangement to achieve this is shown in Fig. 5.7.

This form of adder, which includes no carry facilities is called a *half-adder*. The more complicated arrangement that generates a carry and takes into account the carry from the previous addition is called a *full-adder*.

The circuit shown could be simplified by replacing the AND and I

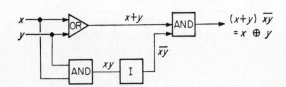

Fig. 5.7

by a NAND. This would mean that there would be a general requirement for yet another unit, making four. It is common practice to work either within the framework of AND, OR, NOT or NAND or NOR, but not to mix them.

5.6 The design of a full adder

The first step in any design is to define the requirement as precisely as possible. This may be done in words as a word statement, but in logical design it is frequently done by writing down the truth table. We have already evolved a truth table for full addition in Chapter 4. We repeat it here for convenience.

a	b	c	sum $= d$	carry $= c'$
0	0	0	0	0
1	0	0	1	0
0	1	0	1	0
1	1	0	0	1
0	0	1	1	0
1	0	1	0	1
0	1	1	0	1
1	1	1	1	1

Truth table of addition of a to b, with c the carry from the previous addition.

Examination of the truth table leads to several useful considerations:

(a) the first half, that is, the addition when there is no carry figure, c, indicates the requirement for a half-adder to generate d, the sum digit, and an AND unit to generate the carry, c'. If we work with AND, OR, NOT units, we have already accomplished the design of this in the previous section; the output of the AND gate into the inverter will provide the carry c';

b) if there is a carry from the previous stage, that is, $c = 1$, then the sum digit d is the inverse, or complement, of the d for $c = 0$. The carry c required for the condition $c = 1$ is given by $c' = a + b$, that is, an OR gate.

Using the considerations in (a) and (b) it is not difficult now to construct a network of logic elements which will produce the desired result and it is a worthwhile exercise for the student to do so. This method does not necessarily produce the simplest or most convenient arrangement. Let us, instead, use an algebraic method, using combinational logic.

5.7 Combinational logic design of a full adder

We commence by examining the truth table, as before, but this time we examine the input combinations for each output for which a one is required. Consider first the digit sum d: we require it to equal one for the following inputs:

$$a = 1, \quad b = 0, \quad c = 0$$
$$a = 0, \quad b = 1, \quad c = 0$$
$$a = 0, \quad b = 0, \quad c = 1$$
$$a = 1, \quad b = 1, \quad c = 1$$

We can express this requirement in terms of *literals* and connectives as follows:

$$a\bar{b}\bar{c} + \bar{a}b\bar{c} + \bar{a}\bar{b}c + abc = d.$$

The term literal means a letter symbol, say, a or $\bar{a}$, denoting a particular value of the variable, a.

For the carry digit c' we obtain, using the same procedure:

$$ab\bar{c} + a\bar{b}c + \bar{a}bc + abc = c'$$

From these two expressions we can immediately put together networks of elements which will produce the required outputs:

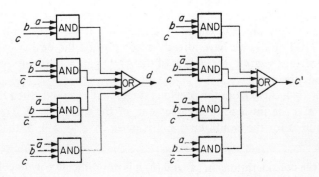

Fig. 5.8

The networks evolved come directly from the algebraic expressions: there is no guess-work or trial and error. They are, in this case, not the minimal, or most simple economic arrangement, either. We can improve matters by operating on the algebraic expressions using logical simplification techniques. It may be possible to reduce the complexity of the expressions, and the number of literals, or gate inputs used, or to change the design to fit a different series of logic elements. Until the final algebraic simplification is obtained, the network need not be designed. There are processes, which we shall study later, of ensuring that the network is *minimal* that is, that there is no redundancy and the design is as simple as possible.

5.8 Redundancy

Let us examine the expression we have evolved for the carry digit c'.

$$c' = abc + \bar{a}bc + a\bar{b}c + ab\bar{c}$$

Taking the first two terms on the right-hand side and factorising we get:

$$abc + \bar{a}bc = (a + \bar{a})bc = bc$$

Now $a + \bar{a}$ always equals one, therefore these two terms together only equal bc and the value of a is immaterial. Similarly taking the first and third terms we get:

$$abc + a\bar{b}c = ac(b + \bar{b}) = ac$$

The first and fourth give:

$$abc + ab\bar{c} = ab(c + \bar{c}) = ab$$

The expression then need not be written out in full; the combination $ab + bc + ca$ will give a one for every condition when c' needs to be one, and a zero otherwise. We can check this by making a truth table and finding if the two expressions give identical outputs for every set of input conditions, that is, proof by perfect induction.

The literals and terms we have dispensed with are said to be *redundant*. The systematic elimination of redundancy is the key process of minimisation.

The network to generate c' now is simplified to the following:

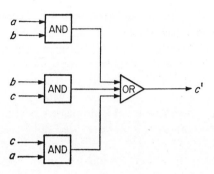

Fig. 5.9

This is the same form of network as before but manifestly simpler: only three AND gates are now required instead of four, and each has two inputs instead of three.

5.9 'Product of sums' and 'sum of products' terms

The expressions we evolved in designing the adder consist of groups of literals multiplied together, and the groups are then added. We refer to this pattern of expression as a *sum of products* expression. It leads to a network having a group of AND gates feeding into an OR gate.

There is another type of expression which is compounded of literals added in groups and the groups multiplied together; we call this type *product of sums*. An example of a product of sums is:

$$(a + b + c) (\bar{a} + b + \bar{c}) (a + \bar{b} + \bar{c}) (\bar{a} + \bar{b} + c)$$

This leads to a network having a group of OR gates feeding into an AND gate. It is possible to convert from sums of products to products of sums, or the reverse, by using De Morgan's Theorem. It will be remembered that each of the De Morgan identities had a product on one side and a sum on the other. So far we have only considered it to apply to simple expressions.

5.10 De Morgan's Theorems

'A product of literals may be complemented by changing the product to a sum of the literals and complementing each literal.'
Likewise:

'A sum of literals may be complemented by changing the sum to a product of the literals and complementing each literal.'
For example:

$$\overline{(w + \bar{x} + y + \bar{z})} = \bar{w}x\bar{y}z$$

and, naturally:

$$\overline{(\bar{w}x\bar{y}z)} = w + \bar{x} + y + \bar{z}$$

Since a whole expression or group of literals may be denoted by a literal, the theorem can be used in manipulation of expressions consisting of many terms and groups of terms. Expressing the theorems in the simplest form we can say that the complement of a Boolean expression is obtained by:

changing all . to + (AND to OR);
changing all + to . (OR to AND);
changing all 1 to 0;
changing all 0 to 1;
and complementing each literal.

5.11 Duals

The *dual* of a Boolean expression is obtained by

changing all . to + ;
changing all + to . ;
changing all 1 to 0;
changing all 0 to 1;
but *not* complementing each literal

or example the dual of $a + \bar{b}c = a(\bar{b} + c)$ or more fully $1.a + \bar{b}c + 0$ $= (0 + a)(\bar{b} + c).1$
The dual does not have any direct connection with the truth table values. t is useful sometimes in simplification, when it saves complementation. t must be used with care.

.12 Conversion from sum of products to product of sums

ı) Complement the expression, using De Morgan's Theorem;
٥) multiply out this complement into sum of products form;
٠) complement the resultant expression, which will lead to a product of

sums. (Twice complementing leads back to an expression equivalent to the original.)

We may proceed instead using the dual in place of the complement. The procedure is the same, and the resulting dual of a dual is equivalent to the original expression. For example: determine an equivalent product of sums expression to $\bar{a}c\bar{d} + a\bar{b}d + a\bar{c}$.

The dual is: $(\bar{a} + c + \bar{d})(a + \bar{b} + d)(a + \bar{c})$.
Multiply out: $a\bar{b}\bar{c} + \bar{a}\bar{c}d + ac + a\bar{d} + \bar{b}\bar{c}\bar{d}$.
The dual of this is: $(\bar{a} + \bar{b} + \bar{c})(\bar{a} + \bar{c} + d)(a + c)(a + \bar{d})(\bar{b} + \bar{c} + \bar{d})$.

The same result could have been obtained using De Morgan's Theorem, but the use of the dual saved complementing all the literals twice.

5.13 Logic circuit minimisation

After the evolution of a logic network, designed by any method, it is often possible to reduce its complexity, or the number of gates used, or the number of connections. This is done by seeking out and rejecting redundant elements.

Whether a network or logic arrangement is in fact minimal depends on the criteria chosen for judgement; these in turn, depend on circumstances, which are usually limited by economic or speed requirements.

For instance it may be possible to achieve a desired result with n gates each having up to p inputs. The minimal solution may be chosen different from this because gates having less than p inputs are more readily available cheaper, or have less delay time associated with them. The chosen minimal solution may have more than n gates, limited to less than p inputs. In general however, a circuit is minimal if there is no redundancy, but there may be several different minimal solutions. The speed requirement usually dictates that the required solution has the lowest number of levels. Most work of this kind is aimed at producing two-level networks.

The process of minimisation starts with the Boolean algebraic expression derived from the design specification. There are then three basic methods of minimisation:

(*a*) direct algebraic simplification by inspection and use of theorems;
(*b*) systematic elimination of redundancy by a tabular method;
(*c*) 'mapping' techniques.

We shall deal with each of them in turn.

5.13.1 Algebraic simplification

This approach is similar to the conventional simplification procedure in ordinary algebra, and is performed by factorisation and the application of some simple theorems. The following is a summary of the simplification theorems; some are self-evident truths, but others require explanation or proof.

$$0.x = 0; \quad 1 + x = 1; \quad 1 + \bar{x} = 1 \tag{i}$$

These follow from our study of Venn diagrams.

$$1.x = x; \quad 0 + x = x$$
$$xx = x \quad \text{and} \quad x + x = x$$
$$x\bar{x} = 0 \quad \text{and} \quad x + \bar{x} = 1 \tag{ii}$$

If $x = 0$, or $x = 1$, and one is the universal class, these again follow from the Venn diagrams.

$$xy + xz = x(y + z), \quad \text{and} \quad (x + y)(x + z) = x + yz \tag{iii}$$

The former is as normal algebra; the latter is proved using the Venn diagram.

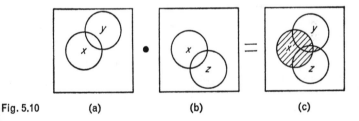

Fig. 5.10   (a)   (b)   (c)

The areas enclosed by the rings in (a) and (b) are $(x + y)$ and $(x + z)$. The intersection of these areas is the shaded area in (c), that is, all $x +$ (the intersection of yz) $= x + yz$.

$$xy + x\bar{y} = x \tag{iv}$$

Factorising: $x(y + \bar{y}) = x.1 = x$. This is the most important redundancy theorem and has important extensions.

Let m be a group of variables and n a further group, all of which are multiplied together to form mn: if terms mn exist so that all possible forms of the variables n occur, then n is redundant and the whole expression reduces to m. This is best illustrated by examples:

$$xy + x\bar{y} = x(y + \bar{y}) = x \qquad \text{(i)}$$

$$xyz + x\bar{y}\bar{z} + x\bar{y}z + xy\bar{z} = x(yz + \bar{y}z + y\bar{z} + \bar{y}\bar{z}) = x \qquad \text{(ii)}$$

Since the bracket (the terms n) contains all possible forms of the two variables, y, z, it is equal to one for all y, z.

The dual of this theorem yields another identity.

$$(x + y)(x + \bar{y}) = x \qquad \text{(iii)}$$

This can be proved by Venn diagrams or easily by algebra, for:

$$\begin{aligned}
(x + y)(x + \bar{y}) &= x.x + xy + x\bar{y} + y\bar{y} \\
&= x + x(y + \bar{y}) + 0 \\
&= x
\end{aligned}$$

$$x + xy = x, \quad \text{and} \quad x(x + y) = x \qquad \text{(iv)}$$

These are easily seen from the Venn diagrams.

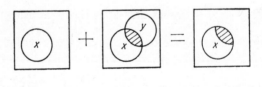

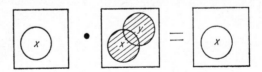

Fig. 5.11

$$x + \bar{x}y = (x + y) \quad \text{and} \quad x(\bar{x} + y) = xy \qquad \text{(v)}$$

The Venn diagrams give the results immediately.

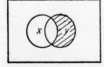

Shaded area = $\bar{x}y$
$x + \bar{x}y = x + y$

Shaded area = $\bar{x} + y$
Intersection with x
gives xy

Fig. 5.12

The following identities are sometimes useful; they should be proved as an exercise.

$$xy + \bar{x}yz = xy + yz \qquad \text{(vi)}$$

$$(x + z)(\bar{x} + y + z) = (x + z)(y + z) \qquad \text{(vii)}$$

$$xy + \bar{x}z + yz = xy + \bar{x}z \qquad \text{(viii)}$$

$$(x + y)(\bar{x} + z)(y + z) = (x + y)(\bar{x} + z) \qquad \text{(ix)}$$

We have, furthermore, De Morgan's Theorems which we have examined previously.

5.13.2 The canonical form of expressions

Consider the expression $wx + w\bar{y} + yz + \bar{x}z$; there are four variables involved in the expression but only two appear in any term. This implies that so long as the conditions called for in each term are met with respect to its own pair of variables, the values of the other variables do not matter. In simplifying expressions of the type shown, the minimal solution may not be obtainable from the grouping of the variables in the expression. We therefore expand the expression so that each term contains all variables: the expression is then called the *canonical expansion* of the original expression. To make this expansion we employ the theorem (iv) above, that is: $xy + x\bar{y} = x$, and its extensions.

The canonical expansion of the expression chosen above is produced as follows:

$$wx + x\bar{y} + yz + \bar{x}z$$
$$= wx(yz + \bar{y}z + y\bar{z} + \bar{y}\bar{z}) + x\bar{y}(wz + w\bar{z} + \bar{w}z + \bar{w}\bar{z})$$
$$+ yz(wx + \bar{w}x + w\bar{x} + \bar{w}\bar{x}) + \bar{x}z(wy + \bar{w}y + w\bar{y} + \bar{w}\bar{y})$$
$$= wxyz + wx\bar{y}z + wxy\bar{z} + wx\bar{y}\bar{z} + \bar{w}x\bar{y}z + \bar{w}x\bar{y}\bar{z} + \bar{w}xyz +$$
$$w\bar{x}yz + \bar{w}\bar{x}yz + w\bar{x}\bar{y}z + \bar{w}\bar{x}\bar{y}z$$

If this is now simplified, the minimal expression $wx + x\bar{y} + z$ results. It is not easy to see a direct simplification to achieve this. It is also very laborious to simplify an expression like this by direct algebraic simplification. We should note that there are eleven terms, and the remaining five terms out of the possible sixteen must be the complement of the required expression. It is sometimes easier to operate on these terms to obtain a simplification and then to complement this result. Usually, how-ever, unless an easy way is immediately apparent the *tabular* or *map* methods should be applied.

5.13.3 The tabular method

This method is based almost entirely on the fourth theorem, $xy + x\bar{y} = x$. The expression to be simplified is first expanded into canonical sums of products form. The theorem is then applied exhaustively to all terms in pairs to obtain all irreducible terms and reject redundancies. As each term is matched with each other term, new terms are produced which contain one literal less. These are entered as a second column of the table and examined in pairs in the same way. As successful matchings are made, the terms reduced by two literals are entered as the third column of the table and so on.

By this means every combination of terms is matched and the reduced terms tabulated. Any terms that cannot be matched are irreducible. When all possible matching has been done, all remaining terms are irreducible; these are called the *prime implicants* of the expression.

Referring back to the theorem $xy + x\bar{y} = x$, the literal x implies the terms $xy + x\bar{y}$, that is, if $x = 1$, then $xy + x\bar{y} = 1$ and the y literals are redundant.

The details of the process are most easily understood by means of an example: we shall choose the expression $= wx + x\bar{y} + yz + \bar{x}z$ which we have already expanded. The working is shown in the table opposite.

The expression has been written in columnar form, starting with $\bar{w}x\bar{y}$, which has only one uncomplemented variable, or 1. The term $\bar{w}\bar{x}\bar{y}\bar{z}$ does not appear or it would head the table. We then make up column (i) in which we substitute numerical values for the literals. There are only two terms having only one uncomplemented variable: we therefore draw a line after $\bar{w}x\bar{y}\bar{z} = 0100$, and list the terms with two uncomplemented variables. After $w\bar{x}\bar{y}\bar{z} = 1001$, we draw another line and list the terms contained three 1's. Finally, we are left with one term of four 1's, wxy. Taking the first term, 0001, we match it with each in the second group starting with 1100, with which it will not match. We then match it with the next term, 0101, and we see that it will match: 0101 differs from 000 only in the second digit. This then corresponds to applying theorem (v) to $\bar{w}x\bar{y}z$ and $\bar{w}\bar{x}\bar{y}z$, and we see that $\bar{w}\bar{y}z$ implies both terms. In our tab we place a tick or check mark against both terms, and open column (with 0–01.

	(i)	(ii)	(iii)		
$\bar{w}\bar{x}\bar{y}z$	0001 √	0–01 √	0—1 √	—1	
$\bar{w}x\bar{y}\bar{z}$	0100 √	00–1 √	—01 √		
$wx\bar{y}\bar{z}$	1100 √	–001 √			
		–100 √			
$\bar{w}x\bar{y}z$	0101 √	010– √	–0–1 √		prime implicants
$\bar{w}\bar{x}yz$	0011 √	110– √	—01 √		are given by:
$w\bar{x}\bar{y}z$	1001 √	11–0 √	–10–		—1 = z
$wx\bar{y}z$	1101 √	–101 √	11—		–10– = $x\bar{y}$
$wxy\bar{z}$	1110 √	01–1 √	–1–1 √		11— = wx
$\bar{w}xyz$	0111 √	0–11 √	—11 √		
$w\bar{x}yz$	1011 √	–011 √	1—1 √		
		1–01 √			
$wxyz$	1111 √	10–1 √			
		11–1 √			
		111– √			
		–111 √			
		1–11 √			

Tabular method of determining the minimal form of $f = wx + x\bar{y} + yz + \bar{x}z$.
f expanded into canonical form:

$$F = wxyz + wx\bar{y}z + wxy\bar{z} + wx\bar{y}\bar{z} + \bar{w}x\bar{y}z + \bar{w}x\bar{y}\bar{z}$$
$$+ \ \bar{w}xyz + w\bar{x}yz + \bar{w}\bar{x}yz + w\bar{x}\bar{y}z + \bar{w}\bar{x}\bar{y}z$$

These terms are written in a column; the terms with most barred literals first, so that the number of ones increases as we go down the column.

We go on with this process matching each term with every term in the next group and wherever we make a successful match we enter the implicant in column (ii). A term once ticked does not require a further tick but it must be considered in the matching process each time, since it may be of help to produce a further implicant.

When column (ii) is complete we partition off the groups and match the first term with each term in the second group exactly as before. We note here that the only terms that can match successfully have a blank in the same position, and this makes matching more easy. For instance 0–01 matches for the first time with 0–11 to give 0—1 which is entered in column (iii).

When we have completed column (iii) we attempt to match within that column. We find in this case that the only matches we get produce —1, and two terms remain having no check marks, and are therefore not implied by any other term.

We now examine the table and write down all terms which have not been checked off; in this case there are none in any column but column (iii). but in general there might be unmatched terms in any column. We find in this example that we are left with:

$$-\!\!-1 = z$$
$$-10- = x\bar{y}$$
$$11-\!\!- = wx$$

These are the prime implicants, that is, the expression $wx + x\bar{y} + z$ implies all terms of the original expanded expression, and naturally, of the original expression $wx + x\bar{y} + yz + \bar{x}z$.

We see that, although the technique is somewhat laborious we have achieved a reduction in the complexity of the original expression. The reduction achieved is not an obvious one by direct algebraic simplification, and unless a designer had a considerable flair for this kind of operation it is unlikely that a simplification would have been achieved.

The final expression should now be tested by perfect induction, or truth table, for equivalence to the original, that is, that

$$wx + x\bar{y} + yz + \bar{x}z = x(w + \bar{y}) + z$$

The algebra shows that the circuits shown in Fig. 5.13 are equivalent.

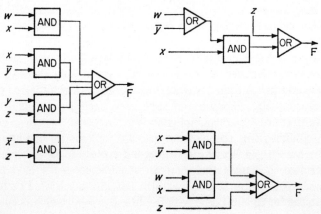

Fig. 5.13

5.14 Simplification by mapping

The term *mapping* in mathematics has a wider use than in geography: the Venn diagrams we have examined are maps. The graphs we are familiar with are also maps: mapping, in general, means a spatial representation of a function, and often gives great advantages to the user in observing the characteristic behaviour of functions. The mapping technique which we will now study is mainly due to Karnaugh and Veitch, and is a remarkably powerful method of simplification. The final minimisation of the simplified expression, however, may still require a tabular method. The Venn diagram forms the basis of the method.

The technique of simplification by mapping is best illustrated by example. To start with a simple example, let us examine theorem (v)

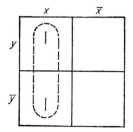

$$f = xy + x\bar{y}$$

Fig. 5.14

The simple map in two variables gives a space for each combination of the variables. These are only two terms in the expression and the two appropriate squares are marked with a one. We can see immediately that both terms are implied by x only; y and $\bar{y}$ are not needed to define the whole group which is shown encircled. Suppose a further term is added and we make a new expression $f' = xy + x\bar{y} + \bar{x}\bar{y}$. We will then have a one in the lower right-hand corner; we know we can represent the first two terms by x so the expression could be written $f' = x + \bar{x}\bar{y}$. By applying theorem (v) exhaustively we could simplify this: $x\bar{y} + \bar{x}\bar{y} = \bar{y}$, and then we have $f' = x + \bar{y}$. Referring again to the map we see that we would ring the lower two squares; $\bar{y}$ would then imply both terms in the lower half and we could read off directly that $xy + x\bar{y} + \bar{x}\bar{y} = x + \bar{y}$.

We will progress further to the three variable map, which is usually formed as shown in Fig. 5.15.

There are eight possible combinations of three variables, each being

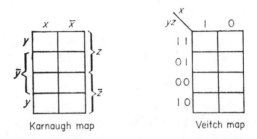

Karnaugh map   Veitch map

Fig. 5.15

two-valued. The map has eight squares, each corresponding to a possible term.

We will examine the expression f = $xyz + \bar{x}yz + \bar{x}\bar{y}z + \bar{x}\bar{y}\bar{z} + \bar{x}y\bar{z} + xy\bar{z}$ which is shown in Fig. 5.16 entered on the map. The expression can be seen to give considerable scope for algebraic simplification. From the map we can simplify it very easily by ringing groups; we ring groups in fours which can be implied by the literals, that is, a line of four, or a block of four. We cannot obviously ring two diagonally and achieve any simplification, but two adjacent in line or column can be taken.

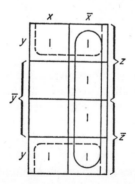

Fig. 5.16

The line of four implied by $\bar{x}$ is an obvious choice. There are then left two groups of two, the top line and bottom line. We must note here that these are only 'top' and 'bottom' arbitrarily owing to our choice of map layout. We can consider the map continuous, that is the top edge corresponds also to the bottom edge, as in Fig. 5.17.

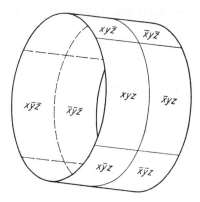

Fig. 5.17

We can then combine our two groups of two into a block of four as shown by the dotted ring in Fig. 5.16. Reading off the map we then have

$$f = \bar{x} + y$$

and this expression implies the whole previous expression. The prime implicants are $\bar{x}$ and y only. Note that the two vacant squares are given by $x\bar{y}$ and its complement is $\bar{x} + y$.

We can expand the technique now, to take in terms of four variables. For this we need 2^4 squares which equals sixteen squares. The map takes the form shown in Fig. 5.18.

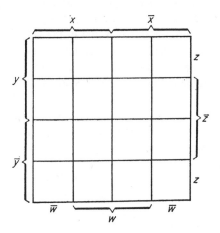

Fig. 5.18

We will mark in the expression we used to demonstrate the tabular method:

$$f = wx + x\bar{y} + yz + \bar{x}z$$

We find immediately that wx cannot be inserted as one square, since it implies four squares and we have to enter it as such. Doing this produces the canonical form which we had to do so laboriously by algebra. The map becomes:

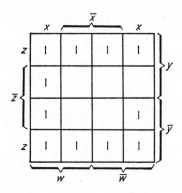

Fig. 5.19

We have changed the co-ordinate arrangement in the second map merely to emphasize that it is immaterial in which order we lay out the map so long as we make it as though it were continuous and repetitive in each direction. The first term, wx, takes the left-hand column; $x\bar{y}$ takes the lower pair of the right-hand column and also that of the left-hand column which are already entered: this indicates a redundancy in the expanded expression, if not in the original one. The third term, yz, gives the top line; the fourth, $\bar{x}z$, completes the bottom line, the mid position of the top line being already filled.

The problem now is to ring the groups in the most advantageous manner. There need be no unique solution, nor one better than any other, and therefore this technique calls for some skill, and trial and error methods. We already know the solution to this problem: we ring the top and bottom lines to give a block of eight, corresponding to z. We can also ring one line of four, wx. We are left with only one square to cover, $\bar{w}x\bar{y}z$. As a pair we could ring the lower two in the right-hand column giving $\bar{w}x\bar{y}$; we can, however, combine this pair with the pair in the lower left giving $x\bar{y}$, which was one of our original terms in this case. We have then the same result as by the tabular method.

$$f = z + wx + x\bar{y}$$

The method of mapping gives an easy, quick solution but we may still need to determine the most advantageous choice. It can be extended to more than four variables by placing maps side by side, but this technique requires considerable practice to be effective. The technique, if required, can be looked up in the quoted references at the end of this chapter.

5.14.1 Complements

It should be noted that both the map and tabular method can operate on the complement of the desired expression, and the simplified result can be complemented, in turn. In the example chosen we have eleven terms in the desired expanded expression: this means that the remaining five, out of the possible sixteen, would be the complement. The map is particularly useful as a method of producing complements to long unwieldy expressions.

5.14.2 Final selection of prime implicants

For simple expressions it is not difficult to see which of the prime implicants derived are themselves redundant. There is however a tabular method which uses Boolean algebra to determine the minimal combination. We commence by allotting a letter symbol to each of the prime implicants which we have derived; we then make up a Boolean expression, in product of sums form, which implies the original expression, and simplify this.

Referring to the expression we have used to demonstrate the map and tabulation methods, we allot symbols:

$$z = A$$
$$wx = B$$
$$x\bar{y} = C$$

We now tabulate the original expanded expression and mark with a tick each term implied by A, B, C as in the following table.

	A	B	C
$\overline{w}\overline{x}\overline{y}z$	✓		
$\overline{w}x\overline{y}\overline{z}$			✓
$wx\overline{y}\overline{z}$		✓	✓
$\overline{w}x\overline{y}z$	✓		✓
$\overline{w}\overline{x}yz$	✓		
$w\overline{x}\overline{y}z$	✓		
$wx\overline{y}z$	✓	✓	✓
$wxy\overline{z}$		✓	
$\overline{w}xyz$	✓		
$w\overline{x}yz$	✓		
$wxyz$	✓	✓	

The significance of this procedure is this: the term A represents, that is, implies, all the terms ticked under A. The terms B and C imply the terms ticked against them. The term $\overline{w}\overline{x}\overline{y}z$ is implied by A. The term $wx\overline{y}z$ is implied by A or B or C. If we form a product of all the sums, e.g. (A + B + C) that are formed it will account for all the combinations in the table. If we now minimise this product of sums, this will be the minimal expression accounting for all the combinations. In this case we have:

$$A.C.(B + C)(A + C)A.A.(A + B + C)B.A.A.(A + B)$$

This simplifies immediately to:

$$ABC(A + B + C)(A + C)(B + C)(C + A)$$

and this again, simply to ABC. The minimal result is A and B and C; in this case the final steps have been trivial since it was already apparent that the three terms were all necessary, on inspection of the columns A, B, C. The term $\overline{w}\overline{x}\overline{y}z$ is implied only by A and therefore A is necessary. The term $wxy\overline{z}$ is implied only by B and therefore B must also be in the final expression. Finally $\overline{w}x\overline{y}\overline{z}$ is only implied by C and this entails the presence of C in the final expression. The first step is, therefore, to search the table for terms which are represented only by one implicant, and then this implicant is essential. Each selected implicant can account for several other terms and these can be marked off. The remaining terms may be representable in several ways, and this accounts for the sums in the Boolean expression.

In a more complicated problem we simplify the product of sums and then convert it to a sum of products of the prime implicants. The significance of this final expression is that the original expression can be represented by any of the groups of symbols forming the products. Suppose the final expression were of the form;

$$ABC + ABD + AD$$

this would be interpreted: the final simplification is (A AND B AND C) OR (A AND B AND D) OR (A AND D). The implicants are then substituted for their letter symbols A, B, C.

5.15 Summary

We have examined combinational logic, starting with the representation of gates and operations by algebraic symbols. We have seen the analogy between symbolic logic and the logic we require for computer logic design. The operations of use to us have been tabulated, and examples of manipulation have been demonstrated. Finally we have examined the technique of algebraic simplification to achieve minimisation of circuits. To become familiar with the subject the student requires to work through examples of each topic covered. To become really proficient a considerable amount or practice is required.

The subject of combinational logic has been covered in this chapter rather brusquely, in a 'once over lightly' kind of way. The student who wishes to enquire more deeply into the subject is advised to read some of the excellent theses on the subject listed in the reference section at the end of this chapter. But best of all is practice, and the evolution and working of examples: there is no substitute for this.

5.16 Sequential logic

This is an extension of combinational logic, intended as a means of orderly analysis and synthesis of switching circuits that contain delays, memories, and feedback loops. In comparison with combinational logic, it is a somewhat intractable topic: whereas the development of combinational logic, as a design technique, was based on the well established symbolic logic of Boole, Venn, Pierce, and others, sequential logic is quite a new development, with little previous work to draw from. A detailed exposition of the techniques of sequential logic is beyond the scope of this book; it is worthwhile, though, to examine the basic concepts. For the reader who wishes to follow the topic further there is a list of references after this chapter.

Systematic research into sequential logic was initiated in order to deal with relay circuits that functioned improperly due to their slow and variable switching speeds. The designers of relay computing devices, and automatic telephone switching circuits, ran into difficulties as circuits grew in complexity: circuit outputs tended to lock on wrong conditions and, occasionally, whole banks of relays lapsed into oscillation. We shall study here a simple relay holding circuit, since it has some interesting properties.

5.17 Stable and unstable conditions

Fig. 5.20 shows a simple 'hold on' relay.

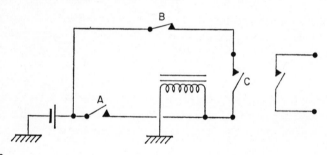

Fig. 5.20

Suppose switch A is normally open, and B closed. The relay coil is not energised, and C will be open. We will call this state (*a*); it is stable. Now we close switch A, and the coil is energised: after a delay due to the switching time of the relay, C becomes closed; we release switch A, but the coil remains energised, through B and C. Once more, the relay is in a stable state. We now open B; after the duration of the switching-off time, the circuit reverts to state (*a*).

The cycle of operations includes four states:

(*a*) in which the cycle starts and finishes, and is of indefinite duration;
(*b*) in which the coil is energised but the relay contact has not yet closed; the duration of this period is finite, and equal to the switching time of the relay;
(*c*) in which the relay holds on, indefinitely;
(*d*) in which the coil is de-energised, but the relay has not fallen back; the duration of this state is finite, and depends on the relay.

States (*a*) and (*c*) are stable, that is, they can be maintained indefinitely, if there is no external influence applied to the relay. States (*b*) and (*d*) are unstable, and once started follow a definite program without further outside intervention. They are transient states between stable states. We call states (*a*) and (*c*) which are set externally, *primary states*, while states (*b*) and (*d*), which occur as a consequence of primary changes, we call *secondary states*.

The basic concepts of sequential logic depend on recognition of stable and unstable states, and defining the logical relationships between them.

5.18 Feedback

Consider the network shown in Fig. 5.21.

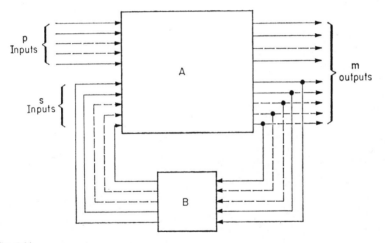

Fig. 5.21

The network A is 'combinational', that is, it has a unique set of *m* outputs for every possible combination of states of its *p* + *s* inputs. Let us consider the feedback network B as an open circuit, to start with: by combinational logic methods we can determine the states of the *m* outputs for any set of states of *p* and *s*. If B is now connected, and some of the outputs fed back to *s* are different from the original states, then there will be, in general, a change in the states of the *m* outputs, and these may again be fed back to the inputs, *s*.

The resultant set of *m* states at the output may settle, or lock, in a static state, or may cycle continuously, depending on the relationships between *p*, *s*, and *m*, the delay in each feedback path, and the gain round the loop.

Manifestly, the determination of the output states is a difficult problem to solve analytically: we make some simplifying assumptions, to solve it. We impose the limitation that the *m* outputs are allowed enough time to staticise in a condition, combinationally dependent on the *p* and *s* inputs, before any subsequent changes in *s* are allowed to take place; in other words, we impose a delay in network B, longer than any switching time in network A. We can, by this artifice, examine the changes that are about to take place at the *s* inputs; imposing the same limitation of delay, we can derive a new set of values for *m*, and subsequent values of *s*, and so on.

If a network has several loops and delays vary between paths, the solution is very complicated and difficult. Normally, we have to restrict our analysis of real problems to fairly simple networks; circuits which are pulsed, or governed by a clock waveform, allow the assumption of equal delays, and in this case the network behaviour is analytically determinable. The work of Flegg, and Campeau's earlier work, using Boolean matrices shows promise of being very useful in problems of this kind.

5.19 Hazards, races and cycles

Hazards are typical of circuits which contain switching elements having finite, different switching times – that is, in the end, all switching circuits; if the hazards are of sufficiently short duration they may be negligible; this is, fortunately, the condition under which we work in most circuits. Consider the simple case of two inputs to a logic circuit, AND or OR: suppose input *a* precedes *b* by a short time; if *a* and *b* are one, then the OR gate output goes to one with *a*, and stays at one until *b* goes down. The AND gate output goes to one, only when *b* goes to one, and goes to zero when *a* does. If the following circuit depended on the output of these two gates, its output would not, at all times, give an output according to the steady-state truth table. A more interesting case arises in the circuit shown in Fig. 5.22.

Suppose *b* = *c* = 1, then the output should be always one, irrespective of the value of *a*. Now *a* and *ā* come from a real logic element, say a flip-flop; there may be a time, during the change-over, in which neither *a* nor *ā* are up, or completely up, and during this time, the network output will go down. In the relay case, this might allow a relay to open or, in an electronic circuit, a flip-flop might be set or reset, by this brief change. One of the objects of sequential logic analysis and synthesis is to determine likely

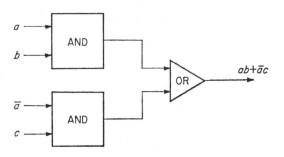

Fig. 5.22

occurrences of this kind and avoid them. For instance, by the addition of a third AND gate to the circuit above, having inputs b and c, the redundant term, bc, would be added; we note that it is no longer redundant, in this case. Huffman and Caldwell have made an intensive study of relay combinations and their hazards, using the concepts of lift sets and drop sets, and these form the basis for hazard-free electronic logic design.

It is quite possible for there to be alternative sequences of secondary operations, that may be traversed to reach a final stable condition. If this occurs, we call it a *race condition*. Race conditions may generate hazard conditions, but in some case we get a more serious malfunction. Suppose we have two secondaries, a and b, which might well be flip-flops; they are in the state $\bar{a}\bar{b}$, say, at the commencement, and we desire them to assume the state ab. Simply, we consider them to switch instantaneously and together, but sometimes we are unable to do this. If, as must generally be the case, one switches before the other, then there must occur one of two alternative intermediate states: $\bar{a}b$ or $a\bar{b}$. Now, in a computing circuit, it might be that $\bar{a}b$, for instance, was itself a valid stable state, or would give an output of an unwanted condition. We are then faced with a critical race, and having spotted it, we should have to arrange the change from $\bar{a}\bar{b}$ to ab so that it always went through the $a\bar{b}$ stage, and not through the other. It is possible, of course, for circumstances to arise when both $\bar{a}b$ and $a\bar{b}$ are unwanted transitions. In this case, a third variable has to be introduced.

Cycling occurs when a secondary element, in seeking its stable state, causes another secondary to go unstable; this in turn puts the former unstable again and the two oscillate – we can cause this, intentionally, with relays, or with transistor switches, to make relaxation oscillators; due to power gain and delays in circuits, it sometimes occurs inadvertently and sometimes, round a loop of many elements. Sequential logic is one method by which this behaviour can be analysed, as yet, in only the simplest cases.

Suggestions for further reading

Combinational logic:

Switching Circuits for Engineers by M.P.Marcus. Prentice-Hall, 1962.
    Chapters 1–3, 6 and 7 are of particular interest.

The Mathematical Analysis of Logic by G.Boole. Cambridge, 1847.

An Investigation of the Laws of Thought by G.Boole. London, 1854,
    reprinted by Dover, New York, 1951.

A Symbolic Analysis of Relay and Switching Circuits by Claude E.
    Shannon. Trans. A.I.E.E., 1938, **57**, pp. 713–23.

A Way to Simplify Truth Functions by W.V.Quine. American Mathematical Monthly, November, 1955, **62**.

Minimisation of Boolean Functions by E.J.McCluskey. Bell Syst. Tech.
    Journal, November 1956, **35**, No. 6, pp. 1417–44.

*A Direct Determination of the Irredundant Forms of a Boolean Function,
    from the Set of Prime Implicants* by S.R.Patrick. Air Force Cambridge
    Research Centre Tech. Report 56–110, April 1956.

A Chart Method of Simplifying Truth Functions by E.W.Veitch. Proc.
    of the Association for Computing Machinery, May 1952, pp. 127–33.

The Map Method for Synthesis of Combinational Logic Circuits by
    M.Karnaugh. Trans. A.I.E.E., November 1953, **72**, Part 1, pp.
    593–99.

A Map Method for Synthesis of Logic Circuits by M.Karnaugh. Trans.
    A.I.E.E., 1953, **73**, Part 1, p. 136.

Sequential logic:

Switching Circuits and Logical Design by S.H.Caldwell. Wiley, 1958.
    Chapters 12–15 may be studied in particular.

Boolean Algebra and Its Applications by G.H.Flegg. Blackie, 1963.
    Chapters 9 and 10 on matrix methods are of interest.

The Design and Use of Hazard-free Switching Networks by
    D.A.Huffman. Journal A.C.M., 1957, **4**, pp. 47–62.

The Synthesis of Sequential Switching Circuits by D.A.Huffman.
    Journal of the Franklin Institute, 1954, **257**, pp. 275–303.

A Method of Synthesising Sequential Circuits by G.H.Mealy. Bell
    Syst. Tech. Journal, 1955, **34**, pp. 1045–80.

6 Information and data

When a computer is first built and switched on it can be considered as empty; it is just a mass of transistors, wires, solder and components, joined together according to a design or pattern. To make it compute, it is programmed; this entails the writing of information on to some suitable medium such as punched paper tape, and feeding this into the machine in a specified form. The machine is required to store the information and then process it; this generates new information which the programmer wishes to know, and this the machine should put out on tape, or by some similar means, so that it may be read and used.

All intelligent beings are interested in information; by it they learn and communicate. Engineers have a further interest in it; telecommunication engineers live by transmitting it, computer engineers work to process it; control engineers harness it to control things. To handle information, as engineers, we need to understand it; we like to measure things we work with, to specify them and define them accurately. We need to relate information to things like speed, cost, and efficiency, and to define it in these terms, There is a branch of engineering science in which it is especially studied, that of information theory. It is rather a formidable subject but full of philosophic and mathematical interest; for our purposes, at this stage, we do not need to study it very deeply, but we do need to have a general idea of what it is all about. We shall be particularly interested in how information can be measured and what is called *information content*.

1 The nature of information

Information is imparted knowledge. It has many possible valid definitions, none of which are very precise. From the point of view from which we are studying it, there is an interesting definition of information as 'the negative entropy.' Most electrical engineering students have some acquaintance with thermodynamics, and this definition may cause them misgiving. The meaning of this definition may be clarified by the statement that the information content of any waveform, or collection of symbols, or any other ordered pattern, can be assessed *mathematically* by the same process as that used to define its entropy. An illustration of this concept, that must not be taken too literally, is with a pack of cards. If a pack of playing cards is arranged in order of suits, and numbers within the suits, it can be said to be a minimum entropy state. If the pack is opened at any part, and a card examined, the neighbouring cards are completely identifiable. The number of cards, given from the top or bottom of the pack will likewise define a particular card. The cards are in an ordered pattern, and using the co-ordinates of the pattern the position of every card is determinable exactly. If the pack is now shuffled once or twice in the conventional manner, the ordered state is spoiled to some extent. Opening the pack and looking at a card, we can say with only a fair probability what the neighbouring cards are. Our information is now less complete. Several shuffles and our information becomes less reliable still, as the chance of our knowing anything about the positions of cards is decreased. The state of the pack is that of increasing entropy with every shuffle.

Another concept used in information theory can be introduced at this stage. The disorder of the pack or confusion of it, introduces *noise* into the information, in the same way that the reliability of the information in a telegram may be reduced if the transmission is mutilated by noise. It is apparent that, as the noise increases, the information decreases or becomes degraded. This is as far as it is wise to push the analogy of the cards.

6.2 Hartley's Law, noise and redundancy

Before passing on to some concrete considerations we shall look briefly at another concept in information theory; this is known as Hartley's Law, which states that the maximum rate of information transmission over a channel liable to interference (noise) is a function jointly of frequency-bandwidth and signal-to-noise ratio. This will not be a new concept to most engineers, but may well have not been named to them or expressed in these terms. A morse signal can be transmitted over a very narrow-band channel fairly slowly. High speed morse, such as auto-transmission, demands a wider band, and certainly tends to occupy one, but the rate of information passage is not high. With television and multichannel transmission systems the rate of information transmission is much higher and the bandwidth is likewise much greater.

Now if there is noise on a channel the traffic is likely to be mutilated. A morse operator may be constrained to send every word twice, for instance, in these conditions. The information rate is then reduced to half. Every word he requires to send as a result of noise interference slows down the rate of transmission. Speaking over a telephone it is common experience that we can have an intelligible conversation through severe noise interference. The telephone demands a wider bandwidth than the morse signal, but the principal factor in this consideration is the 'redundancy' content of our speech. Normal speech contains many redundant words and sounds; it therefore could have a higher information content than it has, per word spoken. It is this margin of redundancy which allows the intelligibility over the noisy circuit—but at the expense of information which might have been transmitted.

The illustrations we have examined are not in any sense proofs; the object in introducing them is to suggest to the reader a line of thought which will help him comprehend some of the implications of information theory, notably with regard to noise, redundancy and information content.

6.3 Measurement of information

Information implies ideas; it cannot therefore be directly measurable. We simplify the problem by considering potential information, that is, possible information content. For instance the possible information content of a book must be proportional in some way to the number of words in it. For the same number of words, reference books are apt to have a higher information content than books written to be read for relaxation; this need not be true, of course, in every case. One new idea may imply an enormous amount of information. It is for reasons of this kind that we restrict ourselves to the simpler concept, that information content is a function of book length. Telegrams are charged on the number of words transmitted, and telephone calls on the time allowed. These charges are based less on information than on the material cost of providing and running the facilities, but experience indicates, in the long term, that the charge is proportional to the information passed or to which it is possible to pass. A great number of nebulous considerations come in here: redundancy is usually high in speech and written language. It may be reduced by telegraphic language though this often reduces intelligibility. The tone of voice of the speaker can communicate information; this is a matter of bandwidth, since if the bandwidth is narrow, as on a poor telephone, the speaker's voice is changed, and recognisable tone and inflexion may be lost.

A very important consideration of possible information content is that of explicit and implicit information. A telegraphic reply to a complicated proposition may be one word; it could be argued that this word carries a higher information content than any word in the original message. It needs to be considered in fact as a part of the original message; the addition of yes or no, which is binary to the end of the message has the same effect as adding a binary digit position to a number—it increases the precision. A binary number is a pattern: the addition of one more digit increases the possible scope of the pattern by doubling the possible combinations, that is, doubling the precision. A further example illustrating this point is in missile guidance or interception. The predicted course may be the required result from a computation. The actual course of a real object such as a missile is not random for its changes of position and direction of motion are governed by physical laws, and the limits of its behaviour are defined; the prediction of its future course is possible within these limits. The information content of the radar information is continuously increased with the time over which the history of the flight is plotted. Much of the missile's future behaviour is implied by its past.

6.4 Quantitive measurement of information content

The paper tape punch and reader are commonly used devices for the output and input of data to computers. This was not their original purpose, which was telegraphy; in the days when this was their prime use they were quite slow mechanical machines. With the growth of computer technique they have been much improved and speeded up. We shall study them in more detail later, as input–output devices. At this stage we will study the information content of punched tape since it provides a convenient illustration for our purpose. The tape punched by the perforator or punch is usually $\frac{5}{8}$ inch wide. The punch has five punch hammers in a line at right-angles to the axis of the tape. To punch a letter or number, that is, a character, one or more of the hammers is driven through the paper, each punching a neat round hole. The tape is then moved on a short distance to allow the next row of holes to be punched for the next character. Each hole punched corresponds to a one and each space not punched, to a zero. The reading device senses the punch holes in the tape; most modern readers do this by means of photo-electric cells.

Each character has a corresponding pattern of holes and spaces. Since each position can have one of two states, the total number of possible combinations is $2^5 = 32$.

Now suppose we punch a tape so that the characters are punched in blocks, or words, of six characters. This gives us a secondary set of combinations, each of six characters, in turn formed of five positions, each of which can assume one of two states. The total number of alternative blocks possible is then $(2^5)^6 = 2^{30}$. We should note that the total number of possible alternatives is independent of the way in which the number of positions is divided up. A tape punched with six punches, having five characters to a block, would yield $(2^6)^5$ possible combinations.

In telegraphy, and in many computers, the characters are transmitted in serial form, that is, each of the five positions causes a pulse if a hole is punched, and no pulse if no hole is punched and the pulses are sent from place to place sequentially. For instance the punched pattern 00111 could be transmitted as three pulses, followed by two spaces, or *pulse absences*. Six characters of a block would be transmitted as a sequence of thirty pulses.

The total number of combinations possible increases with every pulse sent; in a serial transmission the number therefore increases exponentially with time. We have discussed the idea that the possible amount of information transferred is proportional to the number of words transmitted; there will naturally be a constant proportionality due to the person who is transmitting—a 'coefficient of verbosity' might be a suitable term.

We have, then, that the information increases with time; and the number of possible alternative combinations which could be formed increases exponentially with time. From this we can deduce that the possible information content is proportional to the logarithm of the number of different combinations which could be formed.

Systems exist in which each position has more than two states. For instance the tape reader examines five positions simultaneously, character by character; the five positions are then scanned sequentially to generate sequential pulses. From the tape reader's point of view each character is one position having thirty-two states. Six characters again give a possible 2^{30} states.

In general, a system may be able to transmit S^n different combinations in a given time, where n is the number of positions and S the number of states which can be assumed by a position. We have in the above example $S = 2$, $n = 30$ and $S = 32$, $n = 6$, both giving the same number of possible combinations.

If we accept that information increases linearly with time, we can write:

$$\text{information } I = Kn$$

here K is a constant of proportionality, and may depend on S, the possible states, but not on n, which corresponds to time.

The total information is also proportional to the number of combinations S^n. Suppose the same information is transmitted over two systems, having S_1 and S_2 possible states in each position. We have:

$$S_1^{n_1} = S_2^{n_2} \tag{i}$$

$$\text{and} \quad I = K_1 n_1 = K_2 n_2 \tag{ii}$$

From (i) taking logs:

$$n_1 \log S_1 = n_2 \log S_2$$

whence (ii) yields:

$$\frac{K_1}{\log S_1} = \frac{K_2}{\log S_2} = K_0, \text{ say.}$$

Then

$$I = K_0 n_1 \log S_1 = K_0 n_2 \log S_2 \tag{iii}$$

Since K_0 is arbitrary, a convenient value for it is one. By convention, also, we take logarithms to base two. Then the information, or rather, potential information, is measured in *binary digits* or *bits*.

This is particularly convenient for us, since most computers use $S = 2$, that is, the binary system. We have then:

$$I = n \log_2 2 = n \text{ bits}$$

or the possible information content of a 'word' composed of binary digits is equal to the number of digits in the word.

Remembering, once again, the term 'precision', we see that the accuracy of definition of a number is expressed also in binary digit places, like the carpenter's rule, in halves, quarters, eighths, sixteenths, and so on. Precision and potential information content are analogous.

6.5 Choice of radix for computer operation

It has been stated already that computers work most commonly in the binary system, that is, with numbers expressed to radix two, or modulo 2. There are valid engineering reasons for this, since on/off devices have been found the most suitable and easy to make, and have a high degree of reliability in operation. We shall see that engineering considerations and those of information theory reinforce each other.

In a computer we deal primarily in numbers. If we assume a set of N possible numbers, and assume also that they all have an equal probability of occurrence, then in the selection of a number we imply a quantity of information:

$$I = \log_2 N, \text{ by definition,}$$

whatever system of notation we use. Let us compare the use of binary notation with decimal.

6.5.1 Decimal versus binary systems

If we choose a word of b binary digits, then the total number of combinations is 2^b. The range of integers would be from: 0 to $2^b - 1$.

For example, we will choose ten digits to the word. The information content will then be ten bits, and the total combinations:

$$2^{10} = 1\ 024$$

Now a decimal number word, having d decimal digits, gives a total number of combinations of 10^d, a range from 0 to $10^d - 1$.

Let us choose $d = 3$ since this gives 1 000 combinations which is not far from the value of 1 024 chosen from the binary example. If we neglect the odd 24, the number of combinations of each are the same, and the information content is also the same; ten binary digits are, to a first approximation, equivalent to three decimal digits, or 1 decimal digit $= 3.33$ binary digits, approximately, in information content.

More precisely:

$$I = \log_2 10^d \text{ bits}$$

$$= d \log_2 10 = \frac{d}{\log_{10} 2} = 3.322 \text{ bits}$$

This is in fair agreement with our approximate derivation. We can conclude therefore, that to express a decimal number in binary digits requires 3.322 times as many binary digits. We can never make an exact equivalence with integral numbers since 10^d and 2^b do not compare exactly. For $d = 3$, $b = 10$ we get a fairly close equivalence, as we have seen.

6.6 Binary coded decimal system

There are some electronic devices such as ring counters and dekatron tubes which have ten unambiguous stable states, but they are not particularly suitable for modern computer applications. For this reason, when computers are operated in the decimal mode, their actual mode of operation is binary coded decimal. This entails using four binary digits to represent each decimal place. Ten of the sixteen possible combinations of the four binary digits are used to represent the integers 0–9. The remaining six positions are unused, and are therefore effectively wasted, from the point of view of information. We use four binary digits to represent a theoretical 3·322 binary digits, that is, 4/3·322 times as many digits as ideally required. This entails 4/3·322 times as many storage elements, register stages, and similar elements, in a binary coded decimal system, as would be required in a pure binary system. A useful expression to convey this comparison, is that of *storage efficiency*. Using this we can say that the maximum storage efficiency of a BCD system is only: 3·322/4 = 83 per cent. Frequently computer systems for engineering and other reasons use five digits to represent a decimal digit, or as many as eight. The storage efficiency of these systems is proportionately less than 83 per cent.

6.7 Optimum radix

If still more evidence is needed to show the benefits of using the binary system in preference to any other, an interesting calculation is advanced by Bucholz. If we let a given number N be represented, to radix r, by n radix positions, then $N = r^n$. Assume the cost of providing a radix position is proportional to the radix, as well it could be, then the cost of representing the number N is:

$$C = krn = kr \frac{\log_e N}{\log_e r}$$

If we assume also that r and n could be continuously variable, then to determine a minimum cost we put $dc/dr = 0$. This gives a minimum cost for $r = e$. The nearest radices to e are two and three and their values of C are not far above the minimum. Certain magnetic devices lend themselves to ternary operation: a square-loop core could be magnetised in either of two directions or not at all, that is, three stable states. The Russians have built a computer based on the ternary system, and a number of experiments on ternary techniques have been tried here and elsewhere, but, generally, little development has been attempted, probably because programmers and engineers find binary simpler, and satisfactory in use.

Furthermore much of the operation of a computer is a function of logical considerations. Logic as we have seen is very much a binary study: propositions can be true or false, for instance, and things belong in a particular set or do not.

Finally, apart from the larger numbers required in the binary represer tation, it has been pointed out that since the human is accustomed to thinking in decimal terms it leads to inefficient collaboration between man and machine if the machine works in binary. Program techniques for converting decimal to binary, and binary to decimal, are easy and well established and thus the machine itself can do the labour of conversion when necessary. The advantages gained by using the binary system still outweigh any loss of efficiency in the system due to this conversion.

6.8 The nature of data

The information fed into a computer, whether digital or analogue is called *data*. In an analogue machine this is in the form of a voltage, or voltages, and in general, is continuously changing. A changing voltage constitutes a waveform, and Hartley's Law applies. Noise is an important preoccupation of analogue computer and process control engineers. The frequency response and bandwidth of analogue computers and control systems is an important consideration, and we have looked at it briefly in the section on analogue methods. The information content of waveforms of this kind is beyond the scope of this book.

The information fed into a digital machine is basically of two kinds. A scientific machine, that is, a machine used primarily for purposes of scientific research and development, is fed with data of a mathematical kind, such as numbers, and mathematical and logical instructions as to the operations to be performed on the numbers. Very often the information required from the output, does not bulk very large: the answer 0, or no, or –, might be all that is required after laborious calculation. The input data, too, need not be very large in quantity.

Data processing or business machines may be fed with voluminous data, and have to output more voluminous data after little calculation. A typical example of this kind of work is file up-dating for a business organisation in which many thousands of ledger entries have to be checked through and, where necessary, altered in a fairly trivial manner. Owing to the cost of computers there is a necessity to employ their working time to the maximum, and they are usually designed, as far as possible, to be universal, that is, to operate on widely differing kinds of data, and to do scientific calculation as well as business data-processing. The design in this case calls for considerable compromise; one of the basic considerations which must be investigated at the commencement of a design is the size of the *data unit* that is, the word length. Computers may work in serial mode or parallel mode; serial mode means that data is operated on, digit by digit, sequentially, and the data all passes along a single channel; in the parallel mode, data is transferred over as many channels as there are digits in the sample of data, and all digits are operated on simultaneously. In both of these systems there is a machine-imposed limitation on the size of the sample of data that can be handled in one process.

6.9 Machine data units

In general the data unit or word length of a machine is defined as the number of digits of data which are stored in one address location in the memory store, and which can be transferred from one unit to another as part of a single instruction. For instance, if the register length of a machine for all working registers is twenty digits, its data unit is twenty-digit word. Its storage will be organised so that data is stored also in parcels of twenty digits.

The data unit of most machines has, in the past, been arrived at as a compromise between many factors. The working precision required defines the minimum number of digits which must be used to represent the data; the number of digits will be a multiple of four for BCD systems; pure binary systems tend to have a number which is a power of two, say sixteen, thirty-two or sixty-four. Finally there is the requirement dictated by the *order word* of the machine, that is the instruction which the machine must have in order to do its computation. A typical order decrees a mathematical function and the *address* of the store in which the information is to be found.

If there are, say, sixteen possible machine functions, then there need to be four binary digits to designate the particular function required. If the memory store holds 1 000 words, $(1\ 024 = 2^{10})$ then ten digits are required to designate any one word. As we shall see later there are several other possible requirements in the order word, and storage systems on modern computers are not limited to 1 000 addressable words. The order word must therefore be at least twenty or so digits in length. The main data unit is not the only data unit imposed by the computer itself (or by its designer). There are other data units in the machine whose length is dictated by engineering and other considerations. For instance, information may be stored on magnetic tape or in delay lines, or on a magnetic drum or disc. Generally in systems using these types of storage, a word of information is not addressable directly when on the tape, or in the delay line, or on the drum. Information is held in these devices as *blocks* of words, and these blocks are transferred into the working store when required. The block length which is transferred is a data unit, and this may impose a limit on programming or on efficiency. We have mentioned BCD representation: each decimal digit on this system has a natural data length of four digits, or maybe more, if checking and similar facilities are provided. The representation of the alphabet requires a minimum of twenty-six combinations of digits, that is, in fact, $2^5 = 32$, practically. If upper and lower case letters, suffixes, logical and mathematical signs are required, the combinations necessary may be many more and call for up to eight digits to define them. Whatever system is chosen will have its specified series of data units. Finally the binary digit itself is a natural data unit.

6.10 Data units external to the machine

The length of units of scientific data is infinitely variable and it is hard to make any useful generalisations. Business applications, however, have somewhat more firmly defined patterns mostly descending from punched card processing techniques. The patterns are not clearly defined as to length but at least the form of the data is well established in many applications. It is useful to examine the two data unit systems side by side: the closer they can be made to agree the higher the system efficiency that is likely to be attained.

Business data can be divided up generally in the following convention:

character;
field or item;
record;
file.

The *character* is typically a letter, decimal digit or symbol or punctuation mark, such as is found on a typewriter keyboard. This corresponds, in general, to the same term 'character' in the computer data unit system; as discussed before, it may call for from four to eight binary bits to represent it.

The *field* or *item* is typically a group of letters or numbers, in association, to mean a name, or reference number, or a heading of some kind. In a computer system this will normally be contained within a computer word and will have a store location.

The *record* is a group of fields or words that are related. For instance, in a payroll calculation, a record might be the whole particulars of one individual on the payroll. Records are generally themselves a pattern, that is, each record in a programme is identical in form, though the details differ. For instance, the name, or basic pay rate, of the particular individual to whom the record applies would always appear in the same position in each record, and could be extracted from the record without scanning the whole of it. The corresponding computer data unit to a record would be the block. Efficiency would be highest if a record completely occupied a block in every application or if two, or an integral number of records, exactly filled a block. Efficiency suffers if blocks are only part filled by records.

A *file* is a group of records and may be a very large unit indeed. A particular record would have a specified position in the file. Customarily, in computer applications, a file may be a reel of magnetic tape, and may be detached entirely from the machine by mechanical means, whereas the other data units we have described would generally need to be fed to and from the machine through its input or output devices.

We have, then, the following correspondence:

External Data	*Machine Data*
character	character (or byte)
field	word
record	block
file	tape reel, for instance

The word *byte* has been aptly coined in the U.S.A: the spelling is to prevent confusion with bit.

6.11 Efficiency

We have seen that a computer using BCD can only be about 83 per cent efficient in its use of storage as compared with a pure binary machine. This efficiency can only be obtained in the ideal case when all stores are full, and all numbers have an equal probability of occurrence. There are many reasons why practical systems are not ideal and have efficiencies well below the theoretical maximum. Some of the reasons for loss in efficiency will be listed below. They should be borne in mind when designing computer systems, when choosing a computer to do a practical job, and when programming.

Numbers do not have an equal probability of occurrence if we are working in a binary coded decimal system; the binary characters for 10–15 do not occur at all. In a system having a number range of 1 000, there will normally be 1 024 possible combinations: the highest twenty-four numbers will not be used.

The precision of the data will be variable; it is uneconomic to allow for a higher precision than is necessary. It may well be more economic to deal with high precision numbers piece-meal by a quite complicated program procedure, rather than build in a larger data unit.

A word subdivided into fields, such as an order word, will generally have less information content than a whole word: each field will provide a certain number of combinations. All combinations of each field may not be appropriate for use with all the others, and the total number of useful combinations will be less than the possible number.

Block lengths are usually dictated by the designer to fit in with engineering considerations. Scanning half empty blocks takes time and this is wasted. Programme preparation takes time and much of this may be spent wastefully trying to pack storage efficiently. In the design of machines for special purposes this feature can be examined in detail. In design of universal machines there needs to be a good deal of thought given to the optimum block size.

Such a list as this could be extended much further. We shall deal with some of the considerations which occur, in the sections on storage organisation, addressing systems and the like.

Suggestions for further reading

Information theory:
Information Theory and Coding by N.Abramson. McGraw-Hill, 1963.
Information Theory and its Engineering Applications by D.A.Bell.
Pitman, 1953.
Mathematical Theory of Communication by C.E.Shannon. Bell Syst.
Tech. Journal, 1948, **27**, pp. 379–423; 623–56.

Codes and error detection and correction:
Switching Circuits and Logical Design by S.H.Caldwell. Wiley, 1958.
Chapter 10 is of particular interest.
Switching Circuits for Engineers by M.P.Marcus. Prentice-Hall, 1962.
Chapter 12 is of interest.
Error Detecting and Error Correcting Codes by R.W.Hamming. Bell
Syst. Tech. Journal, 1950, **29**, pp. 147–50.

7 Instructions and functions

In the preceding chapters we examined some of the processes of arithmetic, and noted that binary arithmetic in particular, lends itself to logical adaptation. We also saw the methods by which it is possible to make up logic arrangements to do arithmetic functions. A computer is able only to do the simplest processes directly, but it can do them very quickly indeed. The complicated processes called for in automatic computation have to be compounded from the simple ones.

In solving a problem by means of a computer, two people are primarily responsible for arranging the computer and the problem so that the problem can be solved: the designer and the programmer. The designer builds circuits and contrives logic networks to perform a range of functions. The programmer lays out the problem in such a way that it is soluble with the range of functions provided. All the brainwork must be done by the men; the machine does the slaving.

In order to design a computer, an engineer must know the kind of problems it is required to solve and how the programmer formulates them for solution. The programmer needs to know the facilities the engineer offers him, and how they can be used to best advantage; the two must function as a team.

We are concerned with the engineering of computers, and so we must spend a little time looking at the programmer's problem.

7.1 The organisation of a computer

A computer must contain these organs:

(a) a unit which performs arithmetic or logic; this we style the *arithmetic unit*, *function unit*, or *system centre*;
(b) a unit which stores information, both data and instructions, which we call the *store* or *memory*;
(c) a unit which directs and co-ordinates the operations within the machine according to its instructions; this is the *control unit*;

Information must be got into the machine and the answer recovered from it; this requires devices under the heading of *input-output* or *peripheral* equipment.

We shall deal with all these in some detail; here we concern ourselves with the basic functions of the control unit, which are:

(a) *sequence control:* this maintains the automatic step-by-step operation of the system, so that, as each instruction is completed, the next is selected and commenced;

(b) *beat control:* the execution of an instruction follows the decoding of the instruction as written into the computer. The two parts of the process are often known as beats – the 'instruction and execution beats' or 'order and obey beats' are commonly used names;

(c) *instruction* or *order decoding:* this is the translation of the instruction, which is a number or pattern of digits, into a machine process;

(d) *store control:* this means the putting away and recovery of stored information as demanded by the decoded instruction. This and associated functions of internal store organisation are known sometimes as *housekeeping;*

(e) *progress:* the starting and running of function units called for by the instruction. This entails opening and closing of gates, issuing and counting pulses, and doing all the automatic activities which form part of the machine functions;

(f) *timing:* the control of all movements of information, and signalling pulses, to keep them in synchronisation throughout the system.

It is the job of the programmer to formulate his problem as a string of machine instructions which can be obeyed by the control unit. A machine has a limited repertoire of instructions which it is capable of obeying, and these it obeys slavishly. In the initial stages of a design much thought goes into the choice of functions to be provided, in order to choose those which can be most economically implemented, and which can offer the best facilities for problem solution. Once the function unit is built, all programmes must then be reducible into terms of the *function table*, the list of provided functions. Babbage showed, in connection with his difference engine, that the only indispensible function is subtraction. To reduce every problem exclusively to subtraction is laborious and inefficient. All modern computers include add as well as subtract in their arithmetic function table: most include multiply, but many do not provide a divide function directly. There must also be functions to control the *reading-in* and *printing-out* of data and instructions, and for transfers to and from locations in the memory store. Large and versatile machines have been operated on as few as sixteen functions, which included housekeeping. Some modern machines have as many as a hundred or more functions, though many of these are variants of each other, or the combinations of basic functions which most frequently occur.

7.2 Instructions

A problem is fed to a computer as a string of data and a list of instructions or orders for operating on the data. A simple instruction consists of two parts: the function and an address. The function part of the instruction is a number, and this number defines the function unit to be brought into operation as a result of decoding the instruction. The address is that of the *operand*; this is the piece of data on which the function is to be performed. It is placed initially in the memory store in a location. Each location in the memory store has a number and this number is its address, just as houses in a street or in a town have addresses. The information or data held in a location is analogous to the occupier of an apartment; he is identifiable by the address, so long as he lives there, but may move away from it, permanently or temporarily, or change to another. When the program is initially run into the machine, every instruction word and data word is put away in store in a programmed arrangement so that it can be recovered when required, identified by its address. It is the programmer's task to ensure the storage of the data in the appropriate locations; the strength of this technique is that a programme routine may be used over and over again with different data but with the same instructions.

An order consisting only of a function and an address is not sufficiently explicit: there requires to be a second address or a definition of a second operand. *Add four* by itself is not logically complete, but *add four to two* is. In some machines we have to address both operands in each instruction but common practice is to use an *implied operand*. There is a special purpose register in the arithmetic unit of all machines which can be called the *accumulator*, and in this register the greater part of the arithmetic is performed. We use the accumulator contents as the implied operand, and thus the order *add four* means also *to the contents of the accumulator*. In machines, in which both operands require to be specified, the accumulator may be styled *address zero* and then, if the order is to imply the accumulator contents, nothing need be written in the second operand space.

Instructions of the non-mathematical kind conform in pattern to the mathematical ones; for instance an order *store accumulator contents in store location 1 000* fits the pattern. The order *shift the accumulator contents to the right twelve places* can be written in the same form, but here the decod ing device will have to interpret the twelve not as an address but as the number of shift pulses to generate. Both the parts, function and address, of orders are numbers, as are any other parts of the instruction that may be provided. The instruction word is thus no more than a pattern of ones and zeros and this is a suitable form for machine control.

7.3 Sequence

An instruction containing a function and two operands, implied or otherwise, is logically complete in itself, but only for the one operation specified. The control unit, when the operation is finished needs instructions as to what is next to be done and this we call *sequence control*. There are two ways of controlling the step-by-step sequencing of instructions. The first and oldest way is called the *two address system* (really three address if we include the implied address also). The second address in each instruction gives the location of the next instruction, and the programmer can arrange his own sequencing. The system has the advantage that, when used with a slow storage system, the programmer can optimise the arrangement of his programme, and reduce store delays. It is however a complicated system to work, and programming is not simple; it is little used in modern computers.

The commonly used system is to employ a device known as a *sequence control register*, built into the control unit. The register is combined with a binary counter, and the count registered at any time is the number defining the address of the current instruction. When the current instruction has been completed the count is stepped on by one: the new number in the register is then used to call in the required next instruction to the control unit for decoding. The instruction cycle thus becomes:

(a) read the contents of the store location address specified by the sequence control register, into the control unit;

(b) decode the instruction: set up the required function. Bring into the function unit the contents of the location specified in the address part of the instruction;

c) perform the function;

d) advance the sequence control count.

In terms of beats, (c) above is the *order beat* and the remainder the *obey beat*. The order beat will be seen to have much the same form as the obey, that is, decode an address and fetch the contents from store and operate on it. The operation is always the same, whereas in the obey beat the operation is the function.

If the computer had no further facilities than this sequential step-by-step operation it would be no more than a fast calculating machine; to understand the full scope of a computer we must examine two other very important facilities.

7.4 Branch orders

In both the two address and sequence controlled systems, as so far described, the transfer of control from one order to another has been automatic, and unconditional. Branch orders come under the heading of *conditional transfers*; they are also called *jump orders*.

Whatever number is in the sequence control register when an operation is completed, will be used to determine the location of the next instruction. We can contrive to put into the register any other number instead of the next in sequence, and in this case, the next order to be obeyed will be the one defined by the number inserted. This may be done directly by the programmer, when it will cause an unconditional transfer. It may also be done by the computer itself as a result of a decision, and in this case the transfer will be conditional on the result of the decision. The power of the computer of taking decisions is the function which has led to the misleading term 'electronic brain' and given it a magic quality in the popular mind. The computer's 'brain' from this point of view is, in fact, rather inferior to that of a gnat. Its criteria of judgement are extremely simple and are imposed completely by the programmer. Nevertheless, its great calculating speed, coupled with its simple decision facilities do make it a tool of great power, even if not a brain. Branch functions are almost invariably of the form: *test the contents of the accumulator: if zero go to address . . . for next instruction: if non-zero, carry on in sequence.* The test may vary in form: *test for zero, test for negative,* are typical; the test may be on a single digit position in a certain register, or on a whole register or there may be variations of the test function so that it can be applied to several registers. Once the test is made, the pattern is standard, that is *carry on,* or *go to a new location and carry on from there.*

When a branch order is obeyed the control unit usually has also the requirement to meet of storing the contents of the sequence control register, which have been supplanted; this is usually accomplished by maintaining special registers for the purpose. If several branch orders are made in the course of a program it may be necessary to store several numbers in this way, and recover them in the right order.

The value of the branch function can be illustrated by an example. Suppose the object program is the calculation of the values of terms of a series. The programmer decides what value of term is insignificant, and places this value as a number in a store location. The computer computes the values of the terms by a routine, and after completing each term, before commencing the next, it does a decision routine. In this case it will subtract the stored insignificant number from the last calculated value of the term of the series. The branch is arranged so that the machine will continue working out term values until the subtraction gives a negative result; it will then jump or branch to a new location outside the routine and proceed on a new sequence.

The programmer can, by his ingenuity, lay out very complicated and tedious problems so that necessary decisions can be made by the computer, according to criteria arranged for it, and it can be left alone to work until the final result is achieved. We should note, from the example above, that each term of the series, though a separate calculation, will be a routine one having the same instruction sequence but with altered data: the main processing sequence need be written once only. If we can arrange an automatic technique for changing the data we can make the programme shorter still.

7.5 Modification

Both instructions and data in the computer are stored as numbers; data is operated on arithmetically, and so are instructions. The practical implementation of this idea was first put in train by Von Neumann, and in this suggestion he probably made his greatest single contribution to computer science. Reverting to the example above, for each term of the series, the program could call from store a number, by specifying its address, and generate a term by operating on this number. The program would require to place all the numbers for use in store, and would have to be written so as to call them from store in the order required. They could be stored in locations in a set sequence, each location address being a fixed increment bigger than the last, and in this case a routine could be arranged so that the initial instruction required to calculate each term by calling in the data number, could have the necessary increment added to its address. The program would be a routine for developing the terms, used repeatedly, a routine for incrementing the address from which data was to be drawn, also used repeatedly, and a list of data. The latter would be peculiar to the problem; the repeated routines could be used, whenever appropriate, with any other data list. A typical example of this kind of calculation would be the generation of logarithm tables or trigonometrical functions. A common program could be used for four figure tables or for any other; the number criterion for the branch function would need to be specified for each order of accuracy, and the list of data numbers likewise.

This technique of *address modification* is used so frequently and is so effective, that most computers have a built in provision for it. Instead of a separate routine for operating on the instruction in the arithmetic unit, the increment to the address is added within the control unit itself just before the decoding. A part of the instruction word is allotted for modifier instructions: usually this is one or two digits which specify a special register in which the address modifier increment is stored. When the instruction is in the decoding device the decoding process is held until the increment has been added. The programmer must arrange for the increment to be stored and must arrange the addresses of the data to conform to the required pattern.

7.6 Routines and sub-routines

We have mentioned the word *routine* several times: it is used frequently in programming. Most programs are built up of standard forms, or lists of instructions which have been worked out and tested to perform common functions, such as square roots and trigonometrical functions. The instruction sequence is the same wherever the standard method is used, and there is a specified sequence in which the data is inserted. Program standard forms are called routines. Manufacturers and computing establishments build up libraries of complete programs and lists of routines to make for efficiency and save duplication of effort. Sometimes these apply for particular machines, but there are programs and routines in some libraries which are applicable to families of machines, that is ranges of machines of different sizes made by one manufacturer. In this case, it may be a design limitation on a new machine that it conforms to certain program forms already in use.

Usually routines are written into programs and the whole program is run into the machine for a specific calculation. There are some routines however that are normally left in the machine in specified address locations; these are used by programs put into the machines, as and when required.

and effectively form part of the machine's built-in functions. They are then known as sub-routines. Normally they are left unchanged over much of the life of a machine, and it is necessary to ensure that they are not over-written or otherwise destroyed. This is accomplished by the technique of *lock-out* which may be mechanical or merely a prohibition to programmers. The sub-routines can be stored in a block of storage where nothing else is allowed to be stored, or it may be arranged that the block has its 'write to store' circuits disconnected – the latter method is preferred since it also prevents accidental overwriting or interference, due to machine faults or programme errors.

7.7 Microprograms

The sub-routines we have discussed above are written into store by the programmer. They can be changed if required. There is a further routine of similar nature referred to as a *microprogram* which is placed in the store by the builder of the machine. This may be accomplished by a permanent core store, for instance, which has only read out facilities, and since it cannot be written into by accident, or design, it is locked out from the programmer. In rotating store machines these routines are often written on to the drum by the engineers, and then the write circuits are disconnected to achieve lock-out. They are not usually available to the program by addressing methods, but work only at the behest of the function table section of the control register. A typical routine of this kind might be to control the multiply function, or more often, the divide function. These small programs are of particular importance to the designer since they allow him to use the computer's function and timing facilities to do complicated operations which are additional computer functions. The transfer of a block of information from a drum to the core store requires several successive processes to accomplish it, and they are typical computer functions: a microprogram to accomplish this kind of operation is highly economical. Using Atlas as an example we see that it has a private store of some 8 000 words, which are mainly devoted to housekeeping activities, and these are permanently written, locked out, and of a faster cycling speed than the main storage, so that the service given to the main or object program, is as fast as possible. At the other end of the scale, the French S.E.A. CAB 500 computer, has a storage drum capacity of 16 000 words, of which 8 000 are locked out and permanently written with a wide range of microprogram. For Atlas the system gives great speed and flexibility, and for CAB 500 a great economy in hardware.

7.8 The preparation of a program

The programmer commences this task by a detailed analysis of his problem which leads to a list of word statements, each describing a process.
These he compounds into a block diagram, or *flow diagram* which is often
called a *macroprogram*. The blocks in the preparation of a payroll
programme might be: *select employee's index number, bring employee's
data block into working store, calculate gross pay due to hours worked,*
and *deduct tax.* Each block in the flow diagram is now analysed and broken
down into the detailed processes that need to be done. Branches show
where the word statement can be written as a question, for instance, *has
employee any deductions or credits carried forward?* The question is always
capable of a yes or no answer and leads into a sub-routine for either. In an
organisation having library facilities the programmer will normally shape
his flow diagram to incorporate previously worked routines and sub-
routines.

The final stages are the reduction of the detailed processes to machine
instructions and these are written in a symbolic notation, for brevity and
clarity. There is some standardisation of symbols, but, as yet, most
organisations have their own particular conventions, either due to usage
or the type of computer on which they are centred. Typical examples of
symbolic notation are:

$C(A)$	contents of accumulator
$C(n)$	contents of address n
$C(A) = C(n)$	transfer contents of address n to cleared accumulator
$C(A) = 0$	clear accumulator
$C(A) \times C(n)$	multiply contents of accumulator by contents of address n

Finally the detailed programme is reduced to machine language, often
on a specially printed form: every process must be reduced to a symbol
or symbols that the machine can interpret and certain punctuation marks
are allotted which the machine can interpret, also, as word ends, separators
and the like. A list of instructions emerges, of the form: 15/2067/2, for
instance, indicating: function 15, operand address 2067, modified by contents of b-line 2: Normally this is written in decimal or alpha-numeric
notation, that is, numbers and letters. In the original work, on primitive
machines, it was in binary notation, and most laborious to produce.

7.9 Autocodes, compilers, and translation input routines

To save every user from the labour of learning the intricacies of individual machine function tables and addressing, programmers work out routines and sub-routines which translate simply expressed instructions into detailed machine programs for general use. This has become a highly specialised technique, and today the most inexperienced user can get many calculation programs into a machine with little instruction in programming. A fairly straightforward attack on this problem is by *autocodes* which are made up of simple sub-routines, in general, applicable only to a particular machine. The more advanced program languages are known as *compilers* and these are becoming standardised on a world wide basis. In a compiler language the user merely has to restrict his program to a description using a standard vocabulary: a compiler program is written to translate the words and symbols in the compiler language into the particular machine language. The program read into the computer can then be in 'plain' English, and characters and groups of characters in the compiler vocabulary words, are recognised and translated into machine functions through the agency of the compiler program.

The *translation input routine* is a rather more specialised program. We have seen that the problem of storing away data and instructions falls on the programmer when he places a program into the machine. If it were necessary to commence with an empty machine each time, this would be prohibitively laborious.

Before a machine goes into use some sub-routines are written into store, sometimes from another machine, but more often very laboriously, word by word. These are used to control the actions of reading in the object programs when the machine goes into use. A tape reader, for instance, when ordered, will read in a character of four or five binary digits into a register in the computer. An order is required to make room for another character to be read in before a further read order can be given. It may require, say, ten four-digit characters to be read in to make one data word: the necessary program to do this is a fixed sub-routine, together with orders about disposing automatically of successive words in consecutive store locations. The program to do this initial reading in of programs is called an *initial orders* program. In order to facilitate the storage and handling of more complicated and sophisticated programs, programs are written which are run in to prepare the machine to accept them, and to dispose of the instructions and data in a standard way. These are called translation input routines. Different conventions are used in different organisations: the names given here are not general to all, but have been chosen as explanatory, simple ones to help the student to categorise the types of routine.

We have outlined the programming requirement: we have implicitly assumed that the programmer is infallible, which is far from the case. It would be fairly true to say that no complicated program has ever been written that ran perfectly the first time it was applied to a computer. To ensure its immediate success would require much too much checking – the best test is always to try it. This requirement leads to a further engineering consideration, that of supervisory facilities.

7.10 The control desk

A computer is controlled from a position called a control desk, or *console*. On this are concentrated the control switches for starting it and stopping it, the indication that each of its organs is operative or otherwise, the control of its input and output, and the various monitoring facilities required.

The process of getting a program to perfection is called 'debugging' and it is time-consuming, both of programmers' and machine time. The efficiency of the supervisory system can do much to reduce this time. A programmer wants the following facilities for supervision, when his program stops for any reason:

(*a*) the identity of the last order obeyed;
(*b*) the accumulator contents;
(*c*) if the stop was unscheduled, he needs indications to help him see why the stop occurred;
(*d*) a facility for altering an instruction *in situ*.

He may want, among other things, the following facilities:

(*a*) to examine the contents of any working address;
(*b*) an indication of *overflow*, that is a number going out of range by being too large;
(*c*) *underflow* indication of a number out of range by being too small;
(*d*) sign changes beyond control of the machine's functions;
(*e*) indication of division by zero;
(*f*) indication whether an empty accumulator is due to underflow or overflow;
(*g*) indication of machine failure, and its location.

There are many possible facilities, but they all increase the machine's complexity and cost. The indication, (*g*) above, of the location of machine failure is useful to the programmer and the supervising engineer. It is normally restricted, with the exception of power supply failure, to failures of the type known as *parity*. These are failures shown by parity checking systems where a word read by a device, or out of store, contains an obvious inaccuracy. Many of these checking systems are built into machines, and we shall deal with the means of doing this, later.

7.11 The engineering requirement

We have examined rather briefly what are the tasks of the programmer and what are his needs: it is now possible to attempt a summary of the engineering requirements of the control unit of a computer.

The first and most obvious part for consideration is the unit which decodes instructions. For this we need the following:

(*a*) a device to hold the instruction, that is, a register, having a shifting facility so that instructions can be fed to it from store;

(*b*) decoding devices, one to decode a binary number representing a function, and another to decode the address number. The former has to select a function unit and start it going; the latter has to operate on the store to cause it to transmit the contents of the specified address to where it is needed. There may be additional decode facilities required to select any modifiers, and in this case there will require to be also an arithmetic unit in this part of the control to accomplish address modification;

(*c*) a display system such that the contents of the control register can be inspected by the console operator;

(*d*) a manual control system operating from the console to allow the operator to insert an order manually or amend an existing one in the register.

We shall examine next the requirements of the sequence controller; in this we need:

(*a*) a register which holds the address number of the current instruction;

(*b*) a counter or similar device for augmenting the sequence register by unity;

(c) an arrangement by which the number in the sequence register controls the store and causes it to issue the contents of that address to the control register;

(d) an arrangement for replacing the number in the sequence register by another, to allow transfer of control, and for storing the original contents.

The function units themselves are best considered as part of the arithmetic unit. The sub-routine type of function can be considered as a part of the program, though some of the housekeeping sub-routines in big, sophisticated machines operate entirely in storage peculiar to control, and must therefore be studied as part of it. Descriptions of this type of sub-routine operation are given in later chapters: we are interested here in basic requirements, whereas these considerations are of ultimate refinements.

Timing and beat control are the next requirements to be considered. The beat control is usually fairly simple in concept, being some kind of bistable device which is triggered by a completion signal from either the order decode or a function unit. The engineering problems in its design arise, generally, from the multiplicity of sources from which it may be triggered. The inhibition of the beat change is normally the way a machine is stopped, that is, between consecutive operations, but not in the midst of one.

The timing requirements are various, depending on the operation of the machine, the type of components used and their flexibility. Some machines have all operations restricted to the speed of one component, for instance a drum store or delay line, and in this case the master 'clock' timing signal is tied to this component. In some machines it is necessary to wait for information to appear at the output of the store and then to issue it in synchronism with other pulse channels. This arrangement of 'coincidence' in time is the work of the control unit. We shall see this problem in detail when we study storage devices, and speed limitations. Generally there are numerous service waveforms or pulse trains required in various organs of a complete system, and it is most convenient to generate them in the control unit.

Finally the console requirements must be considered. From an engineering point of view it is most convenient to concentrate all the power supply controls, failure indicators, and engineering monitor points. This may well be a part of the function of the main console, though there is a school of thought, especially in connection with very large machines, which believe that the engineer, and all his works, should be locked out securely when the machine is running on programs and that the operator should be locked out when engineering is taking place. In this case there is a separate engineer's console.

For the use of the operator we have to provide a visual inspection system for the accumulator, control, register, and sequence control. This may well be a lamp type display, where a lamp when lit is one and unlit is zero. Most computer operators are so familiar with binary notation that this is commonly regarded as adequate; if the information has to be displayed in decimal form, then this part of the control is complicated by the provision of binary-to-decimal decoders and decimal lamp display devices. The most rudimentary machines provide only a print-out facility on to a telewriter or similar device. This is slow and has the disadvantage that if there is a fault in quite a large part of the total machine we get no print-out facility anyway, and have rather little to go on at the outset of the fault diagnosis.

Other visual facilities are normally required to show which peripheral units are in operation, and in connection with overflow and similar alarms. The proliferation of light indicators on the console may seem, at first, to be a complication without much advantage when we consider the speed at which the machine operates. We find, though, in practice that very much of any machine operation is repetitive and the light indicators develop recognisable behaviour patterns. Our less mathematical and more rhythmic faculties can then help us supervise the machine. It is surprising how quickly we learn a program pattern, and how conspicuous becomes a deviation from it, in case of faulty operation. This has led to the inclusion on many machines of an audio aid also, in the form of a small loudspeaker which is driven merely from the clicks or switching impulses of the beat change or some similar source, which gives impulses at a repetition rate within the human audio range. Using this we get a tonal pattern which is often quite characteristic of a program; we can entertain ourselves and impress the less initiated by making the computer play tunes on festive occasions, by writing a program having the right beat-change frequencies – though this is a costly way to make music and give entertainment. The musical facility is used in a profitable way. The programmer may require to halt his program for monitoring purposes during program. It is easy to write a sub-routine, depending often on a branch order which causes the beat note to emit a recognisable signal to inform the operator that the programme requires attention. The computer, during this sub-routine goes through a series of instructions called a *loop* in which the end instruction causes a jump to the beginning again, and the process goes on until interrupted. This is also called a *dynamic stop*.

The difficulty of meeting the requirement of manual alteration of register contents from the console depends largely on the logic system of the computer. If the registers to which we wish access are flip-flops there is little difficulty. Some other kinds increase the problem very much. Generally a good way of meeting the requirement is the provision of a special register, often called a *number generator* within the console. This has manual access to all positions through push buttons or key switches, and a lamp display to show the register contents. It is completely under the control of the operator who can set it and reset it at will. When a change, or an insertion, is to be made to a register content, usually the accumulator or control register, a button is pressed which locks out the operator temporarily and transfers the contents of the number generator into the location designated, in the manner of an unconditional transfer. The beat is inhibited during the transfer and the machine may be restarted by stimulating the beat change again.

As we shall find so often in our study of computer engineering, few, if any, of the processes detailed above as requirements are very difficult to achieve; their combination in an economical manner without mutual interference, is a much more difficult problem, of an organisational nature. It is however a challenging one.

Suggestions for further reading

Further, fuller, discussions on instructions and functions will be found in many books concerned with programming and the use of digital computers. For a short, basic study, Chapters 13–16 of *Automatic Digital Calculators* by A.D. and K.H.V.Booth, are recommended.

An Introduction to Computational Methods by K.A.Redish. English Universities Press, 1961. This is recommended as a basis for detailed study.

8 Logic elements

The logic we have studied is an aid to the design of logic networks representing arithmetic and logic relationships. The connective operations are performed by circuits we call logic elements; typical examples are circuits which perform AND and OR functions.

In the design of a computer, a major engineering consideration is the kind of logic which will be used and the most effective elements to meet the requirement. A computer necessarily contains a large number of logic circuits; in the early days of development these circuits were built up as required from standard circuit components – valves, resistors, etc. It soon became apparent that a more efficient method was to design basic logic circuits or logic elements as building bricks and to mass-produce these as far as possible. Using this technique the logic is put together by stringing together the bricks, and in this way logic considerations can largely be divorced from electronic.

Specialists in logic circuit design can, in this way, make the elements, and other specialists can concentrate on logic design and system design. This facilitates the team organisation necessary for the design of a large and complex system such as a computer; it also provides an easy conceptual pattern for understanding computer systems, since we can apply ourselves to understanding the different strata separately: the overall system, the major blocks, the logic units and peripheral devices, and the logic elements.

In addition to their use in computers, logic elements today are used extensively in the construction of control systems, such as machine-tool controls, lift controls and railway signalling devices. Some manufacturers specialise in the construction of elements and supply them to computer and system builders, while some computer manufacturers supply the logic units, which they use in their computers, to other organisations. *Solid state* logic elements are rapidly displacing relays and switches in a host of applications. This chapter describes some typical logic elements.

1 General considerations

The systematic design of a logic element, like any other, calls first for a detailed examination of the requirements it has to meet. When these have been defined as exactly as possible, we can review available techniques and choose the most suitable, if there is one. If there is not, then development must be undertaken in order to advance an existing technique or evolve a new one.

Fundamentally, logic elements can be divided into two types: combinational elements, or gates, and sequential elements, or memories. A logic element is required to realise a mathematical or logical expression defined under one of these two headings. Often the same logic element can be used to meet both types of requirement and then its design has to conform to both sets of design parameters.

8.2 The requirements

The primary requirement is purely logical; the output of the element must be unambiguously one of two defined states, and it must depend in a logical way on the combination of input states applied to it.

Normally the permitted input states are restricted exactly to the same two defined states as the output, that is, a voltage or current representing either zero or one, true or false, on or off, or up or down, according to the usage preferred. For instance, an OR element must give an output unambiguously representing a one if any input terminal has applied to it the state representing a one. There are occasions when the defining conditions of the output are different from those of the input, as when an element is used to convert one system of logic to another, but these are not generally encountered, and are merely modifications of the general types.

The second major requirement is electronic and non-logical; this is the switching time. Combinational logic is essentially static, but in a computing system the combinations at the input to an element will be periodically changed. The output will consequently have to change to conform to the different input patterns. Ideally these changes should be instantaneous. In practice there must occur a delay between the input condition being set, and the output achieving its final condition. This delay is called the *switching time*. In computer applications switching time is the fundamental limiting factor on the operating speed.

In addition to these basic requirements there are engineering and economic requirements which are dictated by the circumstances in which the logic element is to be employed. For instance, in a large system containing very many elements there will naturally be limitations imposed on the power requirements of the element and on cost. The loading which an element may be required to sustain on its output, and the load it imposes n its input are always considerations. The reliability of an element and s complexity are often conflicting factors; in most applications the elements have to be completely interchangeable with each other, and this mposes powerful limitations on component tolerances. Most of the onsiderations are interrelated and often conflicting in their requirements. Cost, however, is always of paramount importance since computer systems re complicated and call for large numbers of logic elements.

Sequential logic, or memory elements entail similar general considerations to those of static logical elements and switching speed is likewise of undamental importance. The difference lies in the logical requirements elating output and input. The output has to be, as before, one of two unambiguous states, but the input, in the case of the memory element, may be a past input. The inputs may change state and the output not, according o the logical requirements; for instance, the input to a memory element s generally a pulse of definite duration; the output may be required to stay n the state last defined by the input, for an indefinite period.

Memory elements are essentially bistable elements, that is, elements having two stable states, whereas combinational elements are switches. n a bistable element the transition time between one stable state and the other is the switching time; there may, of course, be two different switching imes if the device is not symmetrical, the time to change from state A to state B, and the time to change back again.

The subsequent sections of this chapter constitute a survey of logic elements in use, and under development, together with some of the design considerations.

.3 Combinational logic elements: diode and resistance combinations

These form the simplest of the electronic logic elements, and may be used o meet the functional requirements of AND and OR logic.

The operation of the circuits in Fig. 8.1 is as follows: the resistance R s large in comparison with the forward resistance of the diodes. In Fig. 8.1(a), if either input In_1 or In_2 is at ground potential, practically the whole voltage $+V$ will be dropped across the resistor R and the output terminal will be nearly at zero volts. A positive voltage on one diode will cause that diode to be back-biased and will not appreciably affect the output. If both inputs are at a voltage U volts where $U < V$ then the output voltage will be very nearly U volts also. If U volts represents the 'on' condition and

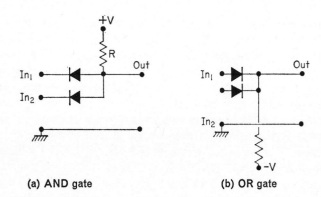

Fig. 8.1   **(a) AND gate**   **(b) OR gate**

zero volts the 'off' (one and zero respectively) then the input will be 'on' only if all inputs are also 'on' which is the required AND condition.

In Fig. 8.1(*b*) assuming R is large, as before, the output voltage will be nearly zero volts, if both In_1 and In_2 are at zero volts. But if either input is raised to $+U$ volts, the output will assume very nearly $+U$ volts also; that is, the OR condition is established. These results are not restricted to two diodes; so long as R is much greater than the diode forward resistances, more inputs could be applied.

The assumptions made with regard to the gates shown, so that they are effective logic circuits, are these:

(*a*) that the diodes are virtually perfect, i.e. they have negligibly small forward resistance in comparison with R, and infinitely high back resistance;

(*b*) that the source impedances of the devices connected to the inputs are so low as to be negligible;

(*c*) that the outputs are connected to circuits which cannot load them sufficiently to affect their functioning.

These conditions can be very nearly met in practice, but not entirely. The output 'on' voltage of the AND gate will be higher than the input voltage by an amount equal to the voltage drop across the diode; in the 'off' condition if the driving device does not offer a truly short circuit to ground at zero volts the output 'off' voltage will not be zero.

In the OR configuration, on the other hand, the output voltage in the on condition will be less than the input voltage causing it. In the off condition, the output voltage will be slightly negative of ground. It may be, in circumstances where there are not many of these gates in cascade, that the

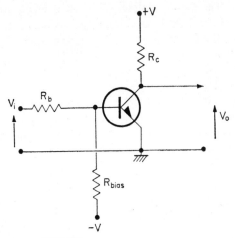

Fig. 8.2 *n-p-n* transistor INVERT

deviations from the exact voltages defined as one and zero can be tolerated. But in general, and in multi-level networks in particular, the deviations are not permissible. To some extent, so long as the elements appear alternately, i.e. AND to OR, and OR to AND, the deviations can be minimized. Otherwise it is necessary to have amplifiers between the networks to restore the voltage levels to the correct value.

Together with AND and OR elements, NOT or INVERT elements are needed to cope with all logical requirements. This can most easily be accomplished with a reversing amplifier, such as can be realised with a single valve or grounded emitter transistor stage. If this is made to have some gain it can be used to provide voltage restoration as well as its logical function. A typical grounded emitter transistor circuit is shown in Fig. 8.2.

The circuit works like this: if V_i is zero volts, due to the negative voltage, $-V$, applied to the base through the resistor, R_{bias} then the transistor is cut off and the collector voltage, V_o, becomes nearly $+V$. If the input voltage is now increased to $+V$ volts the transistor base goes positive of the emitter (ground) and the transistor conducts. The base voltage is arranged to be sufficient to bottom the transistor, that is, to cause sufficient collector current to flow to reduce the output voltage to within a few millivolts of ground. If the logical connection is such that $+V$ volts denotes a one, for zero input, the output voltage corresponds to a zero for a positive input equal to, or approaching, a one. Thus INVERT and level restoration can be achieved. The supply voltage V is often made greater than the voltage defined as logical ONE. In this case the collector voltage needs to be 'caught' with a diode at the required voltage output.

8.4 Transistor-resistor logic

Instead of AND, OR, and INVERT, the universal logic functions of NOT AND (NAND) and NOT OR (NOR) may be realised and used. These elements are a direct development from the inverter described in the previous section. Their concept is quite simple; their realisation, however, is an interesting exercise in circuit arrangement.

Fig. 8.3 shows a typical NAND circuit configuration using a *p–n–p* transistor. The logic convention for use with this unit is: a ONE is represented by 0 volts and a ZERO is represented by $-V$ volts.

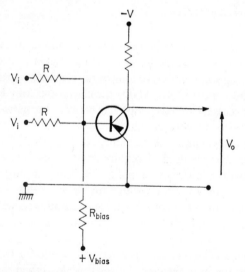

Fig. 8.3 *p-n-p* transistor NAND or NOR

The circuit works like this: when the base voltage is positive to the emitter (ground) the transistor is cut off. The output voltage V_o will closely approach $-V$. When the base voltage is more than about 0·25 volt negative of the emitter, the transistor is arranged to be fully conducting, that is, bottomed, and the collector voltage will closely approach ground potential. The resistor values, R and R_{bias}, are so arranged that if all input voltages V_i are at ground potential, that is, logical ONE, then the transistor is cut off and the output corresponds to logical ZERO. If any of the input voltages V_i are taken to a voltage approaching $-V$ volts, that is, logical ZERO, then the transistor is fully conducting and the output is nearly zero volts corresponding to logical ONE. This corresponds to the logic function NAND using the specified convention.

8.5 The duality of diode-resistor and transistor-resistor elements

If we reverse the logic convention used in the previous section for the NAND gate we have then the correspondence:

$$\begin{array}{ll} 0 \text{ Volts} & \text{ZERO} \\ -V \text{ Volts} & \text{ONE} \end{array}$$

Then when all inputs V_i are at zero volts = ZERO, the output is at $-V$ volts = ONE; if any input V_i approaches $-V$ volts, then the output tends to zero volts = ZERO. This realises the logic requirement for a NOR or NOT OR gate. The circuit arrangement is identical; reversal of the logical voltage convention changes the function of the element to its logical dual.

The diode arrangements can be treated in a similar way. The reversal of the convention changes AND elements to OR and OR elements to AND.

8.6 More complicated transistor logic elements

The elements described so far have been the simplest, but they have disadvantages that limit their use. The diode types have the disadvantage mainly that their use in an actual system entails the existence of three separate unit types, and there are limitations as to the number of logic levels in sequence which can be connected without amplification and, therefore, inversion. The transistor-resistor type of element does not suffer from this limitation, but from two others.

The number of inputs to the base of each unit is limited by the value of β of the transistor and the required resistor values, to ensure unambiguous operation in all circumstances. Likewise the number of inputs which may be driven from one element output is limited. The permissible number of inputs to a transistor-resistor element and the number of permissible outputs are referred to respectively as the input and output *branching factors*, or *fan in* and *fan out*. Since the transistor in the transistor-resistor circuit and in the inverting element are necessarily bottomed in one condi-

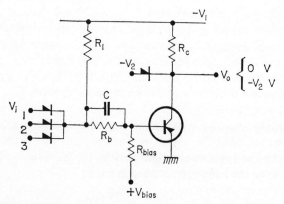

Fig. 8.4 Diode transistor NAND or NOR

tion, their switching time tends to be fairly long. For faster or more flexible operation, more complicated circuits have to be used. Larger branching factors and voltage restoration facilities can be obtained by combining the transistor-resistor and diode-resistor techniques; addition of catching diodes and 'speed up' capacitors gives more speed. A typical diode transistor logic element is shown in Fig. 8.4. Its operation is easily seen to be a combination of the operations discussed before.

In order to gain high speeds of operation logic elements have been designed in the form shown in Fig. 8.5. This kind of element is used in the I.B.M. Stretch computer: it is of a kind known as *low-level, current-switched,*

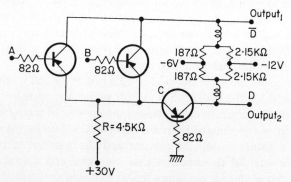

Fig. 8.5 *p-n-p* low-level current-switched AND or NAND

since the voltage difference between the zero and one condition is small, and the device takes virtually constant current, which is switched from one path to another.

The circuit draws 6 milliamps from the $+30$ volt supply: if A or B inputs are negative, their associated transistors conduct and the transistor C is cut off, and the output $\overline{D}$ goes to its positive or one condition. If A and B inputs are made positive, they cut off the transistors A and B: C conducts causing $\overline{D}$ to go down to its negative or zero condition.

There is an exactly equivalent *n–p–n* version of the circuit which restores the reference voltage from -6 volts to zero volts and the circuits are used alternately. The circuit operation is very fast: on the other hand, the transistors are special and fairly costly, the circuit is quite complicated; in computer design, speed and cost are very closely related. There are about 50 000 elements of this kind in a Stretch.

8.7 Sequential logic elements

The most fundamental of these bistable elements is the *flip-flop* or *trigger*. This can be readily made up of two transistor-resistor elements. A simple transistor-resistor flip-flop circuit is shown in Fig. 8.6.

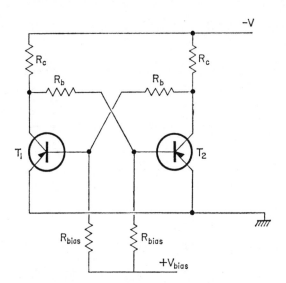

Fig. 8.6 *p-n-p* transistor-resistor flip-flop

The circuit works like this: if the base of T_1 is held slightly positive of the emitter then T_1 is cut off. The collector potential of T_1 is then fairly close to $-V$. The resistor chain $R_c - R_b - R_{bias}$ maintains the base of T_2 negative with respect to the emitter and T_2 is held on. The collector current in T_2 flowing through the collector resistor R_c causes the collector potential of T_2 to be near to ground potential; usually the circuit is arranged so that the transistor is bottomed. Due to T_2 collector potential and the resistor chain $R_b - R_{bias}$, the base of T_1 is held positive of the emitter, which was the original supposition. The circuit, then, maintains itself in a stable state with one side on and the other cut off. If the circuit is symmetrical, then this condition can apply for either side cut off when the other is on, and the circuit is bistable.

Input pulses to change the state of the element can be applied on either base or either collector. Due to the current gain of the transistor the base is the more sensitive trigger point.

Frequently these circuits are made up from two T–R elements cross-connected. In this case the design of the combinational element serves as the design of the flip-flop also; alternatively, the flip-flop may be designed as one entity with special qualities in view.

The flip-flop, as shown, forms the basis of some more complicated sequential elements, the two most important being the binary counter and the shift register. There are several possible configurations, two of which are shown in Figs. 8.7 and 8.8.

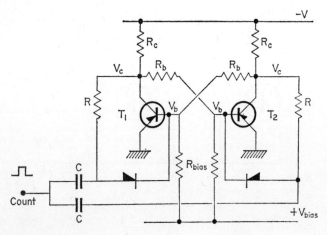

Fig. 8.7 *p-n-p* counter circuit

In Fig. 8.7 when T_1 is on and bottomed, V_c is slightly positive of V_b and the diode D_1 is conducting. T_2 is cut off and its diode is biased off by the negative collector voltage. The input positive pulse goes to the base of T_1 and turns it off and T_2 becomes conducting. The time constant CR is so arranged that the cut off diode remains cut off until the end of the input pulse; this keeps the gate closed until the switching is complete before opening to admit the next pulse, which acts in a similar way cutting off T_1. The output is up for one pulse, down for the next, up for the next and so on, giving one output positive pulse for every two input pulses.

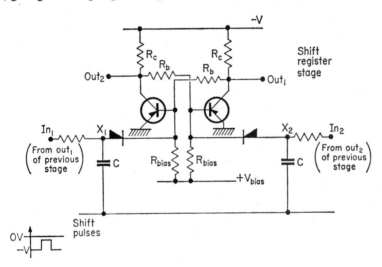

Fig. 8.8

The circuit in Fig. 8.8 works in this way:

The terminals In_1 and In_2 are connected to the output points Out_1 and Out_2 of the previous stage: one must be 'up' and the other 'down', that is, one is close to $-V$ volts, the other close to zero volts (ground). The shift pulse line is normally held negative of ground. Now if In_1 is at zero volts, the capacitor connected to it will be charged to the potential of the shift pulse line. The other capacitor will not be charged since the shift line and In_2 will be nearly at the same negative potential. When the positive shift pulse is applied the point X_1 goes positive of the base of T_1, the diode conducts and cuts T_1 off, if it was in the on condition. If it was in the off condition nothing happens. The input X_2 does not go so far positive that the diode conducts and nothing happens on this side either. Thus a one in one stage will set a one in the next; a zero will set a zero. If the stage is in the same condition as the preceding stage it will stay in that condition.

This circuit can be modified to give a simplification of the coupling circuit; on one side the diode, resistor, and capacitor are left off, and the vacant side is pulsed with a negative-going reset pulse of short duration compared with the positive shift pulse. The action is then as follows: all stages are simultaneously set to zero by the reset pulse. Wherever there was a one prior to the reset pulse the capacitor is charged, as before, and after the reset pulse is over, the capacitor continues to discharge into the base of the following transistor, setting it to a one. In this way each stage transmits a one to the next if it is 'set' but if it is 'reset', i.e. zero, it does nothing and the next stage remains at zero after the reset pulse.

It is frequently necessary for shifts to be performed either way, at will. In this case the coupling circuits have to be duplicated and the second set connected from right to left, and a separate pulser line provided for each direction of shift.

The foregoing remarks have concerned transistor-resistor and diode combinations to realise combinational and sequential logic networks. There is a further well-tried technique which has been used for combinational logic and is still extensively used as a memory element: the ferrite core.

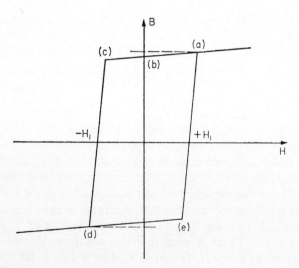

Fig. 8.9   *B-H* loop of ferrite material

8.8 Ferrite core logic

Ferrite materials are formed of a powdered material sintered into a very hard solid. The solid material has what is known as a *square loop* magnetic characteristic, that is, its hysteresis loop is square. Fig. 8.9 shows the form of *B–H* characteristic for a typical ferrite sample.

When a material having a *B–H* loop of this kind is subjected to a magnetic field, of strength $+H_1$ a very rapid flux build-up occurs up to a certain limiting value, when the material saturates. If the field is then decreased to zero again, only a very small flux change occurs shown as (a) to (b) on the diagram. If the field is now increased in a direction opposite to the originally applied field, at a certain clearly defined field strength, $-H_1$ the flux reverses, shown as (c) to (d) on the diagram. Reversing the field again causes the flux to diminish only slightly from (d) to (e) and then at a certain value of field strength in the positive direction again, to reverse and return to (a). Using this characteristic, if a transformer core is made of the ferrite material and a current is applied to the primary, there will be little or no induced e.m.f. in the secondary until a defined number of ampere turns of primary field strength is reached. There will then be a sharp change in flux and a pulse will be induced in the secondary. The core will stay magnetised until the field is reversed, that is, until the ampere turns in the primary are sufficient to switch the core to the opposite condition of magnetisation, when a pulse will be induced into the secondary.

The configuration of a practical core logic element is a small ring of ferrite material with two or three primary windings as logic inputs, a reset winding and an output winding. The core is normally saturated magnetically to one side or the other and Fig. 8.10 shows such an arrangement.

The figure shows a core logic element having two input windings, and at the commencement of operation the core is magnetised in the sense of the

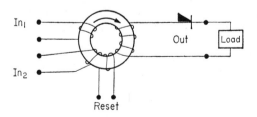

Fig. 8.10

arrow. Suppose the necessary number of ampere turns to switch the core is NI: if either of the inputs has in excess of N turns, and a drive current of I amps is applied, the core will switch and the magnetisation of the core will be reversed. A pulse of e.m.f. will be generated in the output. The diode is so arranged that the direction of the resultant current is the backward direction of the diode, and little current is generated in the output. Since the core is effectively open-circuited no power is drawn from the primary except that necessary to magnetise the core.

A pulse of current is now passed through the reset winding in such a direction as to switch the core back into the first magnetic condition. The flux change induces an e.m.f. and current into the output, this time in the direction of easy conduction of the diode. There may now be power delivered into the output circuit and this will be provided by the reset drive; the output power can be considerably greater than the power consumed in setting the core through the input winding, and the device, therefore, is capable of gain.

If the other input winding is energised in the same way, an output will result likewise. If neither input is energised there will be no flux to be switched by the reset drive and no output will result. The output, though delayed, conforms to that of an OR element.

Now if each input has $N/2$ turns and a current drive of I amps is applied to both they will produce an aggregate amp-turns of NI to set the core, and an output pulse will appear when the core is reset. But if only one input winding is energised the core will not switch: the output to input relationship is then that of logical AND, though delayed.

A number of interesting logic functions can be realised in this way by arranging the number of turns and the value of drive current. For instance the logic function *any two out of three* can be realised. *Inhibit* can be realised by reversing one winding or current.

This type of logic is difficult to categorise as either combinational or sequential. The output is indeed sequential to the input and can be stored indefinitely. It can, however, only be used once; once the reset pulse has generated the output, say a one, the core is reset to zero. Thereafter there will be no output or zero each time the reset is applied, until the core is set again by the input. The gating action is truly combinational, AND, OR and INVERT all being easily realised, but the output is delayed, or rather, held in suspense until the reset pulse is applied. The device can be used as a memory, and we shall see later that its main use is likely to be storage rather than logic.

There are several configurations of core logic: one such system, Symlag, of French origin, uses the cores, in pairs, in a push-pull arrangement. Other systems have been devised with transistor switching between stages, and an ingenious system exists by which a shift register can be made to operate without diodes, giving a very small and most robust register consisting solely of cores, or cores and resistors. A list of some of the literature describing core logic techniques is appended in the bibliography to this chapter.

9 Majority logic

The core logic configuration of Fig. 8.11 is of especial interest: each input winding produces a field strength of a little more than half that needed to switch the core. Thus any two windings together, when pulsed in the same direction, will give an output, that is, conform to the logic expression:

$$f(a,b,c) = ab + bc + ca.$$

This type of element is called a *majority logic element,* or less commonly, *ballot-box logic element.* The expression, f(a,b,c), is the same one that we have previously derived as a carry generator in a full adder circuit, but achieved in this case, by one element, instead of three ANDS and one OR. A transistor-resistor logic element of conventional configuration, can be arranged, likewise, as a majority element.

Suppose, in a circuit with such an element, we tie down one input to logic zero; the expression becomes:

$$f(a,b,c) = bc, \qquad \text{for} \quad a = 0$$

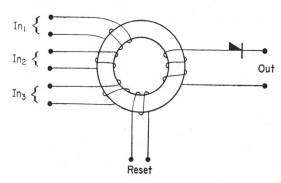

Fig. 8.11   Majority or ballot-box logic element

The element is then an AND gate with two inputs. Likewise, if $a = 1$,

$$f(a,b,c) = b + c.$$

The element is in this case an OR gate. The majority element can be seen to be a kind of universal element of a different kind, and in some ways more universal than a NAND or NOR gate, though restricted to two inputs in AND/OR or NAND/NOR configuration. It is becoming increasingly popular with computer designers, since its T–R form, and a rather ingenious form using tunnel diodes, lend themselves particularly to very high speed logic applications. At very high pulse repetition rates, the interconnections between logic elements require to be treated as transmission lines, that is, they require to be *matched-in* to the sending and receiving elements, and these need to have resistive input and output impedances; T–R logic elements are easy to arrange in this form.

The major problem in using this kind of logic is that there is no suitable systematic minimisation technique available to the circuit designer. On the other hand, the concept of being able to change an AND gate to an OR gate, by a logical switching process, seems to offer interesting possibilities.

8.10 Fluid logic elements

We should remind ourselves, once more, that the relationship between automatic computation and electronics is analogous to that of the grin on the Cheshire cat in *Alice in Wonderland* – remove the cat, but the grin remains. To conclude this chapter, we shall study some computing elements which have no dependence on electricity whatever.

Fig. 8.12 shows the configuration of three *pure fluid* elements, so called

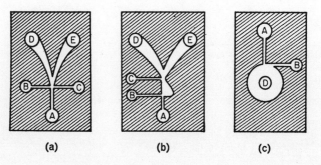

Fig. 8.12   (a)   (b)   (c)

because they have no moving mechanical parts and depend for their action only on the dynamic behaviour of the fluid used, usually air.

The principle of operation is this: compressed air is ducted in at port A. In (*a*) and (*b*) there are two outlet ports, D and E, which are the outputs. The sides of the air chamber are designed so as to make use of a hydro-dynamic phenomenon known as the *Coanda effect*: the fluid jet from A, instead of splitting between D and E, tends to cling to one side or other of the chamber, and leave by one orifice only. There is, as a result, a considerable pressure difference between the orifices. With configuration (*a*) a small pressure of air in B or C, causes the air stream to move across from one wall to the other, that is, from one orifice to the other, and the element becomes a bistable, or flip-flop. By interconnecting the outputs and inputs, the device can be made into an oscillator. Additional chambers can be used as capacitances to adjust the frequency of oscillation; frequencies have been achieved of up to 100 kc/s.

Elements can be made with several inputs to form OR gates; inputs can be opposed, and one side biased, to give AND gates, or an element such as (*b*) can be used for this purpose. The element (*c*) is an inverter. The fluid is sent in at port A and emerges at D; if B is not energised, the air stream out at D will have much the same pressure as at the input. But if a jet of air is sent in at B, tangentially, the contents of the chamber whirl and there is a considerable pressure drop between A and D. Carefully designed elements give a virtually linear inversion of the pressure at B.

Elements of this kind, for computing purposes, can be very small and are cheaply fabricated from die-cast plastic or print metal. They can be used also as control elements, to control large quantities of fluid; they are particularly valuable for the control of flow of corrosive gases and liquids. One such system is made of concrete, with chambers and ducts many feet wide, and is used for the control of sewage effluent. Computing and control systems engineers can find wide scope for their ingenuity.

uggestions for further reading

Digital Computer Design by E.L.Braun. Academic Press, 1963.
   Chapter 4 is comprehensive and includes a valuable list of references.

transistor-resistor logic:
   Basic Transistor Circuit for the Construction of Digital Computing Systems by P.L.Cloot. Proc. I.E.E., 1958, **105**, B, No. 21, p. 213.

Transistor-Resistor Logical Circuits by P.D.T.Hawker. Mullard Technical Communications, September 1960, **5**, No. 45, p. 174.

Transistor switching behaviour:
Large Signal Behaviour of Junction Transistors by J.J.Ebers and J.L.Moll. Proc. I.R.E., 1954, **42**, p. 1761.
Large Signal Transient Response of Junction Transistors by J.L.Moll. Proc. I.R.E., 1954, **42**, p. 1773.

Core logic:
The Design and Use of Logical Devices Using Saturated Magnetic Cores by G.G.Scarrott, W.J.Harwood and K.C.Johnson. Proc. I.E.E., March 1956, **103**, B, Suppt. 2, paper No. 2065 M, p. 302.

Pneumatic logic:
Fluid Amplifiers – Capabilities and Applications by W.A.Gray and H.Stern. Control Engineering, February 1964, **11**, No. 2, pp. 57–64.

9 The arithmetic unit

This is the unit which does the real work of the computer – computation. It consists of an *ad hoc* assemblage of registers and function units, interconnected by gates. It is fed with information from the memory store or the *reading in* devices and is controlled by the control unit in accordance with the wishes of the programmer. The function units it contains are dictated by the tasks demanded of it; their type is dictated by the type of storage, the mode of working, economics, and the subtlety of the designer. The requirements of arithmetic units generally are fairly well defined, but the ways of meeting them are many and various. For this reason we cannot define a standard form or even what might be called current practice.

In this chapter we shall examine in detail some of the more definite requirements and see how we can simply implement them. For the sake of simplicity we shall postulate the existence of a hypothetical computer of which our arithmetic unit forms part. This computer will operate in the *serial mode*, that is, numbers will be operated on digit by digit; it will have a word length of forty digits, with a gap-time between words of one digit duration. We will assume a two beat machine, these being the order beat and the obey beat.

Instructions to the machine will be of simple form, merely a function instruction and an operand address. The sequence control we will take for granted, together with a store organisation which will present, at the input to the arithmetic unit, the operand called for by the instruction address. It will fetch the operand during the order beat, and hold it at our disposal as long as the obey beat is in operation. These arrangements may seem at first an oversimplification. A computer is generally large and complex, and is usually the work of a team of designers. In practice there must be a division of responsibility at the level of detailed design; the designers of the individual units have to have their areas defined in a similar way to his. Where the separate units cannot be made directly compatible, further design of buffer units is required. This is particularly the case when a computer system has to be coupled to its peripherals such as magnetic tape units and input/output equipment. These are often the product of different manufacturers from the makers of the computer proper.

Although the scope of our activities has now been limited by the specification of the hypothetical computer we also have accompanying advantages, in the form of signals and waveforms which we can expect from the control unit; these will make our work much easier.

We will presume on there being available the following:

(a) a clock waveform consisting of a string of forty pulses defining the forty digit times of each word, with a gap, or pause of one digit time, separating the end of one word from the beginning of the next;

(b) a word marker waveform consisting of a single pulse corresponding to the word-separating gap in the clock waveform;

(c) beat waveforms in the form of voltage levels; the order beat waveform to be up during the order beat and the obey beat waveform to be up during the obey beat;

(d) function signals which will stimulate the selected function unit in the arithmetic unit and inhibit the others.

Armed with these aids we can now proceed with our design study.

9.1 Addition and subtraction

In our study of logic we have seen how to design adder and subtractor units for operating on binary numbers, but we have only examined the addition and subtraction of single-digit numbers. We have now the requirement of adding and subtracting long numbers of up to forty digits. Since we are to operate in serial mode this can be done digit by digit. The key to this problem lies in the use of *shifting registers*. A register is a device in which a bit of information can be held, typically a bistable element such as a flip-flop, which can be set one way to represent a one and reset to the other stable state to represent a zero. A binary number or a pattern of ones and zeros can be held in an assembly of single bit registers and the assembly becomes a *multibit* register. For the hypothetical computer a word contains forty digits and a register to hold a word requires forty stages or single bit registers. The shifting register, or more briefly shift register, is an assembly of register stages of the kind typified by tha shown in Chapter 8. Each stage is coupled to its neighbours so that it state may be changed to that of either its left- or right-hand neighbou on receipt of a shift pulse, depending on whether left shift or right shif is called for. Fig. 9.1. illustrates the process for a shift register of five stages

In (a) the register is set with the binary number 10110. The applicatio of a right shift pulse causes the register to assume the state shown in (b

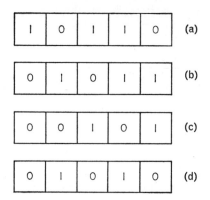

Fig. 9.1 Shifting

where each digit, one or zero, has moved one place to the right. A second right shift pulse causes the assumption of state (*c*).

The left-hand position has nothing preceding it, and becomes zero after shifting. The right-hand space leads to nowhere, hence anything shifted to the right, from it, is lost. Five shifts would empty the register to 'clear' it.

A left shift pulse causes the same effects but in the other direction. The register fills with zeros from the right-hand and after successive left shifts. In the example shown, a left shift from the (*c*) position causes the shifted pattern to become 01010 since the least significant one has been lost.

The shift process has an arithmetical significance. We assume some point of the register to be the radix point; in *integral* working, the radix point would be immediately to the right of the right-hand stage; in *fractional* working, it would be on the left-hand end. We could choose any intermediate point between two stages to give *mixed* working.

Referring back to the condition of the register (*a*): the binary number held, in integral working, is the decimal number twenty-two. After one shift to condition (*b*) the number is now eleven, that is, half the original number. The second shift divides by two again, leaving five in the register, and we have lost the half we should have as a remainder, to the right of the radix point. The lost half is an error called *round-off* error. We should familiar with this kind of error from our conventional arithmetic.

Whenever we express a number to significant figures we are likely to reject some insignificant figures which amount to the round-off error. If the leading insignificant figure is five or more we normally correct the last significant figure: we can do this also in binary if there is a figure following the least significant.

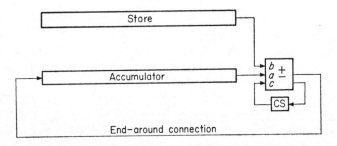

Fig. 9.2

The left shift multiplies the register contents by two each time it is applied. The round-off error in this case is much more serious. If this happens in the course of calculation the programmer will need to be signalled that the register has overflowed.

9.2 The circulating accumulator

To accomplish the addition or subtraction function we must first register the two numbers, i.e., place them in registers. We then need to add them digit by digit and register the resultant. An arrangement for doing this is shown in Fig. 9.2.

The register marked accumulator is connected to the input a of the adder/subtracter unit. The store register is connected to b and there is an additional single bit register shown as CS which denotes 'carry store'. The 'outputs' indicate to the adder/subtracter the state of the digit stage, that is, the least significant figure held in accumulator and store, and the value of the contents of the carry store.

The adder/subtracter gives two outputs, the sum digit corresponding to the binary sum of the inputs a, b, c, and the carry digit resulting. The sum digit is connected 'end-around' to the most significant digit stage of the accumulator, and the value of the sum digit will be set in that register position as the result of a shift pulse. In the same way the carry digit output is connected to the input of the single stage carry store and will set its value as the result of a shift pulse to the carry store.

We will assume integral arithmetic, and that the two numbers we wish to add are in the accumulator and store, aligned by the right-hand end. The carry store is empty. The least significant figure of each of the two numbers is in the right-hand register stage and the sum digit and carry digit representing their addition are at the adder/subtracter outputs.

right shift pulse is now applied. The sum digit due to the first addition is shifted into the left-hand stage of the accumulator, and the original accumulator contents shift one place to the right. The carry digit is shifted into the carry store. The contents of the store register also shift one place to the right.

The position is now that the second least significant digits of the two operands are presented to inputs *a* and *b* of the adder/subtracter, together with the carry store contents due to the operation on the least significant digits. The adder/subtracter new outputs will be the resultant.

A second shift will repeat the action of the first shift and make the same transfers take place, ending with the third least significant digits at the input to the adder, together with the carry due to the operation on the second. If the accumulator has forty stages, as required in our hypothetical computer, then after forty shift pulses, the entire contents of the store have been added to or subtracted from the entire contents of the accumulator, and the resultant is in the accumulator. The store will be empty. We should note, that if we add two numbers of forty significant digits the resultant will contain forty-one: if the left-hand stages of the registers contained ones or if one contained a one, and there was a carry to be added to it, as a result of the fortieth shift pulse, then there would still be a one in the carry store, and overflow has occurred. It is necessary to ensure that the operands are within the permitted range: the existence of the remaining one in the carry store can be used to provide an overflow indication.

If we add two numbers in this way and then place another number in the store and add again, the contents of the accumulator will be the accumulated total of the three numbers. This is the reason for the name; practically every computer has an accumulator, and some have several.

The accumulator and the adder/subtracter as an assembly can be classed a *function unit*; we now require to control it and arrange it suitably to form part of our hypothetical computer. We have considered the store to be a single shift register: the memory store for the computer would contain many registers or similar devices, but it is organised so that when we call for the operand specified by the address contained in the instruction, is immediately available. We have, then, merely to connect the *b* input the adder/subtracter to the memory store output point, via a gate. This gate can be opened by the combination of the *add* or *subtract* function signal and the *obey beat* waveform from the control unit. The only other requirement can also be met with the aid of the control unit waveforms. need forty shift pulses. The add or subtract function signal together with the obey beat waveform can be used to open a gate admitting *clock* to the shift pulse amplifiers. Since they will be 'up' only for the one one word time to accomplish the operation, this will provide the necessary forty pulses.

9.3 Shift pulse amplifiers

The design of pulse amplifiers is amply covered in works on general electronics; we will not spend time on it here. We do need, however, to consider the requirements that these amplifiers must meet. Assume one amplifier to be provided to produce shift pulses for the whole accumulator and carry store; the output of the amplifier will be loaded with forty-one stages in parallel, giving a low load impedance. If each stage draws only a few milliamperes, the total load current will be a substantial fraction of an ampere. The input to the pulse amplifier is from the *clock*, and this is a service waveform and should not be loaded, since it may be used in other units or organs of the system simultaneously.

The input impedance of the pulse amplifier and its gate must, therefore be as high as possible. These requirements pose no great problems in themselves; the problems and snags that do occur are secondary ones. A short rise time on the pulse will give positive shifting action and make for speedy operation of the system. The pulse will, however, apply a heavy transient load to the supply and this has to be carefully decoupled; the inductive coupling of the pulse circuit wiring to adjacent low-level signal wiring is a possible source of spurious signals.

9.4 Clearing

In addition to the pulse amplifier for shifting, there is also the requirement of clearing all stages of the accumulator, which will require a pulse amplifier of similar capability. Generally a separate pulse amplifier is provided for each purpose since gating the high current output pulses is difficult; it is generally easier to do selection and timing processes at logic level, and it is usually more economical to do so, even though more pulse amplifiers are required.

The *clear accumulator* function needs one pulse to stimulate it: convenient source, already provided by the hypothetical computer, is the *word marker* waveform, which would permit clearing to take place between word times.

If we summarise our design, so far, we find that we have provided the following functions:

(a) *add to cleared accumulator*, sometimes called *load;*

(b) *add contents of store location to contents of accumulator,* or just *add;*

(c) *clear accumulator;*

(d) *subtract contents of store from contents of accumulator;*

(e) *subtract contents of store from empty accumulator,* that is *complement* or *negate.* The most important function that remains to be provided is *shift.*

9.5 The shift function

Shift Counting. By gating *clock* to the shift pulse amplifier the accumulator can be made to shift forty places at a time. We can achieve a single shift by gating in *word marker.* The function *shift* calls for an arbitrary number of shifts as required by the programme. The *clock* pulses can still be used but we have to count them and close the gate which admits them when the required number of shifts has taken place. Counters are a regular feature of computers and occur in many forms in different functions.

Counting Circuits. In the chapter on logic elements we have examined a circuit which does a binary division of a train of pulses, that is, it switches to one state for the first pulse, changes to the second for the next, and then reverts to the first state for the third, and so on. It assumes, therefore, a 'one' state after all odd numbers of pulses, and a 'zero' state after none or all even numbers. This behaviour exemplifies the digit pattern of a binary counting sequence. To make a binary counter we couple the individual counting stages together so that the first stage sends a count pulse to the second each time it changes from one to zero.

The second is connected to the third in the same way, the third to the fourth, and so on, until enough stages are coupled to register the binary count called for. The process is detailed more fully in Fig. 9.3.

With the Eccles-Jordan, or flip-flop configuration, each counter stage has two outputs, and we chose the same one in each stage to represent the output, or state of the counter. In the figure we have chosen the left-hand one in each case. To commence the count, all stages are set to zero, that is, the chosen output points are all down. The first count pulse changes the first stage so that its output goes up indicating a one. The second returns it to zero, but this transition sends a count pulse to the second stage, setting it one. The successive states of the four stages give the binary count, and

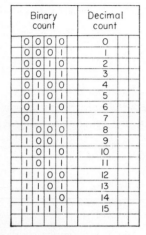

Binary count				Decimal count	
0	0	0	0	0	
0	0	0	1	1	
0	0	1	0	2	
0	0	1	1	3	
0	1	0	0	4	
0	1	0	1	5	
0	1	1	0	6	
0	1	1	1	7	
1	0	0	0	8	
1	0	0	1	9	
1	0	1	0	10	
1	0	1	1	11	
1	1	0	0	12	
1	1	0	1	13	
1	1	1	0	14	
1	1	1	1	15	

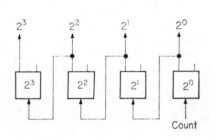

Fig. 9.3 Counting

will continue to the fifteenth pulse which gives the binary combination 1111. The sixteenth pulse resets the counter to 0000; the fourth stage could generate a count pulse to a fifth, and the count would then be extended to thirty-one, that is, thirty-two possible states including zero.

For use with the hypothetical computer a counter is needed which will count to forty. This entails the stages of a count to sixty-three since $2^6 = 64$ is the lowest power of two which is greater than forty; sixty-three can be registered by six binary stages.

The instruction for shift will consist of the allotted function identification number and, in the part normally containing the address of the operand, the number of shifts. The address decoder must be inhibited by the shift function; the number in the address position of the order word can be used to control the shift count. There are several ways of arranging this, but we will use the most direct and most illustrative.

Coincidence. Whatever number is set in the address space of the instruction decoder will be a binary number of ones and zeros. If the counter counts from zero, when it has counted the number of pulses indicated in the instruction, the counter will register the same binary combination as the address decoder. We call the state, when the counter and decoder states are identical, *coincidence*. In this case whenever there is a one in the counter it matches the one in the decoder, and likewise the zeros coincide. This corresponds to the logical operation of coincidence which we have already met, that is, $F = xy + \bar{x}\bar{y}$, where x and y correspond to the counter

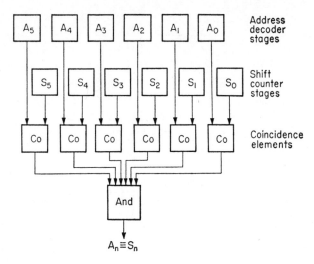

Fig. 9.4   Coincidence

and decoder stage of the same significance. When all stages are coincident the coincidence outputs can be connected to an AND gate, and its output will be up if, and only if, complete coincidence is established. The output of the AND gate in our design can be used to turn off the shift process. The arrangement is shown in Fig. 9.4.

.6 Implementation of shift

hifts to left or right may be called for; both can be arranged electronically t the cost of increasing the complexity of the function unit. Often right hift only is provided, since n shifts to the right is equivalent to $40 - n$ to ie left, in a circulating accumulator of forty digits, such as the one we are iscussing. The logical requirements are the same but two functions have ɔ be provided to give left and right shift. We will only consider one, the ght shift.

To provide automatic right shifting as a result of the programme in-ruction we require to do the following in the arithmetic unit:

) when the beat changes to *obey*, the gate from *clock* to the shift pulse amplifier is opened by the shift signal and obey beat waveform. The

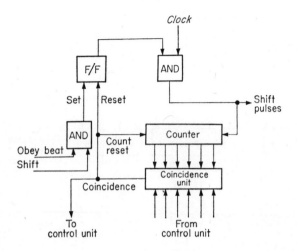

Fig. 9.5

pulses are also applied to the counter. The decoding of the function
part of the order will have caused the address decoder to be gated
through to the coincidence unit;

(*b*) when coincidence occurs, the AND element of the coincidence unit
signals the beat change and closes the gate from *clock*.

We should note that the beat cannot change until the word end and,
therefore, the beat change cannot itself stop the count. There will require
to be an additional flip-flop circuit which is set to open the clock gate, and
reset by coincidence. The count also must be reset to 000000 as a matter of
housekeeping. This can be done by coincidence also. Fig. 9.5 shows the
arrangement of the complete shift function unit.

Other functions

We can quite easily contrive a reverse arrangement of the add function
to transfer the accumulator contents to store. Other functions we need, even
for the most rudimentary computer, are *read in* and *read out* functions to
some kind of input/output unit. Once more there are a variety of methods
we will choose the simplest since it needs little more hardware than we
have already included.

9.7 Read out and read in functions

The simplest of all input and output mechanisms are the paper tape reader and paper tape punch. We shall examine them in detail in the chapter concerned with input/output devices. For the meantime we need to consider them only in so far as they affect our arithmetic unit. The paper tape reader, when interrogated by a *read* pulse, supplies, on five wires in parallel, a binary pattern of ones and zeros corresponding to a character or number. The tape punch, if supplied with a combination of ones and zeros on its five input wires, will punch out that combination on receipt of a *write* pulse.

In a primitive computer system, *read* and *write* are most easily achieved by connecting the five signal wires from the reader or punch to the five least significant digit positions of the accumulator. Gates must be provided on each line which open only when the read or write functions are decoded. The reader then sets the accumulator stages to the number or character pattern in the reading device; or, in writing, the pattern in the last five positions is punched. The only other complications are the provision of the necessary signal from the control unit, to interrogate or punch, and advance the tape.

With our hypothetical computer the procedure for reading in could be programmed as follows:

(a) *clear accumulator;*
(b) *read;*
(c) *shift five places;*
(d) *repeat (b) and (c) seven times more;*
(e) *transfer contents of accumulator to store.*

The converse process, that of *writing* to the punch, is left to the student.

The input and output arrangements we have contrived here are the most primitive. The process of assembling a word, character by character, or number by number, as we have done it, is often called *compilation*. A more sophisticated method is to provide a special register in which compilation is done, with an automatic function unit which not only reads or writes the complete set of numbers of a word as the result of a single order, but also checks the functional accuracy of the input/output device. Transfers to or from the compilation register are done as typical store transfers, at machine speed.

The compiler described, with its attendant control circuits, would be a good example of a buffer unit.

9.8 Branch functions

The branch function is a transfer of control and must be properly considered as a feature of the control unit: it is, however, a conditional function and the conditions determining its operation are necessarily derived from the arithmetic unit. The conditions can be variously defined and depend on examination of registers or digit positions in the arithmetic unit, usually in the accumulator. The word 'examine' is not really descriptive, since the computer has no faculties for examining anything: a better word is 'test'. Typical branch function tests are:

(*a*) test to determine whether the accumulator contents are zero or not;
(*b*) test to determine whether the accumulator contents are negative, or not;
(*c*) test for overflow (if no automatic overflow indication is provided).

The implementation of these tests is a matter of contrivance and ingenuity. The amount of difficulty or complexity depends on the test and the system used. For instance, the branch test for negative accumulator contents is simple if the arithmetic system in use is negative sign by complement modulo 2. If the accumulator content is negative, the left-hand, or most significant digit position will contain a one. This stage is capable of giving an up output for one and a down for zero; the control action as a result of the test can be decided by this output state. The terminology for these tests is *branch fails* if the tested condition is not as stipulated, and *branch succeeds* if it is. The instruction in this instance might be *if accumulator content is negative, jump to the given address; if not, continue in sequence.* If, as a result of the test, the accumulator stage indicates an output defining a one, the branch succeeds and the one signal triggers the jump control arrangement. For a zero output the control merely changes the beat on receipt of the *operation completed* signal, and the original sequence continues.

We should note in this case that the test is immediate, that is, only one condition has to be tested and the condition already exists. If a logical technique is used to determine sign, then this too can be tested immediately a test for zero content of a register or accumulator is likely to be more difficult. One way is to shift the whole register content through a logical ANI unit which has a one on its other input. If a one output occurs it can signal to the control that the branch fails. This operation can use the *collator* function unit which we will shortly describe, and can thus economise in hardware: but it takes a whole word time to perform the test and it is, therefore, not immediate. The test could be performed immediately by an AND gate having one input from each stage of the accumulator or register to be tested.

Gates having five or six inputs are easy to arrange; large multi-input gates are not. For the forty digit accumulator of our hypothetical computer we might well find it more economical to provide seven or eight gates each having five or six inputs connected as a two level system to a further gate, rather than a forty input single gate configuration.

We have mentioned overflow tests and indicators earlier. These are usually contrived by adding additional stages to registers and using such already existent facilities as the carry store. The indication of overflow as such, into the sign digit position when using fractional signed arithmetic offers a subtle problem.

.9 The implementation of less basic functions

A number of functions, which may be provided automatically in sophisticated systems, are often left to the program in simple ones. Typically, multiplication is often done by program or by a sub-routine. The test functions leading to branch are also often left to the programmer to arrange except perhaps one simple one, like the test for negative. If the more complicated tests are left to the programmer, usually some additional functions are provided so that he does not have to examine the register contents himself on the console display, or via the output printer. Typical of this kind of function is *collate*.

The collate function has also the title *mask* and can be used to detect the presence of ones in a register. The function unit is a logical AND element; the register under examination is shifted into one input, while a word from store, arranged by the programmer, is shifted into the other. If the store word is all ones then there will be generated a one output for every occurrence of a one in the tested register. This would be a trivial operation; but it may be that the programmer wishes to test for a one in a single position, or in a group of digit positions. The store word is then arranged to have a one in the desired positions, and the resultant word output from the function unit gate will be all zero with the exception of the desired positions. The diagram below shows the operation for a word of sixteen digits:

word under test	1011010110101110
store word	0000011111100000
resultant	0000010110100000

collation

The centre six digits of the word have been extracted from their context, and the remainder masked.

This function is also considerably used in print-out procedures for selecting a single number or character from a group, and may also be used for store packing, that is, storing several short numbers together in a store word to economise on the use of store locations.

9.10 Multiply

This is a much used function but not simple and, without special artifice, is slow and time-consuming. Since it is important and also most illustrative of computer technique, we shall examine it in some detail.

The simplest, but slowest method, entails some extra provision of hardware: we must include an additional register, in which we will hold the multiplier. Fig. 9.6 shows the arrangement.

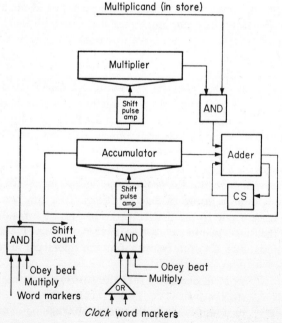

Fig. 9.6 Simple multiplier

The procedure is as follows:

(a) the multiplier is brought from store and placed in the specially provided multiplier register, then the accumulator is cleared;

(b) the add function is triggered: if there is a one in the last stage of the
multiplier register the multiplicand is added into the accumulator. If
there is a zero the store gate is shut and nothing is added in; we remember long multiplication in binary – the least significant digit of
the multiplier indicates whether we add in the multiplicand or not;

(c) the multiply function admits a word marker pulse to the accumulator
and multiplier register shift pulse amplifier. Each shifts one place to
the right.

This places the second least multiplier digit in the last position of the
multiplier register. If it is a one it corresponds to the multiplication of the
multiplicand by two or binary 10. Doing our sums on paper we shift
the multiplicand to the left – here we shift the partial total, that is, the
accumulator content, to the right to achieve the same result.

(d) the *add* function is performed again. If the multiplier last digit is a
one the multiplicand is added to the partial total (accumulator) in the
correct binary significance.

This process is then repeated from stage (b). Meanwhile we employ
the shift counter to count the multiplier register shift pulses: after
forty, the shift count signals the control unit that the operation is
completed and the beat changes.

We should note the following points:

a) the process takes forty word times from the first addition;

b) the accumulator is shifted by *clock* in each word time, and by word
marker in each gap time: in fact, it is in continuous circulation;

c) the multiplicand must be called from the store every time it is needed.
We have assumed that it is immediately accessible, but this might not
be easy to arrange;

d) the multiplication of an m-digit number by an n-digit number yields
a product having $(m + n)$ digits. There must be either a double length
accumulator, or a limitation on the precision of the input numbers, or
overflow will result.

9.11 A faster multiplier

From the considerations we have noted above we can set about improving the multiplier performance. The main improvements to be gained are from eliminating the word times spent in adding zero to the partial total when the tested digit is zero, and by ensuring that the multiplicand is in fact immediately available. Fig. 8.8 shows a possible configuration. As always, there is an attendant added cost for any improvement gained: we need an additional counter up to forty, and a third register which must be a recirculating one, which is used to hold the multiplicand. This additional register need not be attributed entirely to the requirements of multiplication: it can be used as an immediate access store for other purposes. For the sake of clarity we will first examine the reasons for the introduction of the additional counter and register. The details are shown in Fig. 9.7.

The multiplication will be most quickly performed if the single shifts corresponding to zero in the multiplier last position can be continuous, and at any time relative to the computer word time cycle: for instance, if there are several successive zeros in the multiplier, the single shift must be repeated without any additions taking place. In this case the circulation of the multiplicand register, if an addition is required to follow immediately, will be out of synchronism with the computer word time cycle. To allow for this we provide a separate counting cycle which, on being started, will give the register forty shifts and then switch back to zero. This register is connected to a flip-flop which can be set by the multiplier last position to admit pulses to the counter, but is reset by the counter when forty pulses have been counted. While the flip-flop is set to allow the count it inhibits the shifting of the multiplier. The flip-flop is by this means arranged to allow shift pulses either to the multiplier, to give shifts, or to control groups of forty shift pulses to the multiplicand register. Since this is a recirculating register, after forty pulses the contents are back in their original position.

The process in sequence is then:

(*a*) in the order beat the multiplicand is shifted from the accumulator where it would normally be, and placed in the new multiplicand register. The multiplier is brought from store and placed in the multiplier register. The multiplicand shift counter and the shift function counter are reset to zero, and the beat changes;

(*b*) the obey beat commences. In the first pulse time of the new beat, the accumulator is empty, and the least significant digit of the multiplier is in position in the multiplier register. If the last position is a one

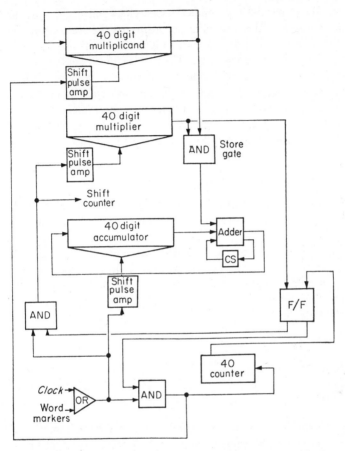

Fig. 9.7 Simplified logic of improved multiplier. Multiplier least significant digit controls store gate and flip-flop (F/F). If least significant digit equals one shifts to the multiplier are inhibited during forty digit times under control of the forty counter, forty digit shifts are performed by the multiplicand register and accumulator adding in the multiplicand. If least significant digit equals zero multiplier and accumulator shift one place.

sets the flip-flop (F/F) and opens the multiplicand shift counter gate to admit shift pulses. It also opens the store gate to the adder admitting the least significant digit of the multiplicand, which sets the adder output accordingly. If the multiplier last digit is a zero, the flip-flop is not set;

(c) when the first pulse time ends the next clock pulse will either shift the multiplicand or the multiplier according to the state of the flip-flop, if the multiplier last digit is a one the multiplier is not shifted and the last digit remains unchanged. Thirty-nine more shifts will then take place, under control of the multiplicand shift counter. This counter then resets itself to zero and resets the flip-flop. The next pulse must then go to the multiplier register, moving a new digit into the multiplier register, moving a new digit into the multiplier last position, which will set or not set the flip-flop according to whether it is one or zero, and the process continues.

The pulses admitted to the multiplier register are counted by the shift function counter, which we have not shown, since its arrangement has already been discussed. When all multiplier digits have been examined this counter will reset and signal that the process is complete, stimulating the beat change. Since the beat only changes in the gap time we would need to provide additional gating in order to inhibit any further shift pulses to the unit until the next occurrence of word marker which would coincide with the beat change.

9.12 Variations

We have explored some of the requirements of an arithmetic unit and examined some of the ways in which the requirements might be satisfied. We have considered only serial operation and flip-flop type registers. The arithmetic processes we have considered have been restricted to unsigned, but could have been used either with fractional or integral ranges. We must note that the examples we have studied are possible solutions to problems having many solutions. In general, simplicity is to be aimed at, but when speed or particular system requirements have to be met the designs are apt to become complicated indeed. This causes two disadvantages principally: the complicated system costs more, and is more difficult to maintain.

There is little to be gained at this stage by the detailed examination of more complicated systems. It is rewarding, however, to examine some other methods of operation.

9.13 Serial mode delay line accumulator

The delay line type of circuit will be considered in more detail in the section on memory stores: a brief description of its function will suffice for our present purpose. The delay line logic circuit consists simply of a pulse amplifier which gives out a pulse every time a logical one is applied to its input. The pulse output is mechanically coupled into an acoustic delay line, in the form of a metal wire or column of mercury. The 'mechanical pulse' applied at one end of the line causes a shock wave down the line which travels at the speed of sound in the line material. A sensing device is connected to the other end of the line, which generates a computer pulse every time it receives a shock wave from the sending end; due to the comparatively slow progression of the acoustic wave, the received pulse arrives a finite time after the pulse is transduced into the line. This time varies from a few tens of microseconds for a line several inches long, to several milliseconds in lines whose length may be measured in feet. We are concerned in this section with lines whose delay length is of one word time or so. Fig. 9.8 shows the arrangement of a delay line accumulator.

The arrangement shown allows addition and subtraction, together with left and right-shifting facilities. Its method of operation is simple, but it poses engineering problems of synchronisation to the rest of the computer system. The line delay time is normally made one digit short of a word time. In this way the received pulse is able to be amplified and shaped to a computer pulse in synchronism with *clock* and emitted from the receiving amplifier exactly one word time later. In the arrangement shown, the line delay time is made two digit times shorter than a complete word time cycle: the operation is as follows:

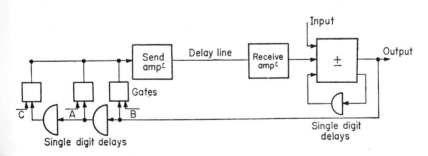

Fig. 9.8

(*a*) add (or subtract): the gates B and C are closed and A is open. For a word-time of n digit times we have an effective circulation time of $(n - 2)$ digits in the line, one in the amplifier, to allow for synchronisation, and one single digit delay element, making the correct total of n digit times. The line is loaded by shifting a word into the input of the adder: this is added to zero if the circulation is empty. The pulse pattern of the word shifted in enters the system and proceeds down the delay line. The first pulse approaches the receiving end amplifier as the last pulse is shifted into the adder. The input gate is closed: the first pulse is regenerated and commences round the circulation again, followed by the subsequent pulses, in exactly the same manner as in a shifting register type of accumulator. To add in another number, the input gate is opened and the least significant digit of the number is admitted to the adder at the same clock pulse instant as the equivalent digit in the circulation. So long as the line contents and added word are synchronised to *clock*, the addition is accomplished in the same manner as in our hypothetical accumulator. To clear the accumulator, the circulation is broken for one word time;

(*b*) shifting: this is accomplished by shortening or lengthening the circulation path by means of the gates B and C. If the path is shortened by opening gate B, the circulation is reduced to $(n - 1)$ digit times. The remainder of the computer system is cycling in n digit times per word, and so for every circulation the accumulator content is right shifted one place. By opening the gate C instead, the circulation is lengthened and the accumulator contents become left shifted one digit per circulation.

This kind of accumulator is most economical from the point of view of hardware. It poses problems of synchronisation, as mentioned before, since the admission of information to the accumulator has to be exactly synchronised with the circulation. This, in turn, depends on the line length which depends on temperature. The shifting technique is simple and economical but, for the case shown, would require at least two gap digits to be allowed in the *clock* system.

9.14 Parallel mode operation

A simple arrangement for parallel addition into a five-digit accumulator is shown in Fig. 9.9. Each adder/subtracter is identical in form with that used in a serial accumulator, but the carry is transferred to the next stage instead of into the carry store. The advantage of parallel operation is

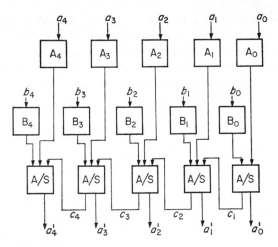

Fig. 9.9 Parallel addition

obvious: however long the word length, all the operations are done simultaneously in one digit time, with an additional time allowance for carry propagation, which should amount, at the most, to one more digit time, but may be made practically instantaneous. The disadvantages are also obvious: there is a great increase in the hardware requirement. Each channel or digit position in the parallel system becomes equivalent to a serial system. For a forty digit accumulator we require forty adder/subtracter units, for instance. Every gate has also to appear in every channel.

Today generally, large, fast computers and data processers are operated in parallel; small machines, necessarily slower, are commonly serial. With the development of very fast logic and arithmetic there is now a trend towards a return to serial operation for arithmetic, using parallel storage and data transmission.

We must not forget that the multiplication of two binary numbers having n and m significant figures gives a product having $(n + m)$ significant figures. Sometimes double precision or double length working is called for. In this case the accumulator length has to be doubled by the addition of another register: this entails twice as many shifts per circulation and complicates the control problem, in addition to demanding a further register. Having gone into double length working it is usually the programmer's responsibility to dispose of the contents of the additional register, but facilities have to be provided so that he can clear it or transfer its contents to store if required.

In the logic diagrams shown control gates have mostly been omitted for simplicity's sake. To make a working arithmetic unit numerous gates have to be provided to allow different function units access to the accumulator and registers, and likewise to deny unwanted pulses from circuits and waveforms not required in the particular function in operation. These are a matter of housekeeping for the designer: the art is to keep them to the minimum number.

We must realise in our study of computer engineering that there are few rules and many accepted practices. The design of function units and the like, is a matter for the ingenuity of the designer; he must do the best he can within the framework of costs and available techniques. A multiplier must produce an answer ab which is equal to the product of the input numbers a and b: how it is done, or whether it is truly multiplication at all, in a mathematical sense, is immaterial. After all, we use logarithms and slide rules for this purpose without a second thought. References to information on short cut methods, fast carry techniques and the like, are given at the end of this chapter.

A more detailed description of the performance of serial arithmetic, including division, is given hereafter.

9.15 A complete arithmetic unit

Immediately after the writing of the first part of this chapter, the author had cause to design and build an arithmetic unit for an instructional computer. Since it was intended for instructional purposes, the design was based on a first principles approach, using the precepts already described. The remainder of this chapter outlines the operation of this unit. The flow diagram is shown in Fig. 9.10; timing waveforms used to control the arithmetic are shown in Fig. 9.11.

9.16 Register arrangement

Three sixteen-bit registers are provided, of conventional, shifting, or flip-flop design. The accumulator and store buffer are recirculating registers: numbers can be set in each by push buttons on the operating panel. The store buffer acts as the memory store for arithmetic demonstration. In the complete system, information to and from store is by parallel transfer through the store buffer. The third register, called the *test register*, is used to hold the multiplicand in multiplication, and is used, also, in division.

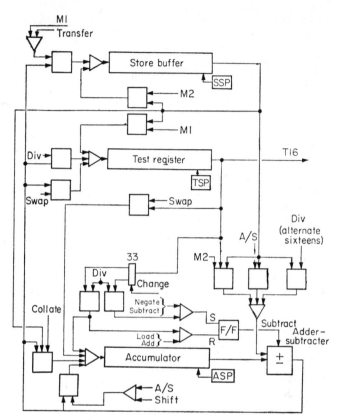

Fig. 9.10

The unit performs the following functions:

Add	store buffer contents to accumulator contents.
Load	add SB contents to cleared accumulator.
Subtract	SB contents from accumulator contents.
Negate	subtract SB contents from cleared accumulator.
Shift	accumulator contents left *n* places.
Multiply	accumulator contents by SB contents.
Divide	accumulator contents by SB contents.
Collate	accumulator contents with SB contents.
Swap	accumulator contents with test register contents.
Transfer	accumulator contents to SB.

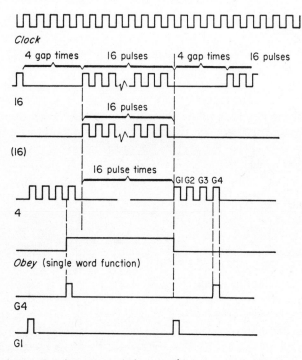

Fig. 9.11   Instructional computer timing waveforms

9.17 Operation and construction

Operands are set in accumulator and SB registers manually by the push buttons. The desired function is set by a multi-position selector switch, and a GO switch is pressed. This switch enables the next 'G4' pulse to set the *obey* flip-flop, which allows the function to be executed. When the function has been completed, the next 'G1' pulse resets *obey*, ready for the setting up of the next operation. For instructional purposes, the *clock* pulse rate can be set to 4 kc/s, or 1 c/s, or operated one pulse at a time, manually.

The unit is built throughout with commercial NAND logic elements; for simplicity the flow diagram is drawn for AND/OR and NOT elements. The state of gates and registers is shown to the operator by display lamps.

9.18 Description of operation

The four functions, *add*, *subtract*, *load* and *negate* are all basically similar. When the function switch is set, and *obey* comes up, the gates marked A/S are opened in G4 time. The waveform (16) is sent to the accumulator and SB shift pulse generators, (ASP and SSP), and sixteen shifts take place. The answer ends up in the accumulator due to the end-around connection. The add/subtract unit is set to *subtract* by the function switch, for *negate* or *subtract*; in the case of *load* or *negate*, G4 is sent to the *clear* pulser as *obey* is set.

9.19 The shift function

This is achieved rather simply. Four push-buttons are provided on the operating panel and, through these, the shift counter is set to the desired number of left-shifts, n. The end-around connection of the accumulator is enabled, and all other connections to it remain shut. When *obey* is set, (16) is applied to the accumulator shift pulse generator causing right shifts to take place; these pulses are also passed to the shift counter. When the shift counter comes to 0000, its outputs are gated together to produce a waveform which prevents further shifting. In this way, the accumulator is shifted to the right $16 - n$ times; this corresponds to n shifts to the left, as were called for.

9.20 Transfer

This is achieved by opening the gate, leading from the accumulator output, into the store buffer register input. All inputs to the adder/subtracter, other than from the accumulator, are closed. The contents of the accumulator are copied into the store buffer, by (16) applied to the accumulator and SB shift pulsers. To clear the accumulator at the conclusion of the transfer, G1 is sent to the *clear* pulser at the same time as *obey* goes down.

9.21 Collate

This is achieved by gating the output of the store buffer register with the contents of the accumulator, in a specially provided, end-around, connection: once more, (16) provides the timing pulses. The collated resultant ends up in the accumulator.

9.22 The multiply function

This is achieved using the improved approach mentioned in the earlier part of this chapter. The operation is divided into two subsidiary beats, called M1 and M2, which are two sides of a flip-flop. A further sixteen-counter is provided to give a complete circulation of the store buffer register, through its end-around connection, during each addition.

The sequence is as follows: M1 comes up with *obey*; the accumulator circulation is gated into the input end of the store buffer register, while its output end is gated to the input of the test register. (16) is applied to all three registers, resulting in the multiplier going to the test register and the multiplicand to the store buffer. At the conclusion of (16), G1 comes up and clears the accumulator, at the same time setting M2, M1 going down. During M2, that is for the rest of the multiplication cycle, *clock* is supplied to the accumulator shift pulser, and also to a gating complex under the control of T16, the least significant digit position of the test register – which contains the multiplier. If there is a one, that is, T16 is up, then *clock* is gated to the store buffer shift pulser, and the store buffer output is connected to the adder/subtracter. In sixteen clock-pulse-times, the store buffer makes a complete circulation, as does the accumulator, and C(SB) is added to C(A), the resultant ending in the accumulator. As a result of the sixteenth pulse, the store buffer circulation counter emits a pulse that resets T16 to zero. T16 is arranged so that, when it is reset, that is, at zero, *clock* is gated to the test register shift pulser and to the shift counter. The test register contents are right shifted one place (the accumulator is shifted likewise since it is directly connected to *clock*); if a further zero arrives in T16, the next *clock* pulse is applied to test register, but if T16 is a one, the adding sequence described above is repeated; we should note that the accumulator contents are right shifted one place, with respect to the store buffer contents, each time the test register is shifted. This gives the additions in the right significance.

The process continues, adding and shifting under control of T16, until the shift counter has counted sixteen shifts of the test register. When this count is complete, each digit of the multiplier has been examined, and the shift counter turns the function off.

The process so far described allows for single precision multiplication. The unit, in fact, works in double precision by the following simple artifice: once the least significant digit of a partial total has been generated in the multiplication process, it is not further modified; whenever T16 is down, that is, whenever there is a shift of the test register, the accumulator circulation (M2.T16) gate closes: a zero is passed to the accumulator. At the same time a gate is opened into the test register and the digit, 'snipped' out of the accumulator circulation, enters the left-hand end of the test register, vacated due to the multiplier shift. At the conclusion of the function, the least significant sixteen digit positions of the result are held in the test register, and the sixteen most significant in the accumulator.

It should be noted that the function takes an integral number of sixteens to complete and, therefore, when the function closes down, the accumulator and store register contents are in exactly the same significance as at the start, but with the accumulator left shifted sixteen places.

9.23 Division

This is the most difficult function to implement, of those attempted in this unit. The process of binary division was outlined in Chapter 4: the non-restoring technique described seemed the only simple method of implementation; it has the disadvantages, in this context, of imposing a programme limitation on the relative and absolute magnitudes of the divisor and dividend. In the interests of simplicity this limitation was accepted. The unit therefore is capable of operating on numbers only in the range $0 < n < 1$, and subject to the limitation that the quotient must be in the same range.

The process starts with the dividend in the accumulator and the divisor in the store buffer. When *obey* comes up to start the function, the test register and accumulator are gated to form a continuous circulation, analogous to the *swap* function, but with the exception that the connection between T16 and the accumulator input is through an additional, special, shift register stage. This makes a total circulation path of thirty-three digits.

The first sixteen digit times perform a normal subtraction of the store buffer contents from the accumulator contents. Due to the long circulation, the remainder ends up in the test register: the accumulator is empty, since there were no contents in the test register at the start, nor in the register stage *33*.

During the second sixteen digit times, the store buffer input to the adder/subtracter is closed; the remainder is shifted back into the accumulator, through stage *33*. The result of this shifting is that the most significant digit of the remainder is left in *33*, while the rest of it is in the accumulator, but shifted one place left, with respect to its original position, due to the thirty-three digit circulation path. Register *33* now sets the adder/subtracter according to whether it is a one or zero, that is, whether the remainder is positive or negative, since we are using a form of sign by complement.

If the sign is positive, in the next sixteen digit times the subtraction process is repeated, from the left shifted remainder; if the sign is negative the adder/subtracter is set to *add*, instead of *subtract*, and the process continues. The reader will see that the unit is now performing the add/subtract and shift routine outlined at the end of Chapter 4. It remains now to develop and store the quotient.

The sign digit in register *33* at each stage is the complement of the quotient digit: this register stage is arranged also as a counter stage, that is, it will change state if driven by a pulse on a common input to both sides. Immediately the add-subtract control flip-flop has been set by the contents of *33*, a count pulse is sent to *33* which inverts it. Thus, sixteen pulses later, that is, at the conclusion of the subsequent subtraction or addition, the required quotient digit is in the least significant digit position of the accumulator, while the new remainder is in the test register. Sixteen digit times later a new quotient digit is formed, and sixteen digits after that, this new quotient digit is in the least significant position of the accumulator, with the previously formed quotient on its left.

If this process is followed through carefully by the reader, it will be seen that the quotient is formed from left to right in the accumulator; the dividend and quotient occupy the test register and accumulator alternately; since all shifts occur in blocks of sixteen, all three registers can be driven directly from *clock*, continuously, including the store buffer. The output from this must be inhibited during alternate sixteens. To turn off the function, on completion, this inhibit waveform is used to operate the shift counter. After sixteen complete cycles the shift counter turns off the function.

9.24 Conclusion

In this chapter we have studied the implementation of binary arithmetic, mostly in serial form, and in the manner based on human performance. Once more, it is stressed that a designer must use what means he can of producing the required answer, within a defined framework of speed, cost and precision considerations. The instructional arithmetic unit described, is chosen to illustrate technique since it does conform to simple practice. Generally, arithmetic units of operational, commercially built computers are not very useful illustrations of first principles since this was not an important preoccupation of their designers.

Suggestions for further reading

Arithmetic Operations in Digital Computers by R.K.Richards.
Van Nostrand, 1955.

The Logic of Computer Arithmetic by I.Flores. Prentice-Hall, 1960.

A Signed Binary Multiplication Technique by A.D.Booth.
Quart. J. Mech. Appl. Math., 1951, **4**, Part 2, p. 236.

Universal High-speed Digital Computers: Serial Computing Circuits by
F.C.Williams, A.A.Robinson and T.Kilburn. Proc. I.E.E., 1952,
99, Part 2, p. 94.

Fast Carry Logic for Digital Computers by B.Gilchrist, J.H.Pomerene
and S.Y.Wong. Trans. I.R.E., 1955, *EC–4*, p. 133.

*Short Cut Multiplication and Division in Automatic Binary Digital
Computers* by M.Lehman. (Proc. I.E.E., 1958, **105**, B, p. 496.

Parallel Addition in Digital Computers – a New Fast 'Carry' Circuit
by T. Kilburn, D.B.G.Edwards and D.Aspinall. Proc. I.E.E., 1959,
106, B, p. 463.

This set of proceedings contains several papers on 'fast carry'.

10 Memory stores

The subject of computer storage systems is a large one; it can most conveniently be divided into two parts. The first part, as we shall approach it, will be the study of memory elements; the second part will be the study of the organisation of memory systems using these elements to meet the requirements of a computer store.

Babbage's memory elements were cog-wheels with ten teeth or multiples of ten teeth, each tooth of which denoted a decimal digit or number. Desk calculators use this system of number registration. There is an analogous electronic device called a *dekatron* which has been used in computers, notably at the Atomic Energy Research Establishment at Harwell; it performed its task adequately but would not meet the requirements of a present-day computer.

Aiken's computer used relays both as logic and as memory elements. These are bulky and slow, and consume a good deal of power. They do, however, illustrate many of the qualities demanded of a memory element, and we shall examine a relay memory element before proceeding to more modern devices.

10.1 Hold-on relay

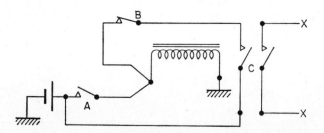

Fig. 10.1

The diagram shows a relay circuit of the type often used as a switch to control electrical machinery. The switch is 'off' when the circuit is in the condition shown in the diagram. The output $x\,x$, is open-circuit.

When contact A is closed, current flows in the relay coil and this closes C and the output circuit, $x\,x$, is closed. We now see that A is redundant: the contacts A and C form an OR combination. Contact A can now open again, but it has no further control of the circuit, which stays 'on' with $x\,x$ closed, until contact B is opened. Contacts B and C form an AND circuit: when B is open the coil circuit is open, the coil becomes de-energised and C opens; $x\,x$ is also made open, and the circuit is back in the initial off condition.

This circuit illustrates two concepts. It is a binary memory or storage element, since the condition of the circuit $x\,x$, shows the past state of A and B contacts. It also introduces sequential logic: although we have introduced the terms AND and OR in a valid way for the contacts A, B, C, their interconnection cannot be dealt with completely by combinational logic. For instance, when A is pressed, first of all, there is a period of instability during which the coil is becoming energised and contact C is closing. During this period A is closed, C is open and $x\,x$ is open. There is another similar period in which B is open but C has not yet become open. It is necessary in some circuit arrangements to take these unstable states into consideration and it is in these applications that we employ sequential logic.

The main characteristic of any memory circuit is demonstrated by the relay arrangement – the circuit is bistable, that is, it has two stable states. It can be set or reset to either state and remains stable in either. If one state is called 'one' and the other 'zero' then the circuit can hold one bit of information.

We have mentioned in the chapter on logic units the classical bistable electronic element called the flip-flop. It will be seen that its behaviour is almost exactly that of the relay circuit: a pulse on one side sets it, a pulse on the other resets it and it can remain stable in the set or reset condition. We also mentioned in the same chapter the ferrite core logic element. We shall investigate this in rather more detail later in this chapter.

10.2 The use of delay as a storage technique

A pulse of electric current takes a finite time to pass through a network, but, even with quite large reactances, the delay time is short in terms of microseconds. The delay due to a sound wave passing down a wire is much longer, and so a delay element can be made in the form shown in Fig. 10.2.

10.3 Delay line system

The device works in this way: nickel is a magnetostrictive material, that is, it changes its linear dimensions when subjected to a magnetic field. When a pulse is applied to the amplifier, A, it is amplified and causes a powerful electric field in the coil. The coil is wound round one end of a nickel wire,

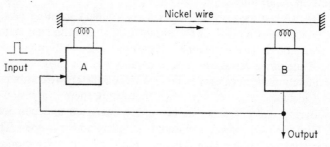

Fig. 10.2

which, as a result of the pulse, contracts and then expands again as the field decays with the current. This contraction and expansion causes a pressure wave to move along the nickel wire. At the other end of the wire there is a second coil connected to a sensitive amplifier. The pressure wave causes the nickel wire within the second coil to change dimension momentarily, which causes a flux change in the coil and induces a pulse in to the amplifier B. The pulse at B follows the input pulse at A a finite, fixed time later, dependent on the length of the wire: the pulse at B is a delayed version of the pulse at A. We can arrange that the pulse at B is fed back to the input of the amplifier A, where it will generate a further pulse, and provided the system loop-gain exceeds unity the system will be regenerative: pulses will continue to circulate once an initial pulse has been introduced at A. Once again we have two stable states, on and off, triggered or set by a pulse at A and reset by inhibiting the circulation for one pulse time, which is usually achieved by closing a gate between B and A.

The technique of using a pulse generator and delay element has been much used in the past as a single bit storage element, usually called by the name *staticiser* or *dynamic flip-flop*. Fig. 10.3 shows the logic diagram of a staticiser.

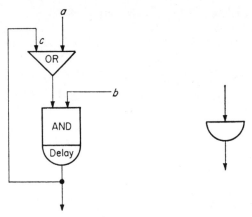

Fig. 10.3 Staticiser   Delay element

10.4 Staticiser or dynamic flip-flop

The AND gate is held open by the input *b*. When a pulse is received at the input *a* it is delayed by the delay unit, and passed back to input *c* of the OR gate. It will continue to circulate until *b* goes down, interrupting the circulation, and the circuit reverts to the zero condition.

The memory circuits we have examined so far have been single bit memories, capable of holding a single digit. We will examine the techniques in rather more detail in the following section when we study multi-bit memories, or storage devices capable of holding a group of digits, such as a computer word or a block of words.

10.5 Multi-bit registers

The first of the memory stores which we need to study is the logic assembly known as a multi-bit register. In general the function of a register is that of a temporary store, in which a group of digits can be set and held during the process of a logic operation. The contents of a register may be required for use in two ways, either serially or in parallel. In the serial mode of operation, the register requires to be a shifting register, that is the contents are fed into one end and shifted along, stage by stage. The output of a shifting register is normally taken from the last position of the register, and the register contents are offered to a logic process of some kind by means of the shifting process. A schematic diagram of a shifting register is shown in Fig. 10.4.

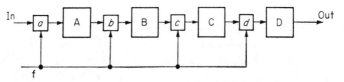

Fig. 10.4

10.5.1 Shifting registers

In the figure the blocks A, B, C, D, represent bistable elements. The gates, *a, b, c, d*, are the input control gates to the bistables. These are normally held closed, and opened only by the presence of a shift pulse on the line (f). The output of the bistable D is normally available at the point marked *out*, and in general this would be connected to the input of a logic element. When the logic process for which the content of D is required has been completed, a shift pulse is applied at (f) and each of the gates *a, b, c, d* is opened for the duration of the shift pulse. The output of A bistable is presented to the input of B, the output of B to C and the output of C to D, and these each set or reset the bistable to which they are connected. Thus a pattern of ones and zeros in the register will move one place to the right for each opening of the gates *a, b, c, d*, by a shift pulse. Whatever state is applied to the input gate *a* will be applied to set or reset the bistable element A.

There is one major complication here which we have glossed over in order to explain the main function of the unit; it comes into the province of sequential logic. If the output of each bistable is, in fact, presented to the input of the next, instantaneously, then it must be that, after the briefest period, all stages will be set to the state as at *a*. In order to make the system work, there requires to be a delay between consecutive stages, at least as long as the shift pulse. Another way of expressing this requirement is to say that the contents of each stage must be remembered during the shift pulse and passed to the next stage. The memory is required to be longer than the shift pulse. This is achieved using coupling networks at *a, b, c, d*, of the kind shown in the shift register stage in Chapter 8, on logic elements.

The memory is effected by the simplest memory element of all, the capacitor. A capacitor will be seen to have the qualities of a memory: it can be charged or uncharged, and therefore have a voltage at its terminals or not, as required. If it is charged, then, when the charging voltage is removed, the output voltage stays at the charged level. This would make the perfect capacitor a perfect memory store device. We live in a real world, however, and real capacitors are imperfect. The charged state can only be maintained for a short time, owing to leakage, and so the capacitor can form a useful transit store but not much more.

Registers get repeated mention in a work of this sort: they are of universal use in computers. For this reason we cannot overlook them in the discussion on storage, but we are more properly concerned with devices of which storage is the prime use.

10.6 The multi-bit delay line store

The basic principle of this element is exactly the same as for the single bit store, but the implementation is a little more difficult. We have left the complications of this method of storage until this stage in order to allow the original survey of memory elements to be fairly brief.

The construction of a delay line store poses some mechanical problems; there are two main types of acoustic delay line used in computer storage, the magnetostrictive type, and the mercury column type.

10.6.1 Mechanical construction of magnetostrictive delay line stores

The speed of sound in a nickel wire is of the order of one foot in 100 micro-seconds. For a delay of one word length in a computer having about thirty digits per word, at three micro-seconds per digit, we need, therefore, about a foot of wire. To store twenty words of the same length, about twenty feet of wire are needed. For a delay line to hold one word, if the wire is not too thin, the delay line could be self-supporting except at the ends. For a longer line the wire will need support at several intermediate points. The mechanical problem is this: at each end the wire support must be a complete absorber of the pressure waves. At each intermediate support the wire must be supported in such a way that there is as little absorption as possible and no reflection. The pressure waves generated by the sending-coil move both ways along the wire; the waves moving towards the anchorage must be completely absorbed. At the receiving end, the waves continue beyond the reading coil to the end of the wire. There must be total absorption here also, or reflections will take place and these will

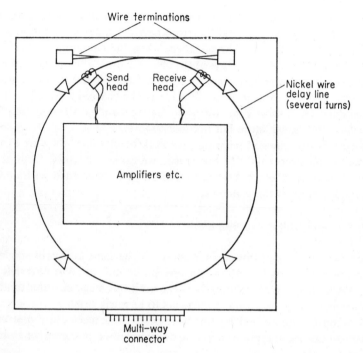

Fig. 10.5

be read by the reading coil as spurious signals. This is not too difficult a problem; the ends of the wire are held in sleeves of plastic that gives the termination a high damping factor; a very high degree of attenuation is achieved in an inch or so of plastic material, properly constructed.

The intermediate supports are less easy. A rigid mechanical support will attenuate the wave train and cause severe reflection. One of the best supports is the crudest – a slot torn or cut in the edge of a piece of kraft paper into which the wire is pushed. This suffices to support the wire. Since there may be several feet of it, it is usually in the form of a coil, and the paper at three or four points around the periphery, supports and separates the turns. The conventional construction for the unit is shown in Fig. 10.5. The whole assembly is mounted in a flat square box, with the delay line in a coil near the outside, and the amplifiers are arranged to occupy the space in the middle.

The attenuation over several feet of wire is fairly high, and so the read amplifier requires to be sensitive; this means that it is susceptible to vibration, but a computer is not generally run in a vibrating environment. The main design problem is that, however square a pulse is applied to the sending-end amplifier, the pulse at the receive end is nothing like square – the received signal must be a differentiated form of whatever flux pulse is generated by the line, due to the way e.m.f. is induced into the reading coil. The problem is dealt with in this way: there is generated within the computer a *clock* waveform of regular shape which is used to synchronise all pulses in the machine. The read amplifier working from the reading coil merely detects the presence or absence of a pulse. If there is a pulse along the line, the read amplifier gates out a *clock* pulse. If there is no detectable pulse down the line, the read amplifier output gate is closed and a pulse is not issued. This is standard practice in computer work: we detect the presence of a pulse or not, and generate a pulse of specified shape and duration if there is a detected pulse. Reference will be made again to this technique when we deal with considerations of computer operating speed. There is a final point about this technique which we should note. We wish to generate the output pulse in time with the appropriate clock pulse. To do this we detect the pulse in the previous clock pulse time and set a bistable memory. At the very commencement of the clock pulse when the output is required, the gate is open and the new pulse is exactly synchronised to the *clock*. This procedure merely entails examining the delay line a pulse earlier than otherwise, that is, the line itself is made one pulse period shorter than a whole word length or block length.

There is a variation of the magnetostrictive delay line, called a *torsional delay line*. In this a wire is used as a delay line, as before, but it need not be of magnetostrictive material. At the sending end a small iron 'paddle' is welded to the wire and a coil placed close to it. When a pulse of current is passed through the coil the paddle is attracted to the coil and twists the wire momentarily. A torsional impulse runs down the wire and a similar paddle the other end acts as an armature in a coil, generating a detectable voltage impulse. This system has proved very satisfactory. The Ferranti Sirius computer uses store elements of this construction, having a capacity of fifty forty-bit words, working at a repetition rate of 500 000 bits per second.

10.6.2 The mercury column delay line store

In this system the delay medium is a column of mercury several feet long, contained in a steel tube. At each end of the tube is a crystal transducer, with a flat surface facing up the axis of the tube. A pulse applied to the

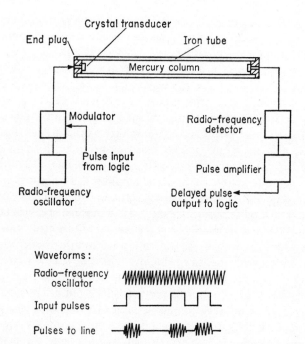

Fig. 10.6

sending-end transducer causes the flat to move by piezo-electric effect. This generates a pressure wave up the tube, which causes a compression of the crystal transducer at the read amplifier end. This crystal generates an e.m.f. which is amplified by the read amplifier and causes the generation of a computer pulse in the same way as the amplifier in the magneto-strictive system; each pulse is, in fact, a burst of radio frequency waves, as illustrated in Fig. 10.6.

Both these systems act as long-term stores by feeding back the output to the input. In this way a full Sirius line, as described above, holds fifty words of information. To recover this information either the whole line contents are read out in sequence to another kind of store, as a block, or the output is sampled only at the period when the wanted word of information is emerging from the read amplifier. The process of arranging to sample only during the word period required is called *coincidence*. Each word in the line has an *address*: this is the number of the word, in sequence, from an arbitrary datum. Each line, too, is numbered, thus an address in this store, which has twenty lines or so, would be, for instance 1836 denoting the 36th word in sequence in the 18th line.

The recirculating delay line system has the advantage of being fairly cheap; it has two main disadvantages. The first is logical – the wanted word of information may not be the next to appear at the line out gate, and time will be wasted awaiting coincidence. In the worst case on a Sirius line this entails forty-nine word times, but the average is twenty-five. In a fast computer, delays of this kind cannot be tolerated. The second disadvantage is a mechanical one. The delay time must be maintained very accurately indeed; it depends on the physical length of the delay line, which in turn depends on ambient temperature. Unless the temperature is strictly controlled the delay lines may become unsynchronised with the rest of the computer. This defect may be overcome, of course, by synchronising the rest of the computer to the delay lines, but this is not always practicable.

10.7 Rotating stores: drums and discs

The most economical form of computer store is the type known as the *rotating magnetic store*. These exist in two forms, rotating drums and discs. In the drum form, the information is recorded on a magnetic coating on the curved surface of a rotating cyclinder. The disc has one or both sides coated and the information is recorded on this, rather in the same way as on a gramophone record. Both types have a very large information capacity, but both suffer from the same defect as the delay line, the requirement of waiting for coincidence to read a particular word.

The mechanical requirements of a rotating store are rather stringent. The drum is a cylinder, usually of dural or similar material, from three to nine inches in diameter, and about the same depth. Larger and smaller versions have been made, but the size quoted covers the more commonly used. The drum is pivoted on fine bearings and spins at a few thousand revolutions per minute. The read/write head arrangement is shown in Fig. 10.7.

The read/write heads are mounted in brackets which are held close to the drum surface. Each head is offered to a band of magnetic material round the drum which passes close to it as the drum revolves. Usually there are several head brackets round the drum, so spaced that the heads on each bracket trace out different tracks from the corresponding heads on other brackets. In this way there can be thirty or so heads per inch of the drum axial length.

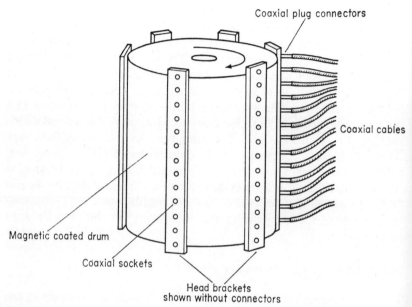

Fig. 10.7

The heads are not run in contact with the drum surface, but at a small distance from it, of the order of 0·001 inch.

The drum surface is coated with a paint in which ferrous oxide, molybdenum ferrite, or similar material is held to the surface as a fine powder, set in a hard glue or varnish. The coating is of the order of 0·001 inch thick and requires to be an even thickness all over, as homogeneous as possible, and with no surface imperfections. This coating is much the same as that used on magnetic recording tape of the highest quality.

The principle of the system operation is this: the drum rotates at a constant speed; a chain of pulses signifying data is fed to a head amplifier which produces reversals of current in the windings of the head. The current is sufficient to cause the magnetic coating immediately under the pole pieces of the head, to be saturated magnetically. There will then be a succession of small segments of the magnetic coating magnetised in one direction or the other according to the pulses to the amplifier at the moment of passing under the head. These segments of the surface will remain magnetised until erased. If the recording amplifier is detached from the head and a sensitive read amplifier attached, the passage of the magnetised segments under the head will induce pulses of e.m.f. which can be amplified; the information which was previously written, can be recovered. For those who are not familiar with magnetic recording technique there is a section appended to this chapter giving brief details of the principles involved, applicable to both drum and tape recording systems.

In order to achieve reliable recording and reading back of digital information the drum system requires to be very precisely constructed. To get a high capacity storage system the drum periphery is normally recorded with between 100 and 300 bits per inch round a recording track, and with up to forty tracks to the inch. The usual packing, achieved reasonably easily, is about 100 to 150 bits per track inch, with twenty to thirty tracks per inch. This gives a packing density of about 2 000 to 4 000 bits per square inch.

The signal level is very dependent on the separation between the head and the drum surface. We can see now some of the mechanical requirements of the drum. To get the packing density the heads need to have very small gaps, and a separation from the track of the order of one thousandth of an inch. This distance should not be allowed to vary more than $\pm 1/10$ of one-thousandth of an inch during a revolution: this entails on a drum, of say 9 inch diameter, a maximum eccentricity of $1/10$ of one-thousandth of one inch. This demands the highest grade machining under conditions of strict temperature control, and bearings of as near perfection as can be obtained. The latter are usually ball races, specially selected and finished for the purpose.

The recording system is designed to work without a separate erasing process. The drum has one track written on it as a clock track, having one digit for every digit position in every word position round the track. A typical track would carry, say, 128 words, of forty digits. In order to write a digit, a one or a zero, the amplifier input is gated with the clock track. In this way in any track, and in any digit position, the recording is always made exactly on the same spot every time. If a zero is written over a previously written one, the track is saturated in the zero direction and the one is completely obliterated. A one or a zero is written always in every digit position and there are thus no ambiguities.

The address of a word on a drum is defined in the same way as on a stack of delay lines: track number, and word number round the track. Due to the large number of words round any track the waiting for coincidence period is long, on average, and for this reason none but the most primitive computer systems now address down to a single drum word. The normal practice is to record blocks of information onto the drum, and to move the information on and off only in blocks. The block with which computing is being carried on will normally be held in a working store or immediate access store of another kind.

The disc store is much the same as the drum in all respects, except the mechanical. The mechanical requirements are just as stringent, but the bearings and the machinery have to be most precise in the axial direction. The length of the recording tracks decreases as the radius decreases, which limits the amount of disc surface that can be used – about the outer third of the radius can be used, normally. By using head brackets which are narrow, several discs can be mounted on one shaft, giving a highly compressed arrangement. The IBM multi-disc store, which has been most effective in operation, has acquired the soubriquet juke-box, by reason of its resemblance to that well-loved machine.

10.8 The cathode ray tube store

The cathode ray tube store was first evolved at Manchester in 1948 by Williams and Kilburn, and for a time was the only large-scale high speed store available for computer systems on either side of the Atlantic.

The basic principle of it is as follows: a cathode ray tube is arranged as shown in Fig. 10.8 with a pick-up plate of metal foil or gauze attached closely to the display surface.

The deflector plates, first and third anodes, and the internal conducting coating of the display surface are all connected to ground. The electron gun, that is cathode and focus electrodes, is connected to a high negative

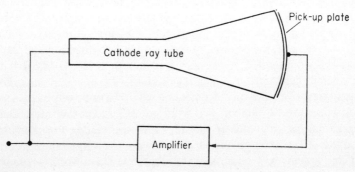

Fig. 10.8

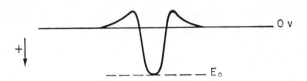

Fig. 10.9

potential, say 2 000 to 3 000 volts. With no beam current, the internal surface of the fluorescent screen will be at ground potential due to leakage between it and the inner conductive coating of the tube face.

Suppose a well focussed beam is directed at a spot on the screen: we have then electrons arriving at the spot at very high speeds and their energy is sufficient to cause secondary emission of electrons in the screen in excess of the number arriving, that is, we have a secondary emission coefficient greater than unity. The spot at which the bombardment takes place gains a positive charge due to its net loss of electrons. Fig. 10.9 shows the potential distribution near to the spot.

The *well*, as it is termed, will reach a potential determined by the energy of the arriving electrons, their number – that is the beam current – and by the rate at which leakage causes the well to tend to refill from its surrounding material. After a short time, of the order of a micro-second or so, an equilibrium state will be reached at which the electron outflow is equal to the inflow. If now the beam is interrupted, the hole will tend to refill, but since the material is of high resistance the time constant is fairly long, of the order of several hundred milliseconds. Switching the beam on again even for a very short time maintains the well, and it can in fact be maintained by very short bursts of bombardment. Here then we have a form of rudimentary memory cell, since a spot that has been bombarded will keep a small positive charge, a spot that has not will be at ground potential. We have the problem now of detecting the charged spots if the memory is to serve a useful purpose in a computer.

Several ways were tried; the first method was to have two spots very close to each other. If the beam is switched to one spot, excavating a hole, and then switched to a second spot very close to the first it will excavate a hole there also. In this second excavation a number of slow-moving secondary electrons will be generated adjacent to the first well and, due to its positive potential, will be attracted to it; it will quickly become partially filled. We call the first spot the *storage spot*. We have now the following conditions possible:

(a) by bombarding a storage spot and not a second spot near it, we are left with a deep well, at the storage spot;

(b) by bombarding a storage spot and then bombarding a spot close to it we are left with a partially filled well.

We have not so far considered the effect on the pick-up plate. If we now apply a pulse of beam current to the storage spot, within a few hundred milliseconds of our action (a) above, a negative pulse will be transmitted to the amplifier at the start of the pulse. But if we bombard the storage spot after action (b) a positive pulse will be sensed by the pick-up plate and transmitted to the amplifier. To make this system into an effective memory store, a good deal of organisation was required. A typical storage cathode ray tube could carry about forty words of forty digits. For a large store, a large number of tubes are necessary with their attendant complications of space, control circuits and power supply. A great disadvantage of this storage system is the necessity for rewriting the data continuously, since the charge pattern on the tube face is transient.

The most practicable and effective method of cathode ray tube storage used a system called focus-defocus instead of the two-spot method described. In this technique, the beam is first focussed tightly on a point to excavate the well; instead of a second spot, the beam remains on its original axis, but is de-focussed slightly to cover an area about five to ten times that of the original spot. The slowly moving electrons to provide a partial filling of the well caused by the tightly focussed spot, are thus generated all round it: but, if condition (a) above is required, the beam is turned off, instead of being defocussed.

The rewriting of information is arranged in this way: the beam is scanned along a 'word' on the tube face; as it arrives at a spot location a positive or negative pulse is generated to the amplifier as described above. If the previous spot was one that had not been partly filled by a defocus, then the beam is turned off. If the amplifier indicates that the spot had been partly filled, then the defocussed beam is applied; the beam is then traversed to the next spot position, repeating the test, and regenerating each spot in the condition it was before.

In such a scan, the output of the amplifier can also be used as the store output, and so the read process is a scan of the required row of spots, with regeneration. The write process is similar, but the initial state of each spot is ignored; the defocussed beam is applied to conform with the write requirement.

There remains the problem of the continuous regeneration of the stored information when it is not actually being used. To do this the whole raster on each tube is scanned regularly and automatically: the automatic scanning is interrupted by demands on the store, which are met immediately, and then the automatic process resumed.

This system is no longer used, but it is considered worthy of description in our study: it illustrates a store system in which the read out is inherently *destructive* but the information is then regenerated, making the overall process a *non-destructive* one. Since this store was evolved, cathode ray tube design has advanced rapidly, like nearly every other electronic technique; the cathode ray tube store is fast, that is, switching and scanning can be done very quickly. Like several other computer engineering techniques it may return to popularity when the right set of circumstances occur.

10.9 Core stores

Core storage is today the most universal storage system used in computers. It combines a reasonable degree of compactness, robustness, reliability and power economy, with a fairly high speed of operation and low access time. It has the advantage that it can be used in series or parallel or both, and it has the ability to retain information when the computer is switched off. Its disadvantage is that it is expensive.

The 'square loop' *B–H* diagram which we examined briefly in Chapter 8 shows that a core will be switched by a certain minimum number of ampere turns of applied field. Below this minimum it will not be switched. This is the simple description of its behaviour on which its memory function is based. A more detailed description of ferrite core behaviour is given later in this chapter, and it is the less simple behaviour described there which causes the comparative complexity of core store systems in practice.

10.10 Construction of the matrix plane

The basic idea of the matrix plane is this: two wires are passed through each core: if both wires carry a current $I/2$, the total ampere-turns applied to the core is I and this value of current is sufficient to saturate, or switch, the core, whereas $I/2$ is not. The wires are assembled in the form of a coordinate grid so that each core has a unique combination of two wires threading it, x and y. If any two wires, x_n, y_n, are selected and currents $I/2$ are passed through them, only the core at their intersection receives the

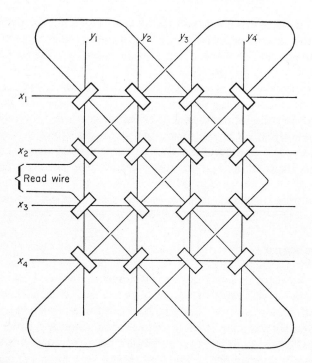

Fig. 10.10

necessary current to switch it. All other cores on wire x_n receive only half drive, as do all other cores on y_n.

Plate 3 shows a typical matrix plane for a core store; Fig. 10.10 shows the wiring arrangement.

Using x and y wires, any core can be set or reset individually and forms a single bit memory. To recover the information, the state of each core must be tested and, because of its nature, this entails switching it. We can set a core by passing half drive currents $I/2$ in each of x and y wires. We can reset it by reversing the current in the same pair. It would be possible to detect the state of a core to which the reverse current pulses are applied by observing the back e.m.f.s in the x and y circuits, but it is easier to incorporate a further wire, called the *read wire* which threads all cores in the plane. If any core is switched in the plane, the read wire will receive an output pulse. Since we arrange which core is pulsed at any instant with the necessary drive, we can arrange for a circuit to detect the pulse and assign it to the core position from which it derives. In sampling each core, however, we have destroyed the information – all reset cores remain reset; all set cores become reset in generating the output pulse.

The cores do not behave perfectly – they do give some output when they receive half drive currents. Thus the read wire will receive an aggregate pulse from the output of every half driven core, as well as the desired output.

The physical size of core planes is limited by engineering factors. They are commonly 32 × 32, 40 × 40, 64 × 64, 64 × 128 cores per plane. Computer word length is dictated by other factors than core plane size; it is uneconomical to manufacture special plane sizes for individual computers.

These three factors, destruction of information on reading, unwanted outputs, and plane size, are the principal ones influencing core store organisation. The designer of a core store must overcome these problems at the outset. The unwanted output problem is largely overcome in the construction of the plane by the way in which the read wire is threaded: this wire is usually threaded in diagonal form, up one diagonal and down another, so that the unwanted outputs occur about equally in each polarity on the wire, and to a great extent cancel one another. This technique is effective but introduces a further problem: the wanted signals occur in either polarity also. The design of the read amplifier must take this into account.

A 32 × 32 plane would be able to store thirty-two words of thirty-two digits: even a large plane such as 64 × 128 would be a small block of storage for a computer, and would hardly be an economic proposition. Most core stores are designed to work in the parallel mode with one digit in each word accommodated in any one plane. The x, y, selection in any plane then defines the word address, and the plane number in the *stack* defines the digit position in the word. The number of planes in a stack is then equated to the word length and thus the store size is limited by the plane size, but the word length is not. Usually the store size is a good deal more flexible a quantity in design than is the word length. This arrangement also lends itself to systems for rewriting information after read out. In a parallel system, it is quite easy to have a register associated with the read out system, in which the word read out can be held, and then re-written.

10.11 The read-rewrite cycle

The method to be described is the most commonly used, but it calls for an additional wire threaded through each matrix plane, known as the *inhibit wire*. This threads all cores of a plane like the read wire, but it is arranged

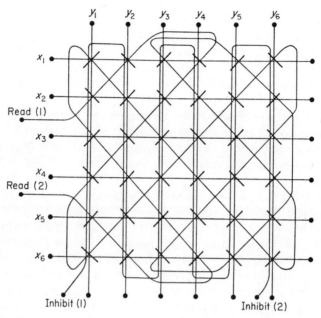

Fig. 10.11

so that it is threaded in the same sense through all cores. Fig. 10.11 shows the arrangement of a typical plane, with x and y write wires, inhibit wire, and read wire.

The stack is wired as follows: all planes have their x wires connected in series, and their y wires in series. The selection of an x circuit and a y circuit selects one core in every plane. Each plane has a read amplifier associated with it, connected to its read wire. The inhibit wire to each plane has a separate drive circuit which is under control of the computer write circuits, and the read amplifier associated with that plane. The operation of the inhibit circuit is such that it opposes and effectively neutralises the write pulses applied by the x and y lines, when it is on. If it is not on then the x and y line write pulses add together to set a core at their intersection.

The cycle of operations proceeds like this: for a *write* operation the inhibit circuits are held 'off' by the computer *write to store* circuits, wherever a one is to be written. A write pulse is then applied through the x and y drive wires selected by the word address circuits. This will write a one into the selected core in each plane where the inhibit is not 'on'. The inhibited planes will stay at zero.

For a *read* operation, the inhibit goes under control of the read amplifiers. To start with it is off on all planes. A *read* pulse is applied to the selected x line and y line; this pulse is of the opposite polarity to the *write* pulse. The x and y selections are accomplished by the address selection circuits, and the combined read half drive pulses switch to zero any core which was a one, in the selected position in each plane. Each one going to zero generates a pulse in the associated read wire which is amplified by the read amplifier to a form suitable for the computer. The read amplifier also triggers a flip-flop in the inhibit control circuit of the plane associated with it. In every plane in which a one was written the inhibit is held off. In all others it goes on as in the normal write operation. Immediately the read pulse has caused the read out to take place a write pulse is sent through the same pair of selected x and y drive lines. This has no effect on any circuit which is inhibited but writes a one in any plane where the inhibit is held off – that is, any plane from which a one has just been read.

The complete read cycle can be seen to be:

(*a*) select x and y lines (word address);
(*b*) *read pulse* to x and y lines;
(*c*) set *inhibit* from read amps receiving zeros;
(*d*) *write pulse* to x and y lines;
(*e*) *operation complete* signal (if required).

The whole process in a fast store system takes about 2 micro-seconds. An operating cycle of 5 micro-seconds is quite easy to achieve.

The pulse outputs on the read wires going into the read amplifiers have a large hump or peak, near the commencement, due to reversible switching processes in all the unswitched cores – the form of such a pulse is shown in Fig. 10.12. This peak is followed by a broader hump of less amplitude which indicates a read one. It is this part of the signal which we wish to use, and so we gate the signal with a strobe pulse at this time; and the strobed output is made to generate a computer pulse. The shape of the read waveform is always as shown in the diagram, but its scale depends on the rise time of the drive pulse. The faster the rise time the shorter the whole pulse, and the larger in proportion to the rest is the unwanted peak due to the reversible phenomena. This is because the leading peak is largely dictated by '$e = L \, di/dt$' considerations, whereas the wanted, or later part of the pulse is dependent on the final amplitude of the drive pulse. The drive pulse amplitude is fixed, between fairly close limits, by the physical characteristics of the core. For $I/2$ must not switch any part of any core, whereas I must switch all parts of any core. When we allow for tolerances on core dimen-

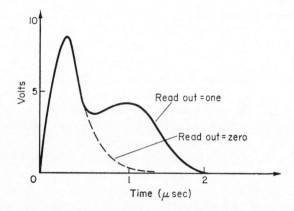

Fig. 10.12

sions, core composition, and tolerances of components in the drive circuits we find that there is not much margin of choice. Customarily the drive currents are limited to within ± 5 per cent of desired value: the sort of values used for $I/2$ are between 300 and 500 milliamps for cores of a suitable size for both fast switching and ease of manufacture – speed calls for smallness, but smallness makes for difficult assembly. Cores for computer applications are normally about one to two millimetres in outside diameter; core planes having cores of 0·030 inch diameter are used in high performance stores, and the use of even smaller cores is envisaged. We can see that circumstances of all kinds dictate our designs in the field of core stores, and we are usually fairly tightly tied to standard ranges of components. The best design must be the best compromise solution to a problem consisting of a large number of compromises. A typical compromise choice is that of pulse rise time for the read and write drive pulses. A fast rise time gives a large 'disturbed core' peak; a slow rise time gives a smaller peak but a longer delay in the wanted output peak. The strobe pulse will have to be arranged after a delay chosen to get the best ratio between *read one* and *read zero*. Now, if the rise time is fast, a 20 per cent tolerance variation in the transistor circuit producing the drive pulses will make a fraction of a micro-second difference to the optimum strobe time. A slower pulse will mean that the same variation may make a whole micro-second difference and the circuit operates outside optimum conditions if any variations occur during operation.

Fig. 10.13 shows a typical set of idealised waveforms for operating a core stack.

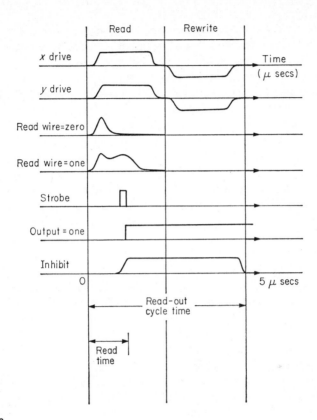

Fig. 10.13

There are many variations of the technique used in operating core stores. The preceding description should acquaint the reader with the basic requirements and how they can be met. An actual design will depend, as we have remarked previously, on a fairly involved set of circumstances – not the least of which will be cost.

10.12 The organisation of computer storage

We can divide up computer storage systems by considering the *access time*, that is the time it takes to recover information for use by the computer, from the store. Convenient, and suitably expressive names for the different categories are as follows:

Immediate access store. This is a store from which a word of information can be recovered immediately the address of the store location is decoded by the control register. This type of storage is provided by registers, usually maintained for special purposes, and by core stores. Single word delay lines have been used for this purpose, but are expensive to provide in numbers; cathode ray tube storage would also be a good method, if it had not other limitations.

Intermediate access store or *working store*. This kind of storage used to be provided by short delay lines, having say eight or sixteen words; nowadays core storage has replaced it in most cases and the working store is all immediate access. Intermediate access stores are now only likely to be encountered where a computer is built under severe budgetary limitations.

Main store. This is the store in which the bulk of the information required for a programme is stored, except in the case of ledgers and similar documents which are processed serially. This storage is commonly provided by drum or disc store units or sets of long delay lines each with a capacity of fifty or so words.

Backing stores. This is the store in which library information is held, ledger files, and the like. Usually this is provided by magnetic tape machines, but it may be provided by stacks of cards, for instance, in census operations and similar tasks. Tapes commonly hold whole programmes such as fault-finding and test routines, payroll ledgers, stock-control ledgers, air traffic time-tables or even dictionaries.

The divisions between one kind of store and another are not easy to define in every circumstance. Immediate access stores are always what their name implies, but working, main and backing stores are not always clearly definable. There is, for instance, a sepcial purpose computer for language translation that uses as a working store a glass plate on which the information is permanently written by a photographic process. This is a 'fixed' store since it cannot be changed in operation. It is not immediate access since coincidence has to be found. It is fast, however, and contains about 300 000 words of dictionary information. It must be a working store or main store but resembles in many ways a backing store.

Ideally, a computer designer or programmer would prefer a computer to have all immediate access storage. This is never possible since there seems to be no upper limit to the amount of storage that users require and any attempt to meet it is extremely costly. The Massachusetts Institute of Technology computer is equipped with a core store of two and a half million cores. It is not within the budgetary capability of every computer user to aspire to this. But what cannot be achieved by luxurious provision can to a large extent be provided by artifice. We are driven to artifice by another consideration also. The arithmetic unit or system centre of a computer can be made to work very fast indeed. The great computers Atlas and Stretch have arithmetic facilities that operate at a pulse repetition rate, or bit rate, of 10 Mc/s. Elliott Brothers (London) Ltd., have now perfected a technique using tunnel diodes, which operates at 50 Mc/s. There are no practical storage devices at this time which are operable at much above 1 Mc/s. The speed of core stores is largely limited by the core size, and at 1 Mc/s the cores are as small as can easily be assembled in matrix planes. We see that, at present, storage operations are slower, by a mathematical order, than logic operations. It seems reasonable to suppose, since stores are built of logic devices, that however fast we make store operation, logic operation will be that much faster. In our first considerations of store organisation, we shall ignore this problem.

Generally, in mathematical or scientific or data processing programs, there are words of information which may be required repeatedly in different phases of the operation. It is advantageous to store these where they are immediately available; also words or numbers occur in calculation and require to be held in store temporarily and require immediate access storage. There are occasions in which the contents of working registers, such as the accumulator, or the sequence control register, need to be put away temporarily. It is customary to provide stores to cope with the latter requirement which may or may not be considered as part of the main storage system of the computer – they may not be available to the programmer for any other purpose. The requirement is usually met by registers, of the flip-flop kind. They are an expensive provision but it is often economical to provide them. Some computers have several accumulators to deal with the immediate access needs we have mentioned. These accumulators are in many cases equipped for some mathematical and logical functions and justify the use of the term accumulators; sometimes however they are merely stores, or registers, and the term accumulator should not be applied to them.

For general immediate requirements, that is, for data required in the current problem, the core store is an adequate provision, and is the working store. Sometimes we can differentiate between the core store locations and register locations acting as temporary stores by their modes of address: the core store is normally addressed as part of the main storage, whereas, in some computer systems, the registers used as temporary stores may not have addresses which are part of the main store address system. These are loaded and used automatically under control of the machine's own built-in micro-programs.

Generally the upper limit to the number of register-type, immediate stores, and core store locations, is dictated by cost; the lower limit is dictated by necessity as defined by the basic specifications for the computer. Assuming that the core store is of so limited a size that the entire data for a computation or programme cannot be held in it, as is usually the case, then the working store is supported by the main store, in many cases, a drum, or disc, or several of them. The information on the drum or disc is stored as blocks of words, and among the functions allowed for in the computer function table will be instructions for reading blocks from the drum into core store locations, and back again. There will need to be sections of the core store especially earmarked for this purpose or it will devolve on the programmer to ensure that the necessary empty locations exist. Normally these transfers are at the discretion of the programmer and it will be his responsibility to arrange the packing of information so that the transfers are used most effectively. The order is sometimes *swap* rather than *transfer*, which means that contents of the selected drum block and core store group are exchanged.

Where the drum or disc main store is insufficient, as is often the case in data processing or business applications, we have a tape store or similar very large storage capacity device as a backing store. The information on the tape is usually, also, in blocks and it seems logical to make these blocks of the same size as the drum blocks, although this is not obligatory. Tape devices are usually manufactured as self-contained units and associated with the parent computer when required, through buffer units. Some indication of the requirements for a tape unit for use with a computer is given in the section on magnetic recording technique at the end of this chapter.

The foregoing has been a discursive survey of storage systems. Let us now recapitulate and see what engineering considerations are likely to arise in the design of a practical system. We will assume that the word length of the computer has already been decided. This affects us in two ways: in the first place, every store location of whatever kind of store has now been fixed in length. In the second it gives us a limit to the number of digits assigned to address in the order word. If the working store is to have, say, 512 words, this will require nine digits to address uniquely every store word location. If the main store is to be large, the number of digits available to assign to drum block numbers may, also, be limited by word length considerations and we may have to borrow digits from the function table assignment – if this is possible.

It is customary to operate drums in the serial mode, that is, we read out from one track at a time, and that track usually supplies an integral number of blocks. Using this method we need only one drum read-and-write amplifier and we switch it from track to track with electronic switching. This is a very economical system. If the computer is serially operated throughout, then the drum transfer to core store can also be serial, but the machine will be slow. If the core store is parallel operated to the computer system centre or arithmetic unit, then serial transfers from drum to core store will take an intolerably long time. Parallel transfers occasion a much larger amount of hardware – say forty times as much, if the word length is forty bits. There will, of course, require to be forty read-write amplifiers for the drum, as well as forty read out amplifiers for the core store. Design decisions of this kind are almost always resolved on the cost versus speed basis.

Introducing tape machines adds further to these problems: we require control functions to control the tape reading and writing, either into the core store or into the drum store. The block-address system applying to the tape may occasion problems, which may well be solved by having built in micro-programs within the computer, in which the tape block-addresses are indexed. Such micro-programs are usually held on the drum. We can see that considerable organisational effort may have to go into the preparation of the tape transfer arrangements or the system may be highly inefficient.

A further interesting engineering problem arises at this stage. The drum store may well work at a different speed from the core store; core stores are apt to work at around 500 kc/s or 1 Mc/s; drums are difficult to operate at speeds approaching this. Tape machines, generally, are slower than drums. We therefore have the speed problems to resolve as well as the control problems. The classical method of dealing with the speed problem is the buffer unit which consists primarily of a register; often these days a matrix plane is used instead of a register or group of registers. The buffer store has the characteristic that it can work at two different speeds, and sometimes in both series and parallel. In the case of a tape-to-drum transfer, for instance, a block of data may be transferred from the tape to a matrix plane, at the tape speed of operation. It may then be transferred to the drum at drum speed, possibly in parallel mode. The buffer unit in the case described will be quite a complicated unit, complete with core store electronics, a method of finding the appropriate tape block, a method of finding also the appropriate drum block, and the necessary control functions to sequence the operation. We should note that tape units are serial: their fastest rate of data transfer is limited normally to about eight parallel channels at about 100 or 200 kc/s. The buffer unit will have the problem of sorting, say, eight parallel channels into words of forty digits in length, for parallel recording on the drum.

Each of the difficulties or problems discussed has a fairly easy solution – but, as ever, each sub-unit costs money and its cost has to be balanced against the possible gain in efficiency. Generally greater speed gives greater economy; certainly, time lost in the computer can only cost money and never save it. The object must be to ensure that the computing section of the machine is kept fully occupied, and this means organising the store, intrinsically slower, anyway, to keep the computing section fed with what it wants; very important, too, is the requirement of getting processed information out of the calculating unit, and preferably out of the system altogether.

Some very ingenious systems exist to accomplish these tasks. The first basic artifice on which these systems operate is that of 'concurrent operation' and of automatic operation of the main organs of the machine and buffer systems. If the buffer systems and transfer orders are made sufficiently automatic, the computing section of the machine operates on working-store data while, in another part of the working store, transfers from drum or tape are taking place. The main object program is only held up while the data transfer orders are decoded and checked for non-interference with the object program orders in process. As soon as the transfer starts, the object program continues. There is nothing very difficult in arranging things this way: it is just rather complicated, and requires careful thought to ensure that the object program is 'locked out' of the transfer sub-program and that this is locked out of the object program. Lock-out techniques are very necessary in many places in computer operations – micro-programs and similar built-in sub-routines must be safeguarded from accidental interference, such as their store locations being over-written, by accident of programming, or by machine faults.

The basic problem of speeding-up the information delivery to the computing section of the machine has been tackled in two ways, very successfully – *look ahead*, and *single level*.

In the look-ahead operation, the process is this: several decode registers are provided and the instructions following the current one in the program are read into these registers. The instructions are examined, by being partially decoded, to see whether they contain demands on address locations that are not immediately available. When these are found the transfer instructions are initiated automatically to bring forward the information into immediate access locations. By this means the store delay can very largely be eliminated and the store appears to be single level the operator or programmer. A true single level store would only exist if all the storage was working store or immediate access but the appearance of single level can be obtained by organisation. The best example of this so far achieved is the Ferranti Atlas, designed jointly by Ferranti and Manchester University, under Professor Kilburn's direction.

10.12.1 The Atlas single level store

The central store of the computer is a drum and core store combination; there are four drums giving a total information capacity of 96 000 words of forty-eight bits, and a core store of four stacks each of 4 096 words. The system can also cope with eight tape machines. In addition to this main and working storage the computer has a fixed store of 8 192 words each of fifty bits, having a very short access time, 0·4 micro-seconds. Associated with this fixed store there is a private store of 1 024 words of core storage giving working space for the programs or micro-programs held in the fixed store. This has a cycle time of 1·8 micro-seconds as does the main core store. The drum store has an average access time of six milliseconds, that is three thousand times the core store cycle time.

In addition to this rather comprehensive armoury the computer is equipped with 128 B stores, or *index registers*, each of twenty-four bits. It would be very difficult for a programmer to arrange his own store-transfer program on a machine as complicated as this; since there are facilities for several programs to be run simultaneously, such an arrangement would not be possible unless the store allocation was divided arbitrarily between programs, and this in general leads to loss of storage efficiency. The difficulty is overcome on Atlas by putting the whole operation of the computing system under the control of a master program known as *Supervisor*, and it is this that uses the very fast stores and fixed stores, securely locked out from any interference from object programs. Supervisor attends to a great many things; here we are concerned with its storage activities.

Drum transfers take place between drum and core stores in blocks of 512 words. The core store blocks which hold these are called *pages*. The main computing unit, then, has thirty-two pages of core store to work on. When a program is put into the machine it is addressed relatively, that is it has a numbered program sequence and store sequence, but these numbers have no absolute position in the overall computer store numbering system. Supervisor places the program in what pages are vacant, and maintains an index of the pages used relative to each program.

Supervisor controls all transfers between core and drum stores. To save time, it transfers any page of core store it wishes to transfer to drum, into the first empty available drum block; the drum store automatically indexes the drum contents. When a block is required for use and is not in a core store page Supervisor finds the required block and transfers it to a vacant page for use.

In order to keep the pages in the working store as up to date as possible, that is, to ensure that current program work is in the core store, there is a learning routine built into Supervisor. This checks all pages in the core store repeatedly; the pages which have not been used recently are returned to drum. The criterion for judgement is by recording each use of the page and timing the frequency of use occurrences. When there is an appreciable gap in use time compared with this frequency, the page is put away to drum store. The strength of this technique is in that instructions in a program, and data in a program most often occur in sequence. A page will get repeated use: there will be a delay when a page is completed, or when a branch instruction causes a jump to a new store location. To the programmer the system seems to be single level, since average information recovery times are about the same as they would be for a single level core-store. Programming is also as though the store were single level. There are other artifices used in Atlas to gain speed, but they are outside the scope of this discussion.

10.12.2 The Stretch look-ahead system

Stretch is the name given to the IBM 7030 computer, a machine of comparable size and specification to Atlas. Stretch has a core store and a disc store. The disc store has a capacity of two million words with a transfer rate of 125 000 words per second. The core store has a capacity of 16 384 words, with a cycle time of about two micro-seconds.

The basic speed organisation of Stretch storage depends on two associated units, the look-ahead operand fetch unit and the instruction unit. As in Atlas, blocks of information are transferred automatically between core store and disc store. Each instruction word of sixty-four digits carries two instructions. The instruction unit holds two instruction words, or four instructions, at any time. These it partially decodes, and does indexing operations on the address sections; then it passes them to an unoccupied level of the look-ahead unit.

This unit has four levels; each level consists of a group of registers to hold the associated instruction, the operand when it becomes available and certain other flag information – *flags* in this context denoting indicator digits, carrying relevant information for controlling the operation's progress. The *fetch operand* part of the unit organises the block transfers necessary to bring the instruction operand right through to the register in the *look ahead* level. When all is complete and ready for use, the level is flagged and the arithmetic unit accepts it for processing as soon as it is clear of its previous commitment.

10.12.3 A comparison of systems

It is difficult to make any valid comparison of these two systems. The description given here is too brief to give the reader anything but an outline of their operation. They do, however, exemplify the very complex store organisation required in a large high-speed computing system. They also serve to illustrate the use of the words immediate, main, working and backing in the storage context.

From an engineering point of view, very large systems introduce interesting problems. The power requirements for the Stretch and Atlas stores run into many kilowatts. The delay on a wire a few feet long is quite appreciable at frequencies of 10 Mc/s and such a large store must also be large mechanically.

Finally there are considerations of cost. Tape storage has the cheapest cost per bit rating, with drum and disc not far behind. Core stores cost generally twenty-five to one hundred times as much, per bit, as drum stores: the latter may be rated at something of the order of one penny per bit. These cost figures are to be conjured with, inside a finite budgetary provision, in any practical design.

No computer yet has met all the requirements asked of it. Storage is often the limiting factor on performance. For the inventive engineer there is great scope for making advances in this field.

10.13 Square loop ferrites: physical principles

The behaviour of the square loop ferrite materials is most easily understood by reference to the Domain Theory of Magnetism. To use a device intelligently an engineer needs not only to know what it does, but if possible, why and how it does it. Since ferrite cores are of great importance in computer systems, we include this study of the fundamental principles as background material.

An atom consists of a heavy positively charged nucleus around which negatively charged electrons rotate in groups of orbits which we call *shells*. In the normally energised state of an atom the inner shells are complete and the only shell that can be incomplete is the outer; the completeness or otherwise, of the outer shell defines the *valency* of the atom, that is, its power to combine with any other atoms. We call the outer shell electrons the valence electrons.

Each electron not only rotates in an orbit about the nucleus but also rotates at a much greater speed about its own axis; this rotation is called the *electron spin*.

When an atom combines with another in chemical combination, or with one of its own kind in crystalline composition, it is the interaction of its valency electrons with those of its neighbours which bonds it to them. In a crystal, the atoms group together in a three-dimensional geometric pattern called a lattice and the form of the lattice depends on the bonding or valence electrons. The inner shell electrons take no part in the bonding process.

Each spinning electron forms a very small but powerful magnet, and when atoms are grouped together in a crystal the fields of the tiny magnets interact. In some materials their resultant is always zero, and these materials are non-ferro-magnetic. In ferro-magnetic materials the electron fields orientate themselves into patterns, and if an external field is applied the pattern may be affected by it, causing electrons and groups of electrons to orientate themselves in line with the applied field. If when the field is removed the imposed pattern of orientation remains, then there is a resultant field in the material, and it is said to be magnetised. The reason for the difference in behaviour between the magnetic and non-magnetic material, is that the exchange forces that bond them align the individual atoms, in the case of non-magnetic material, in such a way that their magnetic moments are all cancelled out; in the magnetic material the exchange forces do not accomplish this completely and there are small residual magnetic moments associated with the atoms in the crystal.

In this case the moments themselves form patterns of alignment giving rise to *domains* in the crystal structure; the domains, then, are zones in the crystal where the residual moments have formed into equilibrium states. Their size and shape are functions of various energy forms - magnetostrictive, magneto-static, and domain-wall energy – and they assume values so as to make the total system energy in the domain a minimum.

Our elementary experiments with magnets and compass needles have shown us that it is difficult to maintain two magnets close together with like poles adjacent. Groups of magnets tend to rest more easily in pairs or rings in such a way as to reduce the reluctance of their field path. The same considerations apply to atoms in a crystal; the residual moments tend to align themselves in groups and these groups become domains. The boundaries between the domains are called *domain walls* or *Bloch walls*. In material having a domain structure the magnetostrictive and magnetostatic energies are least and the majority of the energy is in the wall form.

In a typical unmagnetised crystal the domains will be randomly orientated, along three easy directions of magnetisation due to the lattice form. When an external field is applied, those domains which are most nearly in alignment with the applied field grow in size with respect to the others as the domain pattern changes to conform with the applied field. As the field is increased the unaligned domains disappear altogether and the whole crystal becomes a single domain, having a resultant magnetisation in the direction of the applied field.

Experimenters have been able to observe and record this process by coating the surface of crystals with a magnetic emulsion and observing the changes under a powerful microscope: the technique is a refined form of the pattern experiments using magnets and iron filings by which we convinced ourselves of the existence and form of magnetic fields. Our earlier experiments should also indicate to us why the most non-aligned domains are the first to disappear – the couple applied to a magnet by a field perpendicular to it is reduced as the magnet turns more and more into alignment, as in Fig. 10.14.

While the applied external field is small, the movements of the magnetisation vectors of the most unaligned domains take place and the domain wall movements or rearrangements are reversible, that is, they revert again to their original state when the field is removed. With higher fields the vectors of the domains which are in diametrically opposite alignment

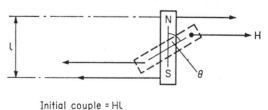

Initial couple = HL
Resultant couple = HL cos θ

Fig. 10.14

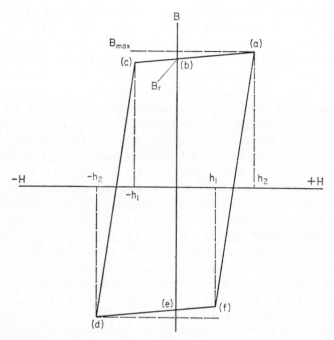

Fig. 10.15

to the applied field are reversed and these domains merge into the aligned ones; the wall movements, in this case, are irreversible, and do not revert to their original state when the field is removed and magnetic remanence is established.

In most iron compounds the degree of remanence, and the domain orientation is a gradual process up to saturation. In the square loop materials, there is a small reversible change until a certain value of field strength is applied, when there is a sharp transition to the saturated state. The $B-H$ loop for such a material is shown in Fig. 10.15; although this is an 'idealised' diagram, some modern ferrite materials approximate very closely to the curve shown.

Referring to Fig. 10.15: commencing with the specimen unmagnetised we increase the applied field to h_1 before any significant change occurs. Increasing the field from h_1 to h_2, causes the wall movement to take place to give almost total alignment and merging of the domains into a single domain. Further increase in field strength makes for little further increase of B_{max}, the maximum value, of flux density, or magnetisation.

Reducing the field once more to zero, the value of B falls to B_r, the remanent value at (b). Reversing the field and increasing it to $-h_1$ in the reverse direction, little change takes place until $-h_1$ is exceeded; then as the field strength increases from $-h_1$ to $-h_2$ the value of B suddenly changes to B_{max} in the opposite polarity, as the whole system reverses its direction, and an irreversible wall movement takes place. Reducing the field to zero causes B to revert to B_r at (e). The ratio of $B_r : B_{max}$ is sometimes called the 'squareness ratio' of the material.

We have so far considered only the static behaviour of the ferrite material. We need also to consider the behaviour of a sample when it is switched, since this is the action which causes flux change, which in turn is responsible for the e.m.f.s induced when using ferrite material as transformer or logic unit cores.

The irreversible phenomena are such by virtue of the fact that not only must energy be supplied to saturate the material but also energy must be supplied to desaturate it or reverse the saturation or remanent induction. The reversible phenomena on the other hand require energy to cause them, but give it back when the field is removed and they revert to the unmagnetised condition.

When a field sufficient to saturate the material is applied, it has to supply the necessary energy to cause the domain wall movement. When sufficient external energy has been supplied by the field, surface imperfections, impurities, and similar irregularities act as nucleation centres and the domain wall movements spread out from them; as the switched areas enlarge they meet and join up and advance together. Imperfections in the path of the movement cause temporary arrests and the wall movement progresses round them and joins up behind them. The islands so formed tend to shrink and patterns form around them, or they vanish. The velocity at which the wall movement takes place depends on eddy currents which cause heat losses, impurities, lattice imperfections and flaws. The impurities cause electron spin relaxation phenomena, known as Jordan lag. The commonest impurity found in ferritic materials, and having this effect, interstitial carbon. Since the rate at which energy can be absorbed depends on the external energy supplied, the velocity depends, also, on the applied field strength. We see, then, that the change of B, the flux density, resulting from a step change in applied field, is a function both of the intensity and time.

The form in which ferrite materials are most commonly used is a small ring core of material which can be wound to make a logic element, in the form of a small teroidal transformer, or which can be threaded onto a grid

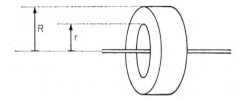

Fig. 10.16

of wires to form part of a matrix plane. We shall consider a ring of ferrite material through which a wire is threaded as in the diagram of Fig. 10.16.

We pass a current through the wire: the wire threaded once through the core amounts to one turn; a current of one ampere along the wire gives a magnetising field strength of one ampere-turn.

The inner diameter of the ring is r and an elemental ring at this radius has a reluctance proportional to r. The field strength effective in the elemental ring will be inversely proportional to r, and until H/r reaches a certain minimum value for the material, saturation of the elemental ring will not take place. The reluctance of an elemental ring at radius R will be considerably greater than the value at radius r, and until H/R reaches the saturation value, the outside elements will not be saturated. By increasing the current slowly the core can be saturated gradually, starting at the inside surface and progressing towards the outside. At some radius between r and R there will be a transition region between the magnetised material and the unmagnetised. Domain wall movement will take place between the inner surface and this transition layer, but none will take place beyond the layer until the field strength is high enough. We can imagine, then, a circular 'front' of domain wall movements which advances from r to R through the material as the current is increased. This picture is close to reality, for a front of domain wall movements does advance through the material more or less uniformly, like a rising tide. Imperfections in the material cause arrests of the advance of the domain wall front, but the advance continues round these imperfections, joins up beyond them and they are engulfed finally, like islands on a sandy beach. These irregularities cause detectable noise.

It would be expected that the rate of progression of the domain wall front would be proportional to the excess applied field strength above the necessary minimum. This has been found to be the case, experimentally, and the speed of front movement through a sample, and its relationship to the applied field strength are not difficult to determine.

If the outer radius were very large, that is, the sample would be a ferrite plate with a hole in it, radius r, then for any current I there would be a maximum radius at which saturation took place and to which the domain wall movement advanced. The speed of advance would decrease as the maximum radius was approached: if the value of current I was achieved instantly and if the reluctance value of all the elemental rings out to the maximum radius were constant, the progress of the wall front would be exponential with time. Since the reluctance changes continuously with radius the expression is rather more complicated. Also, the idea of the instantaneous value of current I is artificial: current pulses may have fast rise times but they are not instantaneous.

In the practical case we apply a current pulse to the circuit under a controlled condition: suppose we attempt an instantaneous rise time. Inductive effects will be experienced and the current driving source will suffer a load changes due to both reversible and irreversible phenomena in the core. The wire itself has an inductance. Thus when applying a current pulse to a core we have the following effects to consider:

(a) the resistance of the circuit wire;
(b) the wire inductance;
(c) the inductance due to the core's reversible behaviour;
(d) the finite speed of movement of the domain walls 'lagging' on the rise of the current pulse.

For the reasons given it is not practicable to calculate and plot the waveform of a current pulse applied to a core, nor more particularly, the current and voltage pulse induced in a secondary winding on the core as a result. The characteristic form of the output pulse is easily determinable by measurement, and it is on the measured characteristic that we have to base our designs. Fig. 10.17 shows a typical pulse shape for the output from a core switched from one state of saturation through to the other by a sufficiently large pulse.

The sharp rise at the start is due to the reversible effects. The central hump in the full curve is achieved at the period at which the domain wall front is moving most rapidly, hence $d\phi/dt$ is at a maximum. The trailing edge of the curve is a Gaussian distribution due to the decay of the domain wall movement as the number of unswitched domains decreases in a random manner. The dotted curve shows the output induced by a second pulse of the same size as the first, and in the same direction. The reversible effects are there for every pulse. The irreversible effects, useful for memory purposes are only there when the core is completely switched.

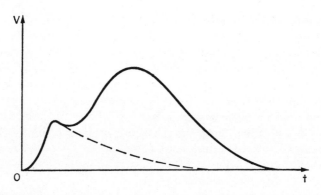

Fig. 10.17

10.14 The behaviour of ferrite cores in matrix planes

When cores are assembled in large numbers in a wire grid known as a matrix plane, the different parts of their behaviour pattern assume particular importance. The perfect plane would have the following characteristics:

(*a*) when no cores were switched, no output should result from a read pulse;
(*b*) when one core was switched a full output should result from a read pulse, of definite size, repeated exactly every time it was switched;
(*c*) the state of switched and unswitched cores should be unchanged by half current pulses;
(*d*) the output pulse should be instantaneous – that is, it should commence exactly at the same time as the read pulse.

We have in practice no perfect planes. A read pulse on a typical matrix store causes outputs as shown earlier, in Fig. 10.12.

The disturbed cores show the reversible effect. It is fortunate that the domain wall movement does occupy a finite time, and is fairly slow, since this allows the hump (one micro-second) to be used as the information indication with little ambiguity.

The foregoing has in no sense been a rigorous treatment of magnetic behaviour or domain theory: it is half model and half truth but it allows us to develop an intuitive understanding of core behaviour.

10.15 Magnetic recording

The technique of magnetic recording is old, by electronic standards; Valdemar Poulson, of Sweden, patented a magnetic recorder in 1890. Early radio programmes were recorded and rebroadcast using steel tape, by the Blattnerphone. Fine steel and nickel wires were also developed as a medium, and then plastic tape, coated with magnetic material. Some quite sophisticated tape systems were evolved by the Germans during the 1939–45 war. The search for storage media for digital computers led to the inclusion of magnetic drums in some of the first computers; notably A. D. Booth's APE(X)C in this country.

Today tape-recording technique is highly developed: audio recorders have become a necessity to certain age groups; many radio and television programmes are recorded and rebroadcast. Nearly every large digital computing system includes drum, or disc, and tape storage. It is widely used in instrumentation and in analogue computing systems.

Like so many of the components of computing systems, the principles of magnetic recording are quite simple to understand, but the refinements demand a good deal of study.

Fig. 10.18 shows a simple recording configuration: the writing head consists of a loop of material of high magnetic permeability, such as iron,

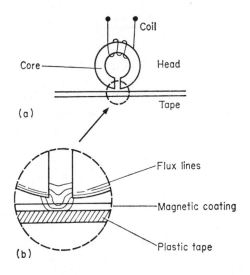

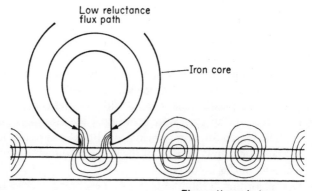

Low reluctance flux path

Iron core

Flux patterns in tape

Fig. 10.19

wound with a coil; the core magnetisation can be varied by currents through the coil. There is a narrow gap in the flux path round the core and the magnetic tape is passed close to this gap, as shown. The reluctance of the gap is high compared with that of the rest of the flux path, and the flux tends to cross the gap by the easiest method; since the coating of the tape is magnetic, much of the flux seeks a path through this coating the material of the coating has a high remanance, and the field intensit in the gap is to some extent recorded in the tape. If the tape is pulled past the gap, and the field is maintained at a steady level, the tape coatin becomes uniformly magnetised; if the field is varied as the tape is moved then the magnetisation of the tape will vary from place to place, i accordance with the changes of field intensity.

Suppose, now, that the current source is removed from the coil and voltage-sensitive device is connected to it: as the magnetised parts of the tape pass the gap, some of the flux associated with the tape will follow the low reluctance path through the core, in preference to the high reluctance air path, as in Fig. 10.19.

Any change in the magnetic field strength, due to the tape movemen will cause a change of flux through the core and therefore through the co This flux change causes a voltage to be induced into the coil windings, and this will be detected by the voltage sensitive device. We should note, par cularly, that the degree of magnetisation of the tape depends on the i stantaneous value of the applied field, and the current. The value of t induced voltage, on the other hand, depends on the rate of change of fl through the core: this depends on the speed at which the tape is moved well as the variation of magnetic intensity of the coating, from place to place.

Our earlier studies of magnetism will have convinced us that the relationships between current, flux and induced voltages in iron circuits are not, in general, linear. It is possible, though, by choice of suitable core material, and current values to get a fairly linear record and play-back characteristic over limited ranges.

The requirements of a recording system differ considerably in analogue and digital applications. We will consider first the analogue; these requirements are in general much the same as for musical recording, that is, we require to record, or store, a pattern of continuously varying intensity, and reproduce it exactly in its original form.

10.16 Analogue recording

Fig. 10.20 shows a typical magnetisation curve for a material such as that for the magnetic material in the tape coating. We should note that the recording head core has a gap in it and this prevents saturation of the core material; we can, in this study, neglect the non-linearity of the core material in comparison with that of the coating.

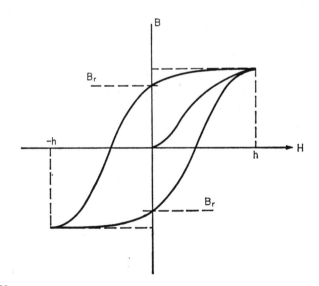

Fig. 10.20

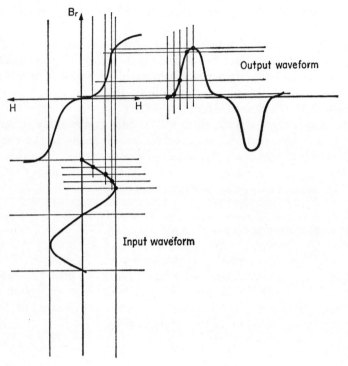

B_r

H

H

Output waveform

Input waveform

Fig. 10.21

The magnetising force, H, which is applied to the portion of tape under the gap, depends on the current and number of turns in the coil; the induced flux density, B, in the tape depends on H, according to the relationship shown on the $B-H$ curve. As H varies between $-h$, and $+h$, the value of B will travel round the hysteresis loop. As the field is reduced to zero from any value, there will be a remanent value, B, corresponding to each value of H, applied and removed: this can be plotted, to give a recording characteristic, as shown in Fig. 10.21.

Manifestly this characteristic would not provide a high-fidelity recording; there is however a portion of the characteristic that is substantially linear; if we can arrange to work only over that portion, we should get quite a reasonably faithful correspondence between output and input. This is achieved by using a high frequency bias signal, to which we add the signal we wish to record.

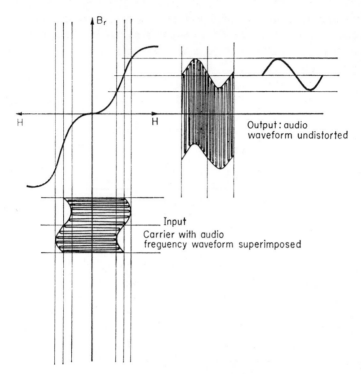

Output: audio
waveform undistorted

Input
Carrier with audio
frequency waveform superimposed

Fig. 10.22

Fig. 10.22 shows the process, simply. We should note that the super-imposition of the one signal on the other is purely additive; it is not 'amplitude modulation' and causes no sum and difference frequencies (these would occur however, if the two signals were mixed in a non-linear circuit). When the biased signal is recorded and played back, the wanted signal component is operated on only in the linear zone of the characteristic; using this technique a highly linear response can be obtained. The bias frequency is much higher than the wanted signal frequency; the reading head acts as a low pass filter and removes the unwanted high frequency waveform, by virtue of its geometry; this is easily seen if we consider the case when one cycle of bias signal occupies a magnetisation pattern of equal length to the air gap. The resultant flux induced into the read head core will be zero; this will be the case if any integral number of bias cycles can be fitted into the head gap, or if the frequency of the bias is such that many cycles fit into the gap, exactly or otherwise.

It is important that the read-back process should not destroy the magnetisation pattern on the tape; to ensure that this is so, the head is constructed as in Fig. 10.23; there is a second gap in the core, on the side remote from the tape.

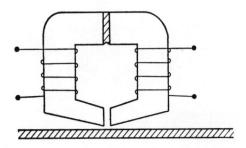

Fig. 10.23

This increases the reluctance of the iron path and reduces the magnetic coupling between the tape and the core to a low enough level not to affect the remanent state of the tape. It also assists in preventing any saturation in the core when the head is used both for recording and playing back and this improves the linearity of the recording. The description, so far, applies to the recording of alternating currents, as in the recording of music. Analogue quantities such as are recorded from telemetry systems and the like, are often d.c. levels. To record these an audio tone is used, and its amplitude can then represent the d.c. value; alternatively, frequency modulation techniques are sometimes advantageous. Once more, we should note that the fidelity of the recording depends on the tape moving at a constant speed. Speed changes not only cause pitch or frequency errors, but also amplitude errors, since the read-back depends on rate of change of flux.

10.17 Digital recording technique

In the recording of a bit we do not need to consider the problems of linearity; so long as every recorded bit can be identified as being present or absent, one or zero, we are not unduly concerned with small variation of amplitude. For this reason digital recording is somewhat simpler and depends on saturating the tape or drum coating material. Now, a piece of saturated coating passing under the head will induce no signal; signals are

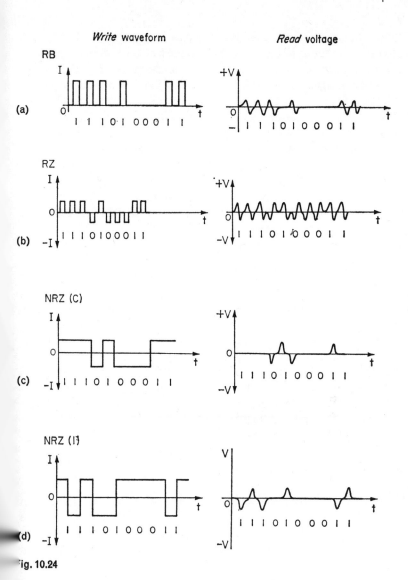

Fig. 10.24

...erived from changes, from one saturated state to the other – a truly ...inary system, in fact.

There are several ways of recording binary digits: Fig. 10.24 shows the ...ost commonly used systems for tape recording. Often drum recording ... by a different system which we will examine later.

The system (*a*) is known as *return to bias* or simply RB. The tape is biased to saturation, in one polarity to represent zero, or no signal; for every one the tape is saturated in the other direction. We note the form of the read-back signal, which will be something like the waveform shown: every one will appear as two brief pulses of opposite polarity, each representing a change of saturation. *No signal* is indistinguishable from zero and no indication is given as to how many zeros there are. This ambiguity can only be eliminated by providing a *clock* waveform to mark out the digit times. Fig. 10.24(*b*) shows a system that does not require an additional *clock* wave. The *no signal* condition is unsaturated, while ones and zeros are represented by excursions to saturation in one direction or the other. The system is referred to as *return to zero*, or RZ. The read-back signal will be like the somewhat idealised waveform in the diagram; we should note that the fundamental frequency of the signal is equal to the pulse repetition rate, and this may be a limiting factor in design.

The remaining two diagrams illustrate *non-return-to-zero* or NRZ methods. Each, manifestly, needs a clockwave, as reference, in order to read it back. Waveform (*c*) is called the NRZ change method; the system stays in saturation in one polarity or other, until we get a change of digit, that is, $0 \rightarrow 1$ or $1 \rightarrow 0$. So long as a string of ones or zeros continues without change, so the polarity of the saturation remains unchanged also.

The waveform depicted in (*d*) is called NRZ (one) or NRZ(1). In this case the system changes polarity each time a one is recorded. The read-back is very simple in this case. We should note that the effective maximum frequency of this system is half the pulse repetition rate. It is, the most commonly used mode in high speed tape storage systems.

10.18 Phase modulation technique

This system is commonly used in drum storage and works well. The reason for its preference is that its effective frequency lies always between the clock frequency, and twice the clock-frequency. Drum record and read heads are not run in contact with the magnetic coating, and the system needs higher gain: the limited frequency bandwidth permits the use of tuned amplifiers, enhancing the gain and giving a better signal to noise ratio.

Fig. 10.25 shows the idealised or logic waveform, and an impression of the actual form of the read-back signal voltage.

Each digit, whether one or zero, is represented by a complete cycle, that is a half cycle, or pulse, to saturation, in each polarity. In practice, the

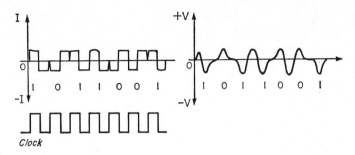

Fig. 10.25

signal is virtually non-return-to-zero, and the square waveform is smoothed out by the electrical and magnetic circuit characteristics. Fig. 10.26 shows the logic for generating the write waveform, and for decoding the read-back signal.

The writing logic is simple: *clock* waveform is supplied to the one gate, and *inverted clock* to the zero gate; according to whether we wish to record a one or a zero the appropriate gate is opened.

The read-back, too, is simple and unambiguous. The signal from the record/read head is amplified and limited, or 'clipped'. The amplified signal is differentiated: the mid section of the recorded pulse will be rising or falling according to whether it represents a one or a zero; due to the differentiation, the rising signal will give a positive pulse, and the falling one a negative. This waveform is gated with a strobe pulse and a one or a zero generated by setting a flip-flop. It is very important to note that the identification of the one or zero takes place half a digit-time later than the start of the actual read-in from the record/read head. The first available *clock* pulse with which it can be gated is a digit time later, within the word-time cycle, than the digit position in which it was written. This is quite a simple logical problem to solve, so long as there is a gap-time between words. It is normally not difficult, then, to write on the drum, in a digit timing one digit ahead of the normal minor cycle: then, when the information is read back, it is in synchronism.

10.19 Magnetic tape stores

Information on magnetic tape is necessarily in serial form, and due to spool length, there may be a long delay in retrieving it; for this reason tape stores can only be used as backing stores, and information is transferred to and from them in large blocks. It is not unusual, too, for tape machines

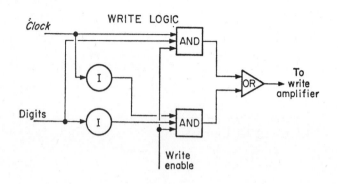

WRITE LOGIC

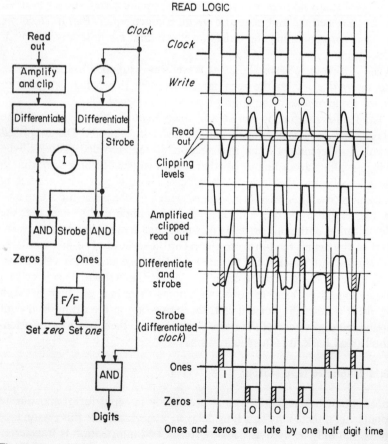

READ LOGIC

Ones and zeros are late by one half digit time

Fig. 10.26

to be a product of one manufacturer, while the computer with which they work, is the product of another. Generally their clock speeds are different, and commonly they use different logic conventions; the tape store is, therefore, a separate entity, and is treated by the computer proper as a piece of input/output, or peripheral equipment. Special sub-routines are arranged to control the transfer of data to and from the tape system and a sophisticated buffer arrangement is necessary to deal with the necessary speed change, and mode change from serial to parallel, and vice versa.

A tape unit can be considered in three parts: the tape transport mechanism, the record-read electronics, and the control logic; of these we shall confine our interest to the first and third.

10.19.1 Tape transport mechanisms

The task of this unit is to pass the tape across the gap in the record/read head. This entails the following:

(a) the tape must be passed through the record/read station in the right direction and at the correct, constant speed;

(b) the inertia of the spool and contents, from which the tape is being drawn, must not be allowed to stretch the tape, or over-run when the tape stops;

(c) the tape emerging from the record/read station must be wound on to the take-up spool at even, correct tension.

A reel of tape contains thousands of feet, and weighs pounds; the difference in inertia between a full reel and an empty spool is considerable. To achieve the three objectives, above, a tape transport has a capstan device which pulls the tape through the record/read station at constant speed, and two servo systems to control the two spools. The spool servos are arranged so that there is always a loop of slack tape on both sides of the read-record station; this ensures that the capstan has only a foot or so of slack tape as an inertial load. In this way it can accelerate or decelerate rapidly and has little difficulty in maintaining its speed constant during the recording and reading process.

The spool drive servos require to be quite powerful; the crux of the problem of the control of their speed is in the control of the tape loop, that is, the length of slack tape between the spool and the record/read capstan. There are two well-tried systems of loop control and these are illustrated in Fig. 10.27.

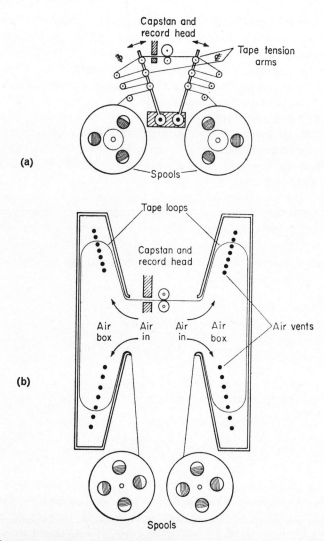

Fig. 10.27 (a) Moving arm tape transport
(b) Air box tape transport

In method (*a*) the tape is threaded over freely running, light rollers, back and forth between the fixed set of rollers, and the sets carried on the pivoted arms. The arms themselves are made as light as possible, but have to be rigid: the pivot is connected to a potentiometer wiper. When the tape is correctly tensioned, the arms are in the centre of their range of travel; if the tape tightens or slackens, the arms are displaced from their central positions, generating control voltages to servo amplifiers which energise the spool motors. The motor torque is bidirectional, that is, the motor can act to accelerate the spool, or decelerate it, and the drive must be precisely controllable, at all speeds, in both directions.

The method (*b*) gives an even lighter loading on the capstan drive, than the method decribed. The loop of tape is contained in an air box on either side. The air boxes are made a very small amount deeper than the breadth of the tape, and the inside surfaces are highly polished. A pneumatic suction pump draws air from the boxes through the ports as shown, and air passes into the box through the tape entry aperture. The tape itself acts as a barrier to the flow of air through the boxes; if the tape loop is too short, most of the suction ports are on the low pressure side of the tape, that is, outside the loop. If the loop is too long, the major part of the ports are at atmospheric pressure. The total pressure difference between the two extreme tape conditions is a few inches, water-gauge, but this suffices to control the servo system. The running condition is with both loops of tape about midway along the ports, giving a mid value of pressure to the sensitive pressure transducer. The actual transducer may be a bellows arrangement, or a thermistor which measures the rate of flow, rather than the pressure. These systems can be made very sensitive indeed, but the servo design has to be of the highest order.

10.19.2 The control logic

This section has the task of locating the wanted information on the tape, and controlling the recording and reading process. To envisage the problem, we must be aware of the following realities:

(*a*) a block of information must be read serially, in the forward direction;
(*b*) demands for information may call for blocks held on either spool;
(*c*) nothing can be read from the tape unless it is moving at the correct speed;
(*d*) a block of information may be held in a few inches of tape;
(*e*) even though the transport mechanism is very highly sophisticated the tape speed cannot be accelerated or reversed instantaneously. In view of (*d*) above, a block length or so needs to be allowed for acceleration or over-run;
(*f*) it is not economical to allow long gaps between information blocks.

To perform its functions adequately the tape control logic needs to be to a great extent automatic, demanding from the computer control only an instruction, in the form of *write* or *read* and a block address. On receipt of such an instruction, the first requirement is to start the tape moving so that its present position is determinable. As the tape accelerates, the clock waveform becomes readable; the signal amplitude depends on tape speed, so this may be used to indicate when the tape is moving fast enough.

When the reading circuits have been enabled, the logic controls the search for a recorded pattern, or character, indicating a block end-marker; when this is received the block address is read in and tested for coincidence with the desired address. If coincidence is found, the block of information is read off the tape.

In general, a demand is not likely to coincide with the first block to be identified; if the block number demanded is greater than that read from the tape, the tape is made to continue to run forward until the wanted block is reached, coincidence occurs, and the information is read out (or recorded).

If the block required is on the take-up spool, the test for coincidence establishes this, and the logic directs the transport mechanism to run back; normally this run back is accompanied by a block count, derived from the original test. When the required number of blocks have been run back, the transport is set to run forward again, and, as it comes up to speed, the required block location should come into the record/read station – provided the necessary allowances have been made for the distance the tape must travel in reversing.

By increasing the complexity of the logic the system can be speeded up to some extent: for instance, a block count can be maintained electronically, which makes it possible for the original direction decision to be made immediately the instruction is received. In systems such as data processors, where blocks will be called for most generally in sequence, the logic can arrange for the tape to be brought to rest, and reversed a short way, after an instruction, so that it can go forward immediately to the next block in sequence when instructed.

The information recorded or read must be dealt with at the tape clock rate: it must then be changed into the mode of operation suitable for the main computing system. Once the tape is moving the information must be stored as the read out takes place. Sometimes a separate buffer store is provided for this purpose, but a more efficient system can be described as buffer in memory. Large systems have their main core memory store divided into sections, and these can be operated separately from each other. *Read* and *record* instructions can be dealt with, at tape machine speed, in one such block of storage, while the rest of the computer is operating normally. Once the block has been transferred, the core store section reverts to being under control of the main computer.

The logic of tape stores is not difficult in principle but is apt to be expensive due to the amount of hardware involved. The speciality in the technique of their construction is mainly in the electro-mechanical field: the highest possible precision is demanded. One of the most effective tape transports now in operation has a tape speed of 150 inches per second, with a start or stop time of 1·5 milli-seconds. This should give food for thought for those of us having a mechanical turn of mind; the others are advised to leave this kind of machine to the experts.

10.20 Disk files

A recent trend, in the U.S.A. has been to develop backing stores in the form of large disk stores, of the type earlier mentioned, but with removable and interchangeable disks; (the spelling of disk in the American way is out of deference to the developers of this very powerful and exacting technique). The disks can be inserted or removed singly or in groups. They are, in some cases, made of light alloy with an oxide coating; but other manufacturers prefer highly machined brass with a finely polished nickel coating, for mechanical reasons.

The head suspension in this type of machine is of particular interest; the head rides on a film of air, by an air-bearing technique. Fig. 10.28 shows the configuration of an air-supported head; the curvature of the head causes air, which is carried round by the disk surface, to be compressed in the gap, and a form of Bernoulli effect takes place at the throat. These

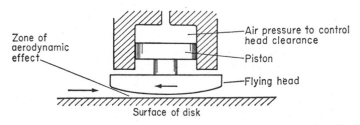

Fig. 10.28   Air supported head. Air pressure above the piston pushes the head towards recording surface, against a light spring (not shown).

are, sometimes, improperly called flying heads; the effect is not, in fact, similar to that experienced by an aerofoil in flight, though it is closely associated with what aerodynamicists call 'ground effect', that is, a kind of flying behaviour which aircraft develop when flying very close to the ground. A surprising quality of air-supported heads is that the air film not only supports the heads at a minimum distance from the drum surface, but also tends to prevent them moving further away – this is due to the Bernoulli action. This quality helps the head to maintain its exact distance from the surface, even though the disk may not be truly flat, or may wobble slightly.

Once more, these systems depend for successful operation on the highest possible mechanical precision. The digit track, for instance, is only a few thousandths of an inch wide. If the read head diverges a small distance from the true track centre there is a severe drop in signal level. What is more serious, however, is that, if a second record process is carried out over a previous one, and is not exactly 'in track', then the new pattern may not completely obliterate the old. Reading, thereafter, may be poor, due to noise, if the head is a little off track, or nearer to the centre of the previously written track.

10.21 The form of recording

A tape system must be basically serial: it is customary however to have eight or nine tracks on one tape; thus, clock and a character, with parity and error checking digits, will normally be read simultaneously, in parallel. Thus we have parallel digit representation to establish characters, and serial character arrangement in words and blocks. Disk files could have more tracks in parallel, but this makes the head arrangement very difficult, and these are usually serial down to digit level. The tapes used in computer systems are of the highest possible quality, and their manufacture, and coating, are most carefully supervised. Nevertheless it is still possible for small imperfections to exist in the recording surface, causing noise, or 'drop outs'. Recording is done, therefore, in a code system having a good deal of redundancy, usually with eight bits to represent a five-bit character and using a 'Hamming', or similar code. Codes of this kind are designed not only to detect errors but also to rectify them by logical means. Additional safeguards are given by overall parity checks and counts over the whole block of information. As ever, there has to be more expense to achieve greater reliability.

Suggestions for further reading

General:
Computer Memories – a Survey of the State of the Art by J.A.Rajchman.
Proc. I.R.E., 1961, **49**, p. 104–27.
Review and Survey of Mass Memories by L.C.Hobbs. A.F.I.P.S.
Conf. Proc., Cleaver-Hume, 1963, **24**, p. 295.
Digital Computer Design by E.L.Braun. Academic Press, 1963.
Chapter 5 includes an extensive bibliography.

Delay lines: mercury and wire:
Ultra-sonic Delay Lines by C.F.Brockelsby, J.S.Palfreeman, and
R.W.Gibson. Iliffe Books Ltd., 1963. Chapters 4 and 6 are of
particular interest.

Single level storage:
One Level Storage System by T.Kilburn, D.B.G.Edwards, M.J.Lanigan,
and F.H.Sumner I.R.E. Trans. El. Comp. 1962, **EC-11**, No. 2,
p. 223.
*The Manchester University Atlas Operating System. Part 1: Internal
Organisation* by T.Kilburn, D.J.Howarth, R.B.Payne, and
F.H.Sumner, Computer Journal, 1961, **4**.

Look-ahead:
Planning a Computer System – Project Stretch by W.Bucholz.
McGraw-Hill, 1962. Chapter 15, pp. 238–47 is of particular
interest.

Ferrites and domain theory:
Self-Saturating Magnetic Amplifiers by G.E.Lynn, T.J.Pula,
J.F.Ringelman, and F.G.Timmel. McGraw-Hill, 1960. Chapter 2,
pp. 17–36 is of interest.
The Magnetic Cell: a New Circuit Element by D.S.Ridler and
R.Grimmond. Proc. I.E.E. Convention on Ferrites, October 1956,
paper No. 2189. Repub. Proc. I.E.E., 1957, **104**, B, pp. 1–2 and
appendixes.

Tape recording:
Digital Techniques by D.W.Davies Blackie, 1963. Chapter 7,
pp. 113–25 is of particular interest.

Tape transport:
Single Capstan Tape Memory by R.A.Kleist, M.A.Lewis and
    B.C.Wang. A.F.I.P.S. Conf. Proc., Cleaver-Hume, 1963, **24**, p. 565.

Supplementary reading:
Square Loop Ferrite Circuitry by C.J.Quartly. Prentice-Hall, 1962.
Digital Storage Systems by W.Renwick. Spon, London, 1964.

11 Input and output

Computers process information, whether analogue or digital. When an analogue computer has been set up, the plug-board and coefficient settings comprise all the information relevant to the mathematical analogue of the system to be analysed. To measure the information imparted to an analogue computer would be difficult; an estimate could be made, perhaps, by programming the same problem for entry into a digital computer, and counting the bit-content of the programme. It would not be a very useful exercise, though it would emphasise a characteristic difference between analogue and digital computers. Analogue computers have a great advantage, particularly for problems of a non-repetitive nature, in that they can be programmed very simply and quickly, and the operator's coding process is close to conventional mathematics. Thus, communication of information to an analogue computer is fast. In the same way, the output may be directly intelligible to the operator; for instance, the output voltage variation may be observed on a meter or oscilloscope. If the problem is, for example, to determine whether a system is oscillatory, and what is the nature of the oscillation, a skilled operator can read off his answer directly. More often a graph is plotted and this conveys a lot of information that may be extracted quickly. Furthermore the output information is in real time.

The digital computer is very different; information must be coded in such a way that it appears as patterns of binary digits and the voltage analogue of these patterns must be generated and got into the computer; likewise the output is only patterns which must be decoded. The process is comparatively slow – we should remember Hartley's Law – and even though the computer is very fast indeed it requires much ingenuity to obtain a result that is even approximately in real time. In an on-line control application, the delay, or *dead-time*, may be tolerable, but it must be considered.

11.1 Analogue outputs

The output from an analogue computer is generally a form of graph; sometimes analogue-digital conversion is used, and a tabulated result is recorded for convenience and, possibly, for graphing at a later time. When the output is directly graphed it may, in fast repetitive mode operation, be recorded on an oscilloscope and photographed. More commonly it is recorded on a paper recorder, either of the strip chart type or on an X–Y plotter. The commonest strip chart recorders are of the pen type; the graph paper is pulled at a controlled speed under a moving pen, and the pen is servo-operated so that its position corresponds to the output voltage on the graph scale. Because of inking problems, and when high speed is required, other forms of trace are sometimes used, but we will not concern ourselves with them here.

The X–Y plotter is a useful output device when we wish to graph a problem in two coordinates, not necessarily against time. In this device the pen is carried by a moving gantry over a stationary graph: the pen is servo-driven along the gantry to give one coordinate, while the gantry itself is servo-driven to provide the other. There is much development and engineering skill behind these recorders and plotters. For further details and specifications the reader is referred to the manufacturer's literature.

11.2 Digital computer input and output

Computer input/output at a speed comparable with the computer's internal speed of processing, provides problems that are far from being solved. Some limited success has been achieved with electronic-reading-automation, that is, arranging for the computer to absorb information from conventional typescript. Some interesting experiments have been done to try and make a computer perform instructions on a spoken word; these are, as yet, only the first steps in the solution of an enormous problem, and from a practical point of view, very limited. Vocal communication with computers, and the translation of spoken language will no doubt be accomplished in the future; at the time of writing the getting of information into and out of computers is a slow business, and any advance in speed demands great complexity and cost.

We commence our study by looking at the simpler systems; from an examination of these we should see what the problems are that must be solved to improve on them. The computer operates on pulse patterns which are directly analogous to binary numbers. A primary requirement of a system for communication with a computer must be the encoding of ideas and data into a binary number form. We are then left with the problem of getting stationary binary patterns into and out of a system where they are moving, or changing, at speed. The philosophy of coding and programming is beyond the scope of this book; our interest is mainly with the second problem, the mechanical process of getting coded data in and out.

Up to the present, the commonest forms of data record for entry into computers are punched tape and punched card systems.

11.3 The punched paper tape system

The early computer designers turned naturally to this medium since it was already highly developed and standardised for telegraphy. An illustration of a piece of paper tape is shown on Plate 4. The system is so well known as to warrant only the briefest description here. Each character is represented by a row of holes punched transversely across the tape. The centre hole, which is smaller, is called the *sprocket hole* and is used for locating each character in the reading station while it is being interpreted. The tape shown is five-bit, that is, up to five information holes may be punched in each row, signifying five bits: a hole punched represents a one, an unpunched location is a zero. Some systems have six, seven or eight bits per character, and in rare cases tapes are used having even greater numbers, e.g. ten or sixteen. Telegraph systems, incorporating conventional teleprinters, use a five-bit code; this allows up to thirty-two different character combinations. The teleprinter has a shift arrangement similar to upper and lower case on a typewriter; the thirty-two combinations thus allow for twenty-six letters, two shifts, (one to letters, one to symbols) and up to thirty-six more symbols, including *erase, carriage return and line feed, space*, figures and punctuation. A computer can be programmed to work in teleprinter code: using five-bit tape there is no possibility of a parity check, and so six-bit tape has become more common. It is often more convenient to work with six-, or seven-bit codes, and this has led to the seven and eight hole tapes. Tapes having more than eight bits have resulted from the use of more complicated codes combined with parity check and error correction techniques.

Programs and data are prepared for entry into the computer system *off-line*, that is on machines not directly connected to the computer. The tape is first punched using a keyboard perforater, having a keyboard similar to a teleprinter. As a key is pressed the character combination is punched in the tape and the tape fed on one space, ready for the next character. Since computer time is much more expensive than keyboard time, it is usual to pass the tape through a verifier, to eliminate punching errors. The verifier has an identical keyboard to the perforater; the verifier operator goes through the motions of punching out the program, and as long as each character agrees with that punched on the tape, the tape feeds on at each step. If there is a discrepancy the machine looks and signals the operator, who checks to see which punching is the correct one, and amends the tape or rejects it if necessary. After verification the tape is spooled, ready for entry to the computer through the tape reader.

11.4 The tape reader

This device is used *on-line*, that is, directly connected to, and under the control of the computer. A typical reader mechanism is illustrated in Fig. 11.1. The reader contains two systems: the electronic system which reads the tape to detect the character punched, and the electro-mechanical system which feeds the tape through the reading station.

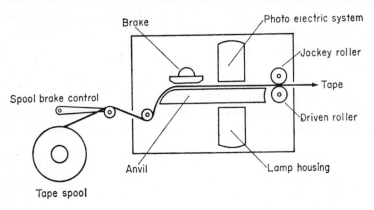

Fig. 11.1

The electronic system is fairly simple: the tape is pulled across an anvil which has holes in it corresponding to the punching locations across the tape. Beneath the anvil there is a lamp which is focussed on the holes. Above the anvil is the reading head containing photo-transistors, so masked that each detects light only through one punching location (including the sprocket hole). The photo-transistor circuits are adjusted so that they produce at their outputs a one voltage level for a hole, and a zero level for no hole. These levels can then be interpreted by the computer during a *read* order.

The demands on the electro-mechanical system are most stringent mechanical systems have inertia, whereas, for most practical purposes we can consider electronic switching as inertialess; mechanical inertia is the root cause of the discrepancy in speed between input/output devices and the computer's electronic operations. The tape reader mechanism functions in this way; when the electronic reading process and any parity check are completed, the mechanism must advance the tape one character distance, in preparation for the next read order. The tape, after leaving the reading station, passes between two rollers, one of which is driven at a constant speed by a motor. The second roller is normally freely pivoted: when the tape is to be moved the two rollers are pressed together by a solenoid action, pinching the tape. When the sprocket hole of the new character comes into alignment with the photo-electric system, the solenoid is de-energised, the rollers cease to pinch the tape and the drive ceases. To prevent it moving during the reading process the tape is clamped between the flat jaws of a brake, also solenoid operated; the brake is situated just in front of the reading station. The mechanism is simple in concept; a tape reader of the type illustrated in Fig. 11.1 can read characters at the rate of one thousand per second, and in case of parity failure the character which fails does not leave the reading station; this entails start-stop operation for every character. It should not, now, be difficult for us to appreciate the mechanical problem. The time per character is one millisecond. The brake must release the tape before the rollers pinch or the tape will be damaged. The rollers must grip the tape right across its width if it is to run straight, and not be torn; the power must be sufficient to accelerate the tape, and the tape spool, so that the movement is completed in less than a millisecond. When the character approaches alignment with the reading station the rollers must release the tape and the brake must be applied. A simple calculation shows that the tape moves at an average speed of about ten feet per second.

Such machines must be carefully designed and the parts manufactured within very precise limits. Naturally it requires most accurate adjustment – but the adjustment must not be delicate, since the reader will be required to read many millions of characters between adjustments, if it is to be satisfactory as part of a practical computing system. At this time the fastest readers operate at about one thousand characters per second; it seems unlikely that this speed will be exceeded substantially by machines working on the same principle.

1.5 The output punch

This mechanism performs the reverse process to the reader: patterns of pulses are sent to the punch by the computer, causing it to punch them into the paper tape. This time, we have two electro-mechanical systems, the tape feed, and the actual punching, but, in this case, the tape feed problem is trivial compared with the punching problem. On receipt of a *punch* order, the punch hammers selected by the pulse pattern have to be driven through the paper and withdrawn; the feed mechanism then advances the paper one character-distance. Both mechanisms are again fairly simple, but very precise. The punching problem is not an easy one; the direct approach would be to have a powerful solenoid to drive each punch; however, powerful solenoids have a high inductance and a long time-constant which limits this method severely. There is an artifice which is commonly used in this kind of mechanism and it is illustrative of how these problems are tackled. An electric motor runs continuously and drives a device called a chopper-bar up and down, just missing the upper end of each punch hammer, or rod, while they are in the zero condition. When a one is called for, a solenoid is energised, which interposes a small metal block between the chopper and the punch rod, while the chopper is in the up position. It takes little power to move this block, since it is small and moves quite freely into the empty space. When the chopper descends it strikes the block against the punch rod and drives the latter just far enough to perforate the paper tape: as the chopper rises again, the punch rod is lifted and the metal block is withdrawn, each by a small spring. In this way the punch selection is a low power operation, though the chopper and perforating action require considerable power. Unsophisticated punch mechanisms operate at rates of tens of characters per second; the fastest punches run at a rate of three hundred characters per second, but they are by no means simple or cheap. Typical of the problems that beset the engineers who design these machines, is that of disposing of the *chads* – the small discs of paper which are punched from the tape. Using six hold tape, in a second, nine hundred chads are generated – they must be prevented from getting into the punch mechanism; they have to be carefully ducted away to a hopper.

Before leaving the topic of paper tape we should look once again at the speed of punching that can be attained. With the really fast punch, we can extract from the computer some three hundred characters a second. Using a five digit code, there can be eight characters stored in a forty digit computer word: we might be able to punch out between thirty and forty word per second, which amounts to about thirty milliseconds per word. A parallel-mode, 10 Mc/s computer could transfer 400 000 words in thi time.

11.6 Punched card systems

The punched card has been a medium for information processing and storage for many years. A typical card is shown in Plate 4; the card is divided into eighty columns, and each column can be punched in twelve locations. It is immediately apparent that one card, having one hole punched in each column, can record, or store, eighty decimal digits. If a second hole is allowed in each column, but restricted to the top two rows, then each column can store one of thirty combinations, 0–9, 10–19, 20–29. By this method alphabetical material can be stored also; there are many ways to make good use of the card as a record, depending on the purpose of the record. Since such cards are in established use and huge libraries of them exist with recorded information, such as census returns and the like, it is natural that they should have come into use for handling computer data also; this allows previous records, used in previous office organisation, to be processed by computer with the minimum of conversion.

We should expect, as engineers, that a medium having more flexibility than paper tape, would give us greater speed, but with greater complexity also. In the first place we should note that the information is not stored in binary form, and if read into the computer it must be converted to binary somewhere in the input system. Likewise the computer output must also be converted. These are not difficult conversions; they are easily accomplished using diode matrix methods, which are discussed in the chapter on control units, in the section on order decoding. They are quite expensive from a hardware point of view; their basic principle is that of a diode gate being provided for every combination of punchings in a column; the gate puts out the binary combination corresponding. Such circuits form an interesting logical exercise since they can be minimised, generally, to use rather fewer diodes than at first seems to be the obvious number. They can be made to be either coders or decoders.

The same basic techniques are used for reading and punching cards as are used for paper tape. There is the added complexity that twelve rows of punchings have to be sensed, and twelve punch hammers have to be provided and controlled. The cards are normally read and punched, column by column, analogously to paper tape, but read in blocks of eighty characters at a time. Simple parity checks are not possible, and a whole card has to be rejected if an error is detected.

The mechanical problems are many and various: the first is the extraction of the card from the pile. Cards are loaded into the machine in stacks; this entails the card reader taking its cards from the bottom of the pack,

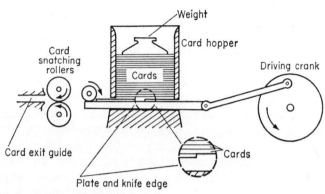

Fig. 11.2 Card reader mechanism

one, and only one, at a time. The method is this: the bottom of the card hopper is open, allowing the cards to rest on a highly polished plate, as shown in Fig. 11.2. The plate has a step or knife edge on it a little smaller than a card thickness. When the plate slides, to the left in the diagram, only the lower card is pushed by the step. The exit aperture leading out of the hopper is wide enough to admit the thickness of one card only, and it thus prevents the tendency of the card above to slide also through the aperture. As the plate reaches the end of its stroke, the extracted card is engaged by the rotating roller which speeds it on its way to the reading head. The plate then slides back ready to push the next card from the bottom of the pile.

Cards are not very stiff and some readers have been designed so that the cards are pushed from the stack broadside-on, to minimise the likelihood of buckling. Others, using the same mechanism, push the cards out, end-on, and yet they do not seem to buckle. The end-on method offers the immediate advantage that the card can then pass directly under the reading station for column-by-column reading. The broadside technique calls for more complications since the card must be stopped after leaving the hopper, and then moved endways by another set of rollers.

The obvious problem is inertia, not only of the card but also of the polished steel plate and knife edge. This has to move over about three inches and is beyond the scope of a solenoid type of motor. Normally a fairly large motor is used to drive a card reader; when a card is to be read, a magnetic clutch is energised, connecting the motor and flywheel through to a crank system that slides the plate forward and back; the clutch releases again after one movement; naturally, the crank linkage requires to be robust, and this adds to the inertia of the system.

A major problem in card handling machines is static electricity. If the cards are dry – as they should be – the action of snatching the card off the bottom of the stack leaves it charged up, and it thereafter tends to stick to the guides and rollers along its route. The cards have to move very fast and there are aerodynamic considerations to take into account, also; if a card is slightly curved it tends to fly or flutter and may miss the centre of the guide or roller system. If it sticks anywhere it becomes a 'wreck' and is soon followed by other cards which wreck also. These have to be extracted and then identified and repunched. Cards are susceptible to atmospheric conditions; a change in humidity may make a well behaved machine quite impossible to use without adjustment; it is good practice to keep cards in airconditioned premises under carefully controlled conditions. We should now have an idea of some of the difficulties of high speed card handling; modern card reading machines process upwards of 600 cards per minute. They are not simple. The punching problem is much the same as for the reading, with the added complication that it must punch each column with the card stationary and exactly in location.

It is worthwhile making a rough and ready estimate of the relative speeds of information handling of paper tape and punched card systems. Each column on the card corresponds very roughly to a five-bit character on tape. Using approximate figures, in one second a tape reader reads in one thousand characters, while a card reader reads in 10×80 columns, so there is no great deal of difference. The same kind of comparison applies for punches. We must remember though, that the card is a comprehensible document, in decimal notation, and can be fed straight into the computer without any conversion or translation. Cards can be processed, sorted, interpreted by other machines, and humans; it is here where the main advantages of the card system accrue.

11.7 Magnetic tape

Punched cards and paper tape are prepared off-line, directly from keyboard machines. They are slow in preparation and compared with the machine very slow indeed when on-line. To obtain faster on-line communication magnetic tape is sometimes used. We do not need to go into any detail here since we have examined magnetic tape as a storage method. There are two ways it can be used; the first is in the same way as paper tape with an input reader and an output recorder; the second way is to insert the tape reel directly into the store on one, or any of the backing store tape machines. This way offers engineering difficulties, since the inserted reel has to be suitable for use in the backing store; that is, the off line tape devices have to conform to those in the on line store. The first system does not impose limitations of this kind and usually the tape devices can be of a lower specification and cost.

The main problem of magnetic tape input/output is the preparation of the tape. Generally it requires a piece of off-line equipment which is nearly a computer in itself. This machine has to read in punched paper tape, or cards, and compile them into suitable form for the magnetic tape, and record them; it requires to do the reverse process when reading out again. Since magnetic recording is very dependent on tape speed the main problem is to write data from cards or punched tape, into the magnetic tape, fast enough; this is exactly akin to the problem of controlling and reading in and out of the computer itself with paper tape or card machines. The system only has real advantages when used on large installations where computer time is very expensive. The recording device time will also be expensive, but less so.

11.8 Line printers

In data processing applications, very often the success of the application depends on the speed of output of information, above all else. A typical case of this is in pay roll calculation: normally the majority of the data required for a pay roll calculations can be fed into the computer beforehand, sometimes a long time beforehand. For instance the main file of information holding the employees' permanent data may be held on a tape file in the backing store; the only information that requires to be fed into the computer is the updating information. In applications such as this, resort is made to *line printers*, that is output devices which print out information a line at a time. These are always expensive and complicated machines: we do not, in this study, need to go into them in great detail, but it is worthwhile to get an idea how they work and of the type of problems to be met in building them, and attaching them to a computer system. The first really successful machine of this kind was the French Bull printer. This was capable of printing out three lines of printed data per second, each line of ninety-two characters. Its mechanism was most ingenious: each character position had a set of type heads round the periphery of a type wheel, and each wheel had its own train of gears. During the print cycle the type wheels all rotated through one revolution, driven by their gear trains, and the paper moved up one line space: each type wheel was caused to impinge on the paper as the required character passed the printing loca tion. The speed of the type wheel and its vertical motion were so arranged that the paper and typehead were moving at the same speed as they came together, ensuring a clear print out. There are many of these machines still in use; the mechanically minded reader should examine one of these mechanisms if the opportunity offers.

More modern designs now in use, print out at rates several times faster than the Bull, using the technique of printing 'on the fly'. These machines have a print cylinder on which the characters are printed in rows along the cylinder, each character appearing along its row as many times as there are characters in a line of print – commonly 160. The rows of characters, figures, letters, symbols, and punctuation marks are spaced evenly round the periphery of the print cylinder. Fig. 11.3 shows the arrangement of the printing mechanism. The paper and inking fabric pass between the print cylinder and the print hammers. The cylinder rotates continuously: as a character is called for in each print position, the print hammer drives the paper against the print roller at the instant that the desired character is passing the hammer head. This is done at very great speed so that the contact between the paper and print cylinder is brief. A clear impression is made since the elasticity of the paper takes up the small movement of the

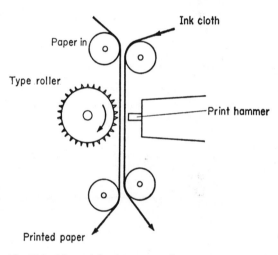

Fig. 11.3   Line printer arrangement

print cylinder during contact. The actuation of the print hammers is by solenoids, and the timing is electronic. Synchronisation between the print cylinder and the timing control circuits is arranged by a photo-electric device coupled to its shaft. The mechanism is quite simple in concept, much more so than that of the Bull printer; we can better understand the mechanical and timing problems when we realise that these printers print some ten to twenty lines per second. The mechanical requirement is to drive the print hammer into the paper for a very brief instant, but exactly as the selected character passes the print position. Since the print roller is driven at a constant speed, and its rotation is continuously indexed by the photo-electric device, the pulse to each solenoid can be accurately timed electronically; once it has been initially adjusted the timing should remain constant. The main mechanical problem is rigidity; the small masses of the print hammers accelerate and decelerate very rapidly, and if the print cylinder and machine frame were not massively constructed, vibrations would occur. The print hammers and type face need to be very hard indeed since they sustain severe loads at a very high repetition rate. Plate 5 shows a typical mechanical line printer, and the massive construction can be seen.

11.9 Xerograph printers

The fastest of all the line printers now in use depend on a non-mechanical principle, that of xerography. This works in the following way: a highly polished cylinder is coated with a thin coating of selenium, a metal that is light sensitive. When light is allowed to fall on the selenium coating, it becomes negatively charged; if a fine powder is dusted over it, the particles adhere to the charged sections of the surface. After picking up the particles the cylinder is rolled against the paper by a hot roller, as shown in Fig. 11.4. The powder used is a resin and, melted by the heat, it sticks to the paper, pulling away from the highly polished surface of the cylinder. After contact with the paper the cylinder rubs against a conducting brush which discharges it, prior to it entering the illuminated zone once more. This is the principle on which the familiar Xerograph duplicating and copying machines work.

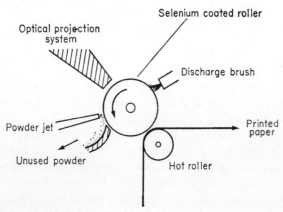

Fig. 11.4 Xerograph principle

In the line printer application, light is shone onto the roller by a projection system; the light is from a cathode ray tube device which generates the selected letters, so that they are effectively written on to the cylinder as a charge pattern and are then printed out. It should be noticed that there are few mechanical moving parts, and these are continuously in rotation during the print process, thus eliminating inertial problems. These printers can output thousands of lines a minute; like mechanical line printers they are not cheap; they require a very large amount of electronics for selection and generation of letters, and for line compilation, as well as a very precise optical system.

11.10 Control and buffer units

Between the readers and printers and the main part of the computing system we require control units and, often, buffer units: these have the following tasks:

(*a*) on receiving a signal from the computer they initiate the read or print actions;

(*b*) they transform the pulse rate of the read or print device to, or from, that of the computer;

(*c*) they maintain a 'busy' indication in the computer control, thus preventing demands for further activity until they are ready to receive it;

(*d*) they signal to the computer that they have completed their last instruction, i.e. they are no longer busy;

(*e*) in the case of readers, they may perform the parity check and having detected a parity failure, signal accordingly.

Control units for simple readers and punches provide no great problems. Their principal feature of interest to us lies in their transformation action to and from computer speed. Fig. 11.5 shows a parallel-serial conversion system for a tape reader; the parallel register is set by the photo-electric system of the reader mechanism.

Each flip-flop output is applied to an AND gate; the other inputs to the AND gates come from the computer and are clock digit pulses, $d1$ to $d6$; to interrogate the reader unit, the computer control sends the *read* signal to the output AND gate of the reader unit: the gate passes pulses into the computer in clock digit times $d1$ to $d6$, as a serial transmission at computer speed.

Fig. 11.6 shows the opposite process to that last described: the transformation of a serial five-digit transmission from the computer into a

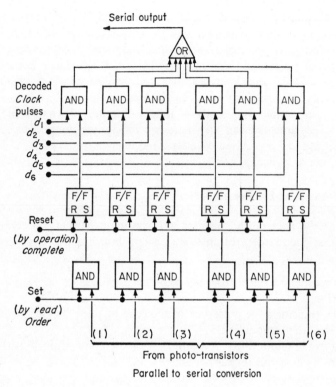

Fig. 11.5

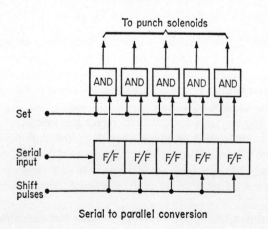

Fig. 11.6

register setting for the punch selector arrangement. Once again we use clock pulses $d1$ to $d5$ which set register stages in turn. These two systems illustrate typical techniques of serial/parallel conversion; in general these systems are of trivial interest: if the input and output to the computer are parallel, the problems are even further simplified. We should note, however, a neat technique of parity checking that can be embodied in a simple reader control. This consists of a single counter stage driven from the serial pulse train, generated as in Fig. 11.5. Assume we are using 'odd' parity. The counter is reset at the commencement of the read operations; if $d6$ is gated with the counter one or set output, a pulse will be passed if parity is correct. Gating $d6$ with the reset output will signal that parity has failed.

The control units for punched card devices are considerably more complicated. In general the card can neither be read nor punched at computer speed. Thus the control unit requires also a buffer store system to hold the complete information of one card. The simplest attack on this problem is to use a small special purpose core store; the core store can then be driven at computer clock speed while in communication with the computer, and at a speed suitable to the reader or punch when working with them. Readers in particular have the problem that it is difficult to pass the card under the reader heads at a constant speed. An asynchronous store, such as a core store, obviates this speed problem since each bit may be written at the instant dictated by the read head, and does not need any further clocking during this process.

The transfer of information from the buffer store to the computer is complicated in that there are generally several computer words to transfer at a time. This is most simply dealt with by a micro-program.

Control units for line printers and magnetic tape machines are very complicated; both these devices need to operate continuously; and this is especially the case with the line printers. Usually there is a large buffer store associated with these systems, which signals to the computer some time before it is empty. The computer can then send further blocks of information and the printer does not need to wait; we shall see more of this technique in the chapter on advanced control systems.

1.11 The operating console

Since this unit is instrumental in controlling the operation of the computer it is often, mistakenly, taken as apart of the control unit; it is truly an input/output device. It serves two purposes: the first is to allow the operator to control the system; the second is to transmit information to the operator.

To understand the requirements of a console, let us first consider what controls are necessary and desirable for operation of the machine and what information the operator may need. There are three modes of operation we should consider:

(*a*) normal running and operation of established programs;
(*b*) program checking, or 'debugging';
(*c*) maintenance or fault finding.

11.11.1 Required facilities

The demands imposed by (*a*) are the simplest. Naturally there must be the necessary controls for switching the machine on and off, preparing it to receive programs, and then running the program in. A program is normally written with built-in checks so that if it goes into fault, it prints out an indicator, or it may be made to stop the machine. Likewise a parity check should stop the operation of a program if there are no self-correcting arrangements. After each stop, the operator requires a means of restarting the program, and if necessary, inserting a correction.

The demands of (*b*) are somewhat more complicated; in general, programs do not work correctly the first time they are tried: to ensure absolute correctness remote from the machine is too time-consuming to be efficient. A long and complicated program may take many hours to get right; furthermore, in many problems, instructions and data have to be amended or added as a result of data computed within the program. The program is usually interspersed with checking arrangements, but even these may be at fault; thus the operator needs to have a continuous idea of how the program is running. When a stop or fault in program does come up, the operator needs to examine the contents of registers and some store locations, and to know which order is in operation at the time of the fault – or as soon after it as possible. It is possible by putting in the right sequence of instructions for the contents of any register or store location to be printed out; this can well be arranged by having a micro-program in the machine for the purpose. It is more satisfactory, in most applications for the operator to receive a display of certain information without having to disturb the machine state; typical information of this kind includes:

(i)   contents of the accumulator;
(ii) contents of the sequence control register;

(iii) contents of the order register;

(iv) indication of the beat on which the operation is halted;

(v) contents of certain immediate access stores;

(vi) indications of which peripheral is in action, or which unit.

There are many other desirable indications, depending on circumstances.

It is possible, also, to write into any location by a micro-program, but once again, it is more convenient if the operator has immediate access to certain registers, with keys or buttons, so that they may be cleared or altered. Typical registers of this kind are the accumulator, the order register, and the sequence control register.

The requirements of (c) are various: if the maintenance engineer is to find faults logically and quickly he needs as much information as he can get. In addition to the facilities for program checking it is useful for him to have a waveform monitoring system and a full display, indicating the condition of power supplies, right through the system and its peripherals. The reader will derive more insight into the maintenance engineer's needs after reading the section on maintenance techniques. We will restrict our consideration at this time, to the needs of operators and programmers.

In highly sophisticated systems, especially where interleaved or multi-program working is provided, the computer control unit has discretionary powers over the disposition of storage space and the distribution of machine time between the programs in operation. In these machines there is little use in providing much visual display to the operator, and it is customary to restrict the information, in and out, to a teleprinter or similar channel. Large machines such as Stretch and Atlas have several consoles; each is attached to a program. Micro-programs control the operators' access to the main system in the same way as they control the separate programs. The choice of console facilities, and the micro-program controlling them, may be under the programmer's control, so that he may arrange them as it seems best in his particular circumstances. The control arrangements of systems like this are very complicated, and involve a good deal of specially provided storage and other hardware; in smaller machines it is usually a requirement not to monopolise more storage than is absolutely necessary: it is then more economical in hardware, if not in machine time, to give the operator much more direct control.

11.11.2 Typical console provision

A typical control console for a medium-size system might include:

(*a*) a display of accumulator contents;
(*b*) a display of order register contents;
(*c*) a display of sequence control register contents;
(*d*) a set of keys or buttons connected with (*a*), (*b*) and (*c*) which can be used to set or reset each register position;
(*e*) a start button causing the beat sequence to commence;
(*f*) a single shot button causing the machine to execute one order only, after which the beat change is held up;
(*g*) a small loudspeaker or hooter.

The function of the latter device is to give an audible signal; it is connected through an amplifier to the beat change circuit, or some similar point, which has an operating frequency, during normal running, within the audio-range. It can be used in several ways; the first is as a dynamic stop indicator. At points in the program where the programmer requires to check its operation, he arranges for the program to go into a loop of instructions round which the machine cycles. By choice of the loop contents the programmer can arrange that the cycling speed causes an audible note of any desired pitch, which calls the operator's attention.

Most programs are highly repetitive; the course of a program through a machine causes a pattern of noises to come from the hooter, and they soon become familiar to the operator. If an irregularity occurs, the operator's attention is attracted at once; this is particularly the case when the maintenance engineers are running test programs; part of the evidence that the machine is working normally, or otherwise, is audible.

The provision of the display and key facilities for the registers is simple when they are of the flip-flop kind. In systems where the registers are either continuously circulating, as in delay line computers, or dormant, as in core-logic types, a requirement is to equip the console with one or more flip-flop type registers, complete with lamp displays and setting buttons; the display is then obtained by having an automatic transfer from the working registers to the console register; insertion of information is by the reverse process, of transferring the information from the static register to the main system under control of the computer clock. The input register is often called a number generator; it is set up by the programmer, who then sets a switch to arrange the destination of the number; the pressing of a further button, or key then initiates a single-shot action, transferring the number to the indicated destination.

The design of single shot devices provides a simple logical exercise; the single shot facility on a computer console controls the beat change. When the button is pressed a gate is opened passing a control pulse, and the beat is changed; the change of beat, when it occurs, closes the gate again so that the next control pulse to the beat change is inhibited until a further operation of the key.

We should understand from the foregoing description, that the design of console arrangements is fairly simple, but, if more than the most elementary facilities are to be provided, expensive in hardware. The most primitive computer systems often have no more than a teleprinter, which acts also as their main input and output device. To change a register contents or examine it, the operator requires to type in a short program. Usually there is no access to the sequence control register in this kind of arrangement, so the operator needs to obtain a print-out of the contents of the order register, and identify it from the program; this process is particularly tedious if the computer works in pure binary, as is often the case with simple or primitive machines.

Suggestions for further reading

Input/output devices are not covered in great detail in textbooks, being of such a specialised nature, but manufacturers' literature is usually very detailed and well illustrated.

The following works are recommended as supplementary reading:

Giant Brains by E.C.Berkeley. Wiley, 1949. Chapter 4, pp. 42–55 covers the subject of punched cards.

Automatic Digital Calculators by A.D. and K.H.V.Booth. Butterworth, 1956. Chapter 8 is of particular interest.

Digital Techniques by D.W.Davies. Blackie, 1963. Chapter 7, pp. 105–13 and Chapter 8, pp. 126–36 are of interest.

12 The control unit

In the preceding chapters we have examined in some detail the parts that go to make up a digital computing system and the functions they perform. We now need to consider the problem of connecting together the various organs to form a working system. The unit which performs the task of interconnection and control of the system parts is the control unit. This unit most characterises the particular computer and, likewise, it is the most difficult upon which to generalise; the design of this part offers the principal challenge to the skill and ingenuity of the system designer.

12.1 The requirements of a control unit

The various functions required of a control unit could be divided up in many ways. We shall make the division under the following headings, since it appears logical and convenient from a conceptual point of view:
(a) sequence control, that is, ensuring the continued step-by-step operation of the computer in accordance with the program;
(b) timing: the provision of timing and counting waveforms to control the sequence of events within the computer functions, and to keep them in synchronism;
(c) order decoding: the interpretation of program instructions, setting up function units, fetching operands, and the like;
(d) arithmetic connected with store addressing;
(e) control of peripheral equipment;
(f) control of store block transfers.

The first part of this chapter is devoted to a more detailed consideration of the control unit requirements as we have enumerated them, for a fairly simple system. The remainder deals with some of the control features of more sophisticated machines such as Stretch and Atlas.

12.2 Sequence control

There are two methods of sequence control which have been commonly used: the *two-address system* and the *augmented count*. The former is now rarely used but is worthy of study since it illustrates very well the *stepping on* action of computers, that is, the completion of each operation initiating the next. An instruction to a machine having this type of control takes the following form:

$$\text{Fn} \quad | \quad \text{X Address} \quad | \quad \text{Y Address}$$

We have remarked in Chapter 7 that an order requires two operands for logical completeness. In the two address system, the address of one operand is implied as being the accumulator. The X address is that of the second operand; the Y address is not that of an operand at all, but the address of the order to be obeyed consequent to the completion of the current one. We could call this system, more exactly, a three address system.

The two address system is simple to implement and most economical in hardware as can be seen from the system flow diagram in Fig. 12.1.

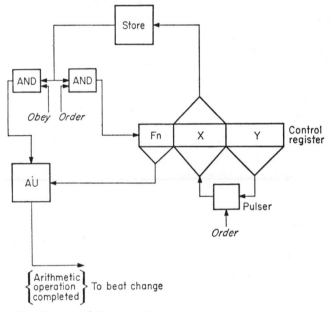

Fig. 12.1 Flow diagram of the two address system

In the arrangement of Fig. 12.1 the X address digits of the control register select the operand in the store. The store outputs this operand to the arithmetic unit (AU), gated in by *obey*. The function digits (Fn), of the control register, control the operation of the arithmetic unit on the operand. On the completion of the specified function, the arithmetic unit signals for the beat to change; the beat changes to *order*, causing the Y address digits to be moved into the position previously occupied by the X address, that is, controlling the store selection. The store output then becomes the Y address specified in the original order; this is gated into the control register, replacing the previous order, and the beat changes back to *obey* when this replacement is complete. The new order is now obeyed and the cycle repeats.

This system has its principal advantage when used with storage systems which can have long waiting times, such as drum stores or delay lines. The programmer selects the location of the next order to be obeyed, allowing the necessary time for the execution of the current one. For example, suppose the drum position is such that the word position n is being read into the arithmetic unit as an operand, and the arithmetic unit is calculated to require two full word times to complete the function: the programmer will write the Y address, specifying the next order as $n + 2$. On completion of the current order the store selection will be set at $n + 2$ and coincidence will occur almost immediately, with waiting time cut to a minimum. This arrangement permits a drum or delay line computer to operate at a speed not much slower than an immediate access machine. We can immediately see the disadvantage: the programmer has a complicated task to perform, requiring a good deal of skill and patience. It will not always be possible to arrange an early coincidence once the program pattern becomes well filled in. Furthermore, some orders, such as multiply, may not have a fixed duration and an optimised Y address can then only be guessed. If the guess is too short the first available coincidence will be nearly a complete drum revolution later.

There are several artifices that can be used to speed up operation on systems of the type described, but usually they demand more cunning on the part of the programmer if they are to be fully exploited. A typical artifice is to number, or address, the drum positions in an alternated sequence: for instance, the address sequence 1–2–3–4–5 ... may be assigned to drum positions 1–4–7–10–13– and so on, so that successive addresses occur round the drum spaced at intervals of three word times. Then if the order in address n is obeyed within two word times, the address position on the drum track approaching the reading heads when the beat changes will be $n + 1$ and coincidence will be almost immediate if this is entered as the Y address. If, for any reason, the instruction requires more time, then the programmer has to use some ingenuity in optimising the program to arrange an early Y address coincidence for the next order.

However, nowadays, due to its comparative ease of programming, and the availability of immediate access storage at reasonable cost, the augmented count system is practically universal. Orders are written in number sequence and the next order is selected automatically by the control unit without it being defined by the previous order. To implement this system of operation the control unit is equipped with a counter, commonly called the sequence control counter, or sequence control register.

The contents of this counter, or register, is used as the address of the order to be read into the control register for decoding during the *order* beat. When the order is obeyed, the counter content is augmented by one. When the beat again returns to *order* the augmented counter content is passed to the store as the address of the next order. Fig. 12.2 shows a simple flow diagram using this system of control.

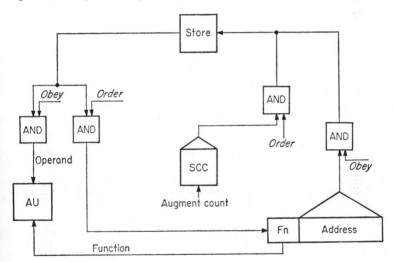

Fig. 12.2 Sequence count control

The sequence control counter (SCC) content is gated by *order* to the store selection logic, causing the store to put out the contents of that numbered address location. This is gated to the control register, decoded and obeyed. When the order has been executed the SCC is augmented by one, or stepped on; the new SCC content calls for the next order from store or the control register, and so on.

The order format for this system needs only one explicit address for the operand, and can therefore be much shorter, that is, require fewer digits to express it, than would an order in the two address system. This has the advantage of simplicity, but is often used to give a still greater advantage; it is common practice to include two complete orders in one word or store location, which gives economical use of store locations. Computers working in this arrangement require a three-beat cycle: an *order* beat, a first *obey* beat and second *obey* beat. We should note that the term 'beat' can be used otherwise from the way we have defined it. In a new and rapidly expanding technology, the terminology varies between different groups of workers in the field. The three beats in a three-beat, two-order, cycle are:

1st beat: fetch order from store;
2nd beat: decode and obey first half;
3rd beat: decode and obey second half.

12.2.1 Conditional transfers of control

Before we leave the topic of sequence control we should consider the operation of *branch* or *jump* orders, that is, conditional transfers of control. It is the execution of these orders that gives the computer its powers of decision. We studied briefly the form of conditional transfers in the chapter on instructions and functions. We can now look into the problem of implementing them. Both the two address and augmented count systems allow fairly easy implementation of these orders. The augmented count system with two orders per word will be seen to have some of the advantages of both systems. We are concerned in this section with the actual transfer of control: we will deal with the technique of decision in the section on order decoding.

The conditional transfer order is essentially a stepping out of one program sequence into another, based on the result of a decision. The control unit must decide if the transfer requirements are met, and if so, to jump or branch into the new sequence. In the two address system the instruction is put together like this: the function 'box' is filled in with the function number assigned to the branch or jump function. The test is performed in the accumulator, that is, on the content of the implied address. The X address, which is normally the operand address is, therefore, not needed as such. If the test shows *branch fails*, that is, no transfer is required, the Y address is passed to store in the normal way to select the next instruction, but if the test shows *branch succeeds* and transfer is required, then the address that must be passed to store is that to which the transfer must be made; this is conveniently arranged by writing this address in the X address box.

With this arrangement the implementation of the logic is quite simple. The order is decoded in the normal way; since no operand needs to be fetched, the function unit associated with the order prevents the X address from being sent to store. Then the test is made. If the branch fails the normal sequence of operations takes place: the Y address is pulsed into the X address position and sent to the store selection system and the beat is changed to *order*; this causes the instruction called for by the Y address to pass into the control register.

If the branch succeeds, then the Y address is not pulsed through into the X address position: the X address is, therefore, sent to the store and its contents pass to the control register to initiate the new sequence. We see that this is exactly the same procedure as for branch fails except that the pulses to transfer the Y address into the X address box are not supplied.

The implementation of a transfer of control in a sequence counter controlled system is rather more difficult. If the branch succeeds, we have to arrange for the sequence counter, or register, to have its contents replaced by another number which has previously been in store. It may also be necessary to store the original contents of the counter, since some branch function applications lead into a loop of instructions, requiring a return to the original sequence once the loop is completed.

In order to change the contents of the sequence control counter we need either some arithmetic facilities, so that it can be augmented or decreased by any specified number, or else we need a shift arrangement to shift in the new number and transfer out the old. Neither method imposes any great difficulty on the designer but it may entail the addition of a good deal of hardware. If the system is one that has two orders per instruction word the problem may be simplified somewhat. As in the two address system, the first half-order is made to be the test or branch function. If the branch fails the second half-order is omitted, or skipped by causing the beat counter to be stepped on two steps instead of one.

12.3 Timing

The timing requirements of a computer depend on a variety of considerations: the machine may operate in serial or parallel mode, with delayed or immediate access storage, synchronously or asynchronously; the machine may be fast or slow. In general, large computers contain parts which can be categorised under all, or any, of these descriptions. We shall in this section look into some of the most important considerations.

12.3.1 Clock waveforms

These waveforms are a particular feature of serially-operating machines. The concept of serial operation is that of the time-divided system of information processing and storage; a minor cycle, or word time, is divided into epochs, or digit times, each epoch having an assigned significance. For instance, in a system which uses binary fractional number representation, with sign by complement modulo 2, a digit time, usually the most significant is assigned, in every word time, to the sign digit. Thus all sign information, in all stored data, is held in the same corresponding time division. Other time divisions or epochs hold numbers to the various powers of two. Some epochs hold no data, for example, gap digits which are used for engineering purposes and separating information blocks or words. Since nearly all computers today operate in the system advocated by Von Neumann, of having all orders and information in a common storage system, the assignment of digit times has a different significance for orders and for data. The first digit of a word time may, in an order, represent the most significant function digit, or any other similar but pre-arranged assignment. We see, from this, that the importance of a clock waveform defining digit times, is not only as a speed control but also as the partitioning system between information epochs. All operations performed in a certain digit time n correspond to the operations in channel n of a parallel system. Having digested this concept we can appreciate why, in the engineering of serially-operated computing systems, there is so much preoccupation with the form, correctness and reliability of the clock wave.

Usually in a clock-controlled computing system there are several associated clocking waveforms. First there is a waveform generated which defines the speed of operation of the machine; this may be square or sinusoidal or any other convenient shape, but the main requirement is for it to be of stable form and frequency. A common name for this waveform is *master clock*. In a system in which a drum or similar rotating storage is used, the drum clock and master clock must be synchronised; in a primitive, single-drum machine this is most easily done by letting the drum generate the master clock wave, and then controlling the speed of the drum as accurately as possible. Where there are several drums, or other limiting factors on the master clock, the drums must be synchronised to it, which provides an interesting problem in drum speed control; the drum must be synchronised not only very accurately in speed, but in position, too, to within a very few seconds of arc, to the rest of the machine, and to other drums or similar devices.

The waveform of the master clock wave is an important consideration since it is used to generate other clock waveforms. If it is generated from a crystal oscillator, as is common to obtain frequency stability, it will commence as a sinusoidal waveform, and will, almost certainly, be required to generate a square wave. To get a true square wave of even mark-space ratio from a sign wave by amplification and clipping, entails that the sign wave remains constant in form and amplitude, with strict symmetry about zero; the square wave must be triggered at the identical point in each sinusoidal oscillation. We do not concern ourselves here with the electronics of good square wave generation, but we are concerned to understand the requirements of the generator.

From the master clock are generated the other timing waves: first the squared clock, commonly termed merely *clock*, and then a waveform defining the word time or minor cycle, which may well be called *digit clock*. Fig. 12.3 shows a typical family of *clock* waveforms for a serially operated computer. Digit clock usually has a digit in each information epoch and these are numbered or named, for reference.

There requires to be a gap time of one or more digits between the blocks of information or words. This gap is to allow for switching time, time for setting up function units and the like, and to accommodate lags in time

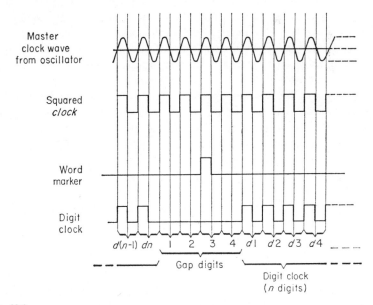

Fig. 12.3

between reading and writing such as we have already discussed in the section on magnetic storage systems. Its length is therefore defined by engineering considerations. It should be as short as possible since it is wasted time from an information point of view. The reduction of one digit gap time in a cycle of thirty-three digits, for instance, gives a 3 per cent gain in processing speed at the same clock frequency. In Fig. 12.3 we have shown four gap digits, which is a fairly generous allotment by normal standards. The information digits are separately identifiable, normally by running a counter from them; then finding coincidence with the counter output will identify a digit in any digit time during the word.

A second important timing waveform generated from the clock is one which defines the ends of the minor cycles or words. The form of this is usually a single digit or 'spike' in a predetermined position in the gap time. In Fig. 12.3 we have shown this corresponding to gap-digit three, that is, it commences in the middle of the gap time; it could equally well be placed anywhere else, to suit engineering requirements. This word marker waveform is commonly used to trigger the beat change; it also may step a counter, the output of which defines the addresses of word times in a major cycle, such as a drum rotation, or delay line cycle.

There is an interesting problem thrown up here which applies particularly to drum store computers. Each word position around the drum periphery is addressed: the counter, if one is used, must always be in phase with the drum word numbering, since information may be permanently stored on the drum. There are two ways of dealing with this fairly simply: the first is to write permanently on one drum track the address of each word location around the track, and thereafter use this for addressing, dispensing with the counter once the drum track has been written. The second is due to A.D. Booth, and was used in his APEX computers; it is typical of the ingenuity of the design. The APEX drum generates both clock and word marker waveforms from engravings on the drum periphery. For the word marker track there are thirty-two evenly spaced engravings corresponding to the thirty-two word positions round each drum track. The thirty-second word marker engraving is followed by another engraving, equivalent to about one digit time later, making thirty-three engravings in all, round the word marker track.

The word positions round the drum are indexed for addressing by counting the word marker impulses; immediately after the counter has counted to thirty-two it generates a blanking pulse which inhibits the input to the counter for a short time. If the drum position is in correct phasing with the counter the blanking pulse prevents the thirty-third engraving from being counted and the drum and counter remain in phase. If, as at starting up, for instance, the counter and drum are out of phase the counter counts all thirty-three engravings and, therefore, moves up one word time per revolution until it does come into phase with the drum, where it remains. One of the most compelling limitations of Booth's designs was economy: this technique is typical of his artifice in overcoming that limitation. Booth's machines were operated on a serial, two address, drum-controlled system, built on the proverbial shoe-string. The system is elegant in its simplicity and economy, and is a most instructive study; reference to Booth's designs will be found in the bibliography at the end of this chapter.

The *clock* waveform has other uses than timing and partitioning of the time-division arrangement of the system. It provides a source of standard pulses for pulse formation and regeneration. We have seen, in the section on magnetic recording, how it can be used to generate write and strobe pulses. We should recall also that it was used as a generator of shift pulses in arithmetic functions.

In fast operating systems using pulses of a few micro-seconds or less, pulses are appreciably delayed and attenuated by passing through gates and logic circuits. One way of regenerating pulses after they have been attenuated and delayed is to pass them through a delay amplifier. Fig. 12.4 shows a diagram of a unit known as a gated delay amplifier.

Consider the inputs, *a*, *b*, *c*, to have come through paths of varying length and different numbers of logic elements; they are, in general, unlikely to arrive all at the same time, and anyway, will lag the clock pulse, to which they should be synchronised. The output of the gate will not be correct until all have arrived, and this will be a finite time after the last input pulse. At this time the flip-flop becomes set in accordance with the gate output. The circuit is so arranged that the pulse generator can only put out a pulse when the *next* clock pulse arrives; since the flip-flop is set first, the pulse generator can put out a pulse synchronised exactly to *clock* and of the correct form and amplitude, though in the clock pulse time immediately following that corresponding to the inputs. This artifice is commonly used in systems operating at high pulse repetition rates. It complicates the logic somewhat, but is effective. Similar devices are used in pulse-coded telephony systems at repeater stations: if the presence or absence of a received pulse can be reliably detected, its attenuation can be completely made good before retransmission one digit time later.

So far we have considered the clock waveform with particular reference to serial systems. In parallel systems its importance lies mostly in synchronisation of the parallel channels. Unless it is limited by having to remain

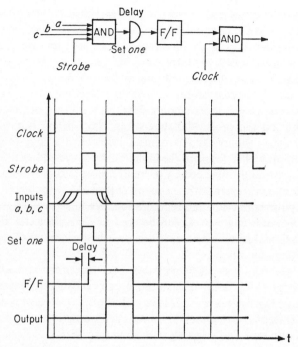

Fig. 12.4 Gated delay to reshape and retime pulses

in synchronism with a rotating store or some similar device, its regularity or frequency are not likely to be so important as in the serial case. Furthermore, there is no requirement to divide it up into words or minor cycles, and interrupt it with gaps. It will be needed, however, in every channel and at every point where synchronism must be ensured. Every point at which it is applied must load the clock generator to some extent: it is easy to see that one of the engineering requirements of a clock generator system is that of being stable under heavy loading. This particularly applies in parallel systems: commonly it is achieved by taking master clock to the various computer organs and major units and, from this, generating a main clock wave in each; the ndividual generators can then be matched to the load imposed by each unit.

In systems where different organs operate at different clock rates, buffering has to be arranged, and this may be controlled by the central control unit. Typically, buffer units need to exist between the arithmetic units and store, between immediate access, delayed access and backing stores, and between the main system and its peripherals such as input and output units. The separate units may each have their own clock systems and typical buffer devices are registers or ferrite core planes in which information may be read in using one clock wave and read out using another. In operations of this kind it is the task of the control unit to ensure that only one of the processes can occur at a time.

12.3.2 'Busy' lines

This term has been borrowed from the field of telecommunications to describe a technique by which a system having several parts running independently is prevented from interfering with them when they are actually in operation. It is a simple and effective technique and is most easily described by example. In some systems, block transfers of information may be made between parts of a storage system automatically, without preventing operation of other units at the same time. For example, a section of a core store may be in process of being loaded from a drum store, while another section of the core store is in use with the arithmetic unit. It may be that, before the former transfer is complete, a new order is commenced entailing the fetching of an operand from an address in the core store section involved in the drum store transfer. Without safeguards, this would cause malfunction; in simple machines it might devolve on the programmer to avoid this circumstance, but in sophisticated systems in which several programmes are run simultaneously, or in which store transfers are fully automatic, this would be beyond the power of the programmer.

The busy lines technique is designed to take care of this; in the example we are considering, registers, or flip-flops of some kind, would be set, indicating that a core-store section and drum are 'busy'. If that core-store section is addressed by the control register to fetch the operand, the combination of that address and its appropriate busy signal inhibits further operation on the order. When the transfer is finished, the busy signal goes down and the inhibition is removed, allowing operation to continue. Many quite simple devices require busy line arrangements, particularly input and output devices. The elementary computer function *read a character* from a tape reader, involves scanning a register of five or six digits set by the reader photo-electric system. This scan may be in parallel, and the reading would then take only one computer pulse time; the parity check, if any, would not take much longer. Meanwhile the tape reader has to advance the tape so that the next character appears under the reading heads. Even with very fast readers this takes a millisecond or more, and thus the computer may well be in a position to call for a further *read in* before the reader is ready. To prevent this happening a read signal to the reader sets the *reader busy* device; this is only reset by the reader mechanism when it is ready for a new read in. If the computer calls for a *read* during the time the busy is set, the combination of the *read* order and the *busy* signal inhibits the beat change; the beat cannot change until the *busy* signal goes down, and the computer has to wait.

12.3.3 Permissive or consequential sequence

The progress of a computer from order to order according to a program is maintained by the timing system. In a primitive system in which every function could be completed within a definite time, say a word time, the clock generator could issue a regular series of trigger pulses, each initiating an operation. This would be an open-loop system and inflexible. The time period allowed between trigger pulses would need to be long enough to allow any function to be completed and would depend, therefore, on the slowest; a safety margin of time would also be necessary. Such a system is easily seen to be wasteful of time. We find this form of time waste in serial operating devices with fixed word length, since the actual data will generally occupy less digit positions than a full word length.

Serial machines are fed with trigger pulses at fixed intervals of one word time, but they are generally not restricted to work at the speed of the slowest function, their timing is worked on a permissive basis, which is somewhat akin to the busy line system we have discussed. When a function is initiated the beat counter is changed by the next permitted trigger pulse. This system is operated by arranging that any function unit, once started in operation inhibits the trigger pulse-train until it has finished. Fig. 12.5 shows a simple system flow diagram, using flip-flop elements and gates.

The beat flip-flop output controls the beat: it is set alternately by trigger pulses from the *clock* system, through gates A and B. Let us assume the *order* beat is in process. This has set flip-flop C, so that its output to the gate A is down and this gate is closed, inhibiting trigger pulses to the beat flip-flop. When the order beat is complete the function decode unit sends a pulse to the C flip-flop, resetting it and thus opening gate A, and closing gate B. The next trigger pulse changes the beat, setting *obey* and this turns on flip-flop D, and closes the gate B. The beat change is inhibited until the function unit in operation sends a signal, indicating that its task is com-

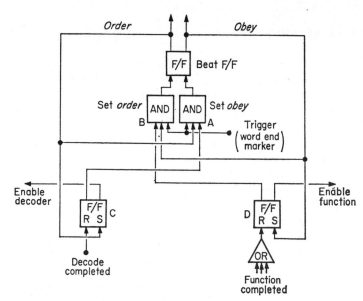

Fig. 12.5 Flow diagram of beat control

pleted, to the flip-flop D; this, in turn, opens gate B allowing the next trigger pulse to change the beat back to *order* once more.

We should note that the timing pulses are supplied after each word-time; the beat is only permitted to change after the work of each beat is completed.

The system described loses time since it has to wait for the timing pulse after each part of the function is complete.

Consequential operation is usually only possible with parallel operating machines; using this system, when an order or function is complete it initiates the trigger for the next function or order, directly, without aid from a clock pulse for which it might otherwise have to wait. This method of operation, when combined with busy lines, as it usually is, becomes most complicated. Each organ or function unit does its own timing, and this allows the system to work without a clock, or with several different clocks. Atlas is an example of a computer operating in this mode. Ultimate speed, or time-saving is obtained, but, as must be, at the expense of cost and complexity. This mode, when used in multi-programmed machines, with a member of peripherals having different needs and priorities is commonly called interrupt operation. We shall study this later in this chapter.

12.4 Order decoding

This is the process by which the programmer's written instructions are translated into computer activity. In simple systems, the process is centred about a register called, commonly, the control register or order register. More complicated systems entail several registers and associated logical and arithmetic facilities.

Instructions or orders to a computer are in the form of binary numbers. These numbers are subdivided into groups of digits, representing functions, addresses and similar information; they may be written in pure binary, or binary coded decimal, or in any alpha-numeric, or convenient notation, but the result is a pattern of ones and zeros, which, so far as the machine is concerned, has little numerical significance. What is the concern of the machine is whether the digit in any particular position in the order word is a one or a zero, that is, up or down, on or off.

In the early stages of the design of a computer, an order format is decided on, and this is directly correspondent with the arrangement of the control register. To obey an order, it is read into the control register so that the instructions and information within it end up in their assigned digit positions. The state of each digit position then acts as a logic input to the control circuits.

A typical instruction to a simple computer consists of three sections: function, address, and modifier, or B-line. The binary representation of each of these is shifted into the appropriate digit positions in the control register, during the order beat. The shift-in may be serial or parallel; it may come from an immediate access memory, or may have to await coincidence, depending on the computer organisation; when the order has been shifted into the control register, decoding commences, and when this is complete, the beat is caused to change to *obey*.

We will consider the decoding process by sections, commencing with the function section.

12.4.1 Function decoding

A small or medium-sized computer probably has at least sixteen functions, though it probably will not have more than thirty-two (these numbers corresponding to four or five binary digits). The most straightforward technique of decoding is by use of a many-one matrix technique. Such an arrangement using diode logic is shown in Fig. 12.6, giving a selection of any one of eight possible outputs from three-digit inputs. It is easy to see

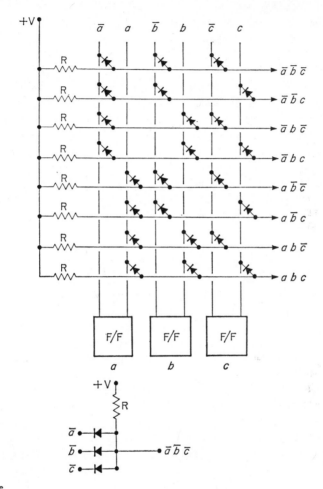

Fig. 12.6

how the system can be enlarged to give sixteen or thirty-two outputs from four or five inputs.

On examination, we see that the matrix arrangement is merely a compact arrangement of eight conventional diode AND gates, the inputs being the eight possible combinations of the three binary digit inputs. It is sometimes more convenient to use separate gates rather than a specially built matrix, particularly if not all possible outputs are required. The process is the same as decoding a binary count; if the computer is limited to binary coded decimal operation, only ten outputs of a possible sixteen can be used and it might well pay to use separate gates.

Each function corresponds to a binary number; sometimes the function numbers are assigned for the convenience of the programmer, or they may conform to any preset order code. There is a system, however, which can often simplify the design of the control circuits; this system allots an engineering or logical significance to each digit. For instance, there might be eight orders which involve a drum, in a system having sixteen or less functions. The setting of the 2^3 digit in the function decode section of the control register could then be used to activate the drum logic. Likewise there might be four instructions calling for the adder/subtracter to be set to *subtract*. The setting of the 2^2 digit could be used directly to control the subtracter. Such a system offers considerable engineering advantages in simple machines and, if well thought out, imposes no particular difficulties on the programmer. A typical example of where this technique could be most effective is in the two address type of machine, such as we discussed in a previous section. The X address digits are normally used to call for an operand from store. Some orders, such as *shift the accumulator, test the accumulator*, and similar ones, which only act on the implied operand address, require the inhibition of the X address digits from being sent to the store. If one digit position can be used to control this inhibition, one of the design problems of the implementation of these orders is met quite simply.

In Chapter 9 we saw that most functions can be arranged easily enough to operate on the receipt of a trigger pulse, or a single voltage-level change. In this case the matrix or other simple decode system is adequate in itself to generate the required level, or trigger pulse. Since the function needs normally to be started at a definite time, that is, at the beat change, the decoder output is gated with *obey*, or *word marker* or any other pulse which is suitably timed.

Some functions are not so simple, since they demand waiting for coincidence, or a sequence of operations. In this case it is good practice to design a separate function unit which controls them from start to finish, on the receipt of a trigger pulse from the decode unit. Functions of this kind are, typically, drum store block transfers, and orders controlled by micro-programs. The provision of the separate function control unit or micro-program operating from a trigger signal has the great advantage that it may allow the remainder of the system to carry on with other instructions once it has been initiated; this arrangement, if it is to be effective, must include busy line safeguards. We can arrange to gate the decoder

utput of functions of this kind with a busy line signal, so that, if they are
alled on when the busy is set, the beat change, or similar control activity,
 inhibited, for the time being.

2.4.2 Address decoding

asically this entails no more than setting the store selection gates from the
ppropriate digits in the control register, and permitting a timing pulse to
rigger the store when this has been done. In immediate access, single-
evel stores, this is, in fact, all that the control unit does need to do, in this
espect. If the store is of a type which requires waiting for coincidence, the
ddress digits of the control register are sent to the coincidence unit; and
he beat is permitted to change when coincidence has been established.

2.5 Arithmetic connected with store addressing

This is the work that the control unit must do to allow modification, when
alled for by the presence of digits or numbers in the B-line part of the
ontrol register. In simple machines the B-line may contain as few as two
ligits or four possible modifications (including no modification at all);
n Atlas there are 128 modifiers permitted.

Modification can take a variety of forms, depending on the designer's
ngenuity, and the amount of additional hardware permitted by cost and
imilar considerations. Generally the B-line digits define the address of an
mmediate access store, or register, specially reserved for the purpose. In
his store the programmer sets a number, which may be an addend to the
ddress digits of the order, or may be a number corresponding to a count
f some kind. In simple techniques the number in the store is added to the
ddress digits of the modified order each time it is used, and, thus, when
sed repetitively the address advances by increments, which causes oper-
nds to be drawn from successive addresses. If this process is primarily
o save programming labour, it may be achieved by using the main arithmetic facilities of the machine, under the direction of a subroutine or
microprogram. More generally it is required also to save machine time
nd, in this case, the control unit requires its own limited arithmetic facili-
ies, in the form of an adder unit; this may work directly into the control
ecode register, adding the increment before the *obey* beat is permitted.
We should note that if the incrementing is to be progressive, the instruc-
ion must be replaced in its old position in store after each modification.
The necessity of returning the modified instruction to store each time can

be avoided by a further complication; the increment in the modified register may itself be incremented each time it is used. In this case the adder must be a part of the modifier register system unless the increment is restricted to being augmented by unity in which case, instead of a register and adder, a counter may be used, and is stepped before each modification.

A further function of the modifier system may be a built-in test facility, which indicates that either the incrementation has reached a specified value, or has reached zero from a specified count; a counter can, of course, be stepped forward or backwards according to the designer's arrangement. In a fairly sophisticated machine these requirements may be met by having a small high speed arithmetic unit to serve some, or all, of the modifier registers. Counting or incrementation may be done in all, or some, of them. It is easy to see that this entails the existence of a primitive computer inside the control unit of the main system, and though it gives efficient and versatile operation it will add considerably to the cost.

12.6 Control of peripheral equipment

This poses particular problems in data processing systems, where peripherals may form the largest part of the installation. Line printers and magnetic tape machinery usually transfer large blocks of information at each operation. The control unit must be prepared to receive these blocks, or send them out, as nearly as possible at the behest of the peripheral buffer units, so that they are not kept waiting. If the system contains several of these large peripherals, the control unit requires to be very ingeniously thought out. It is usual to make line printers, and the like, as automatic as possible, which relieves the control unit of jobs such as compilation of lines: the control is normally on the permissive basis, and the busy lines technique is used extensively.

In simple systems, or systems with primitive input/output devices, the control unit is normally equipped with function units to control each device in the same ways as an arithmetic function; in reading-in it may be required to take action in the event of parity failure: this generally entails the setting up of a dynamic stop or similar indication to the operator.

12.7 Store block transfers

This work is done in most machines under the instructions of the programmer, and is usually controlled by a microprogram. The requirement is to exchange a block of information between the working store and a back ing store. It is a straightforward operation consisting of the following sequence:

(*a*) find coincidence with the block location in the backing store;
(*b*) set a busy line device to prevent access to the working store section being exchanged;
(*c*) progress the transfer, word by word, and count the transferred words;
(*d*) when the whole block transfer is complete, according to the counter, reset the busy line device;
(*e*) if parity checks are in use in the store transfer system, the control must act in the event of parity failure.

It is convenient and time saving if the block transfer can be arranged to operate without holding up the operation of the rest of the computer. In this case the programmer can optimise the program so that all the required operands are in the working store when called for.

There are sundry other housekeeping operations that may necessarily be performed by the control unit, such as clearing registers and store locations after use. Generally it is bad practice to leave this to the control unit since the program should ensure that information left in registers should not be called for unless it has been expressly put there. Function units should clear up after their own operations, and set positions, left in registers and the like, should only occur as faults, and, if they do occur, should not be concealed by general clearing operations. However, we shall see in the following section how, in complex systems such as look ahead, housekeeping of this kind is sometimes inevitable.

12.8 More advanced control systems

In large, very fast computers, computing time is costly. It is necessary to use computing time economically; this entails using every organ of the system to a maximum extent, by making each part work concurrently with as many others as can be. In a medium sized system this can be achieved, to some extent, by making store transfers, print-outs, and the like, as nearly automatic as possible; this allows the programmer to optimise the programme in order to use the arithmetic facilities while the automatic processes are taking place under machine control. Program optimisation is tedious and, in many cases, not much improvement can be gained, since the program may inherently require either calculating, or non-calculating time, predominantly, thus leaving some facilities idle much of the working time.

There have been evolved several very powerful organisational techniques within the control systems of the largest and most sophisticated machines, which give marked economies in machine time. Some of these have been mentioned before, look-ahead and single-level storage, for example; perhaps the most powerful of all is multi-programmed operation, that is, arranging for the machine to process several different programs concurrently.

12.8.1 Multi-programmed operation

This system takes advantage of the fact that different programs, and parts of programs, make different demands on the machine's facilities; some programs are highly mathematical, and need little print-out; others require a great deal of store transfer and print-out, and little arithmetic, and so on. If several programs can be run at once it should be possible to utilise all the machine's facilities much of the time, so long as the machine control system can do the optimisation as it goes along.

Stretch and Atlas make good use of this technique: each is equipped with up to six operating consoles, and these function as sophisticated input/output units. There are also master consoles and engineer's consoles which are used to perform overall control and test functions. We should remember that the computer and its organs are not in the least discommoded by instructions from different programs being processed in succession; one order is like another, so far as a machine is concerned. The primary engineering requirements in a multi-programmed system are these:

(*a*) program identification: the machine must be able to keep track of each program's orders and data right through the system, so that it can compile the result;

(*b*) program sequence: the machine must ensure that the various instructions in each program remain in program sequence even though several orders from the same program are being operated on simultaneously;

(*c*) storage partition: the machine must ensure that one program does not use storage in use by another. The amount of storage used by a particular program during the course of processing is not always easy to assess;

(*d*) program rotation: the machine must select instructions from each of the programs in sequence, either arbitrarily or according to priority. This may be on the basis of programs which have been held up longest being given highest priority, or by a priority list imposed by the user, or both, or sometimes by machine limitations, as we shall see later.

The multi-program technique has a particular advantage when used with programs requiring a good deal of human intervention. It is uneconomical in time for a programmer to check the operation of a program down to the last detail before entering it into the machine. Often it is not even possible to do so; the answer to one part of a problem may dictate the requirements of the next. Thus, program debugging is necessary, which entails running the program through the machine piecemeal, sometimes many times over. In a single-program machine this is very expensive in machine time, since computation is halted during the print out to the operator, and while the programmer is thinking out the modifications required. With multi-programmed operation the machine goes on with other useful work all the time it is not actually dealing with the program that is being debugged.

A further advantage arises in large organisations where a computer may be used to cover business, statistical, mathematical and process control functions simultaneously; process control of systems having long time constants can conveniently be dealt with by quite infrequent sampling. The computer can be used to control a complicated plant and, between-times, do a great deal of other forms of computing.

Storage partition, that is, the allocation of storage to individual programs so that they do not overlap, simplifies the problem of program identification. The program is written as though it is to be entered in a single program machine with the instruction sequence and data addresses starting from zero, or some preassigned starting point. When the program is entered into the machine, the particular console, allocated to the program, causes the control system to modify all the addresses; so that they become relative addresses, this means that, within the machine, the program retains its sequence, but its machine address depends on the block address of the allocated storage space. The machines output of the resultant will automatically come back to the right console and print out device, since it is identifiable within the machine by the address blocks allotted to it.

As we have mentioned before, it is not always easy or even possible, to stipulate an upper limit to the quantity of storage that a program will require during the course of its operation. In Stretch the allocation of storage is done before the program is entered into the machine, and a reason-

able margin of safety must be allowed. To prevent the storage require
ment overflowing the allocation, a complicated system of lock-outs an
alarms is arranged. Atlas has a more flexible system due to its ingeniou
but very elaborate Supervisor program. As the program is read in, Supe
visor allocates its storage, block by block, in pages of the core store; a
the program calls for more storage as it proceeds, this is allocated also
and Supervisor compiles an index of store allocations to each program
In this way the store allocation at any time is only sufficient for th
program at that time; if storage is dispensed with, this is taken back an
reallocated where it is needed, also. This is highly complicated since th
core store pages are transferred to the drum store, and again indexed
when not in immediate use. The identification of each individual program
is maintained by Supervisor through this indexing system.

The sequence control within each program is easy enough to maintair
as in a single program arrangement. When several orders are available
the machine chooses that with the lowest sequence number. The selectio
of orders from several programs, dictated by a priority scheme is cor
siderably more complicated, and should afford the reader considerab
food for thought.

12.9 The pipe-line system

The Stretch system of instruction handling can well be likened to a pipe-line
in that several instructions are held in the system at any time, and the
move from stage to stage as they are processed; like a pipe-line, howeve
once the system is full, the speed of progress does not depend on the lengt
of the pipe-line. It was mentioned, in the chapter on organisation of com
puter storage, that the Stretch system holds in its instruction unit tw
instructions, each containing two orders, before passing them to the ope
and fetch unit, which holds up to four orders; there are, therefore, eigh
orders in the pipe-line at any one instant. Stretch is a very versatile machin
and the processing of these instructions is complicated. In the first plac
Stretch is arranged to work with several different order formats; that i
an instruction word may be made up in several different forms and th
groups of digits within it carry a different significance in these form
Secondly, the machine is organised for variable field length operation, an
so is the storage. This means that a word has no fixed length; the store
addressed down to the individual digit, and the address therefore define
the first digit position of any word, and the number of succeeding digi
which belong to the word. In certain data handling processes the digi

are transmitted continuously in streams many times the length of the basic computer word of sixty-four digits. Order formats all fit, however, into the sixty-four digit framework.

The pipe-line system therefore has the following activities to perform:

(*a*) select the next instruction according to priority, and bring it into the instruction unit;

(*b*) identify it with its own program;

(*c*) determine the order format, from a group of indicator digits within the order;

(*d*) decode it according to the format determined;

(*e*) check for B-line modifications, and make them;

(*f*) flag it with any necessary indicator digits to show its priority, and whether an operand is to be fetched;

(*g*) move it to the *fetch operand* unit and fetch the operand, of whatever length;

(*h*) obey the order when it is all ready;

(*i*) unload the result back to store in the correct section according to the program it belongs to.

It is easy to see why there require to be several steps in the interpretation of instructions and that, to achieve speed and flexibility, great complexity, with its accompanying cost in hardware, must also be accepted.

2.10 Data transfer organisation

Large systems, operating in the multi-programmed mode, demand rapid movements of very large amounts of information. The earlier computers were designed primarily for calculation and mathematical processes, and were thus concentrated around the arithmetic unit, which was sometimes called the system centre. Modern data processing computers require to handle a great deal of data requiring little mathematical treatment, and the true system centre is no longer the arithmetic unit, but the control unit itself. The organisation of Leo III (English Electric-Leo), for instance, is such that the arithmetic unit is virtually a peripheral, that is, it is connected to the control unit and storage, in exactly the same way as the card readers, line printers, and other input/output devices. For a machine whose role is primarily data processing, this is a logical development. We should realise, however, that multi-programmed machines, for whatever purpose, will tend to take this form; the arithmetic unit, since it is for common use, must be fed with complete data for each instruction, and emptied of it completely, before the next. We cannot use the idea of the accumulator being the implied address of an instruction, since its contents do not necessarily belong to the same program during successive operations. The major task of the control unit is that of controlling data flow in and out of store; the volume of it which passes to and from the arithmetic unit will depend on the type of use, and may well be only a small fraction of the whole.

Peripheral equipment such as line printers, and magnetic tape units, have a high data transfer rate and it is usual to have a part of the control unit as an exchange, operating, to a large extent, independently of the central processing part of the computer. Print-out of data is demanded by an instruction and the demand is passed to the exchange; the program then continues – or the main computer then continues with other programs – while the exchange goes independently about the business of retrieving the required output information from the store and transferring it to the buffer system and printer or tape unit. The exchange needs to be very much of a complete data-processing system in itself. Peripheral devices work more efficiently if their operation is continuous; much time is lost if they are required to start and stop at frequent intervals. This recalcitrant behaviour of the peripheral equipments leads to another complication in the control unit, that of interrupt.

12.11 Interrupt operation

The easiest way to consider this problem is by example, for instance, in terms of the operator's teleprinter, attached to one of the slave consoles. When the operator depresses a key it initiates a read a character subroutine in the program associated with that console. It might, at first appear that the programmed operations of arithmetic or some similar process going on within the computer have the highest priority; but if we consider a parallel mode operating system with a basic clock rate of about 10 Mc/s, the subroutine and actual read-in will take a few tenths of micro-second; several million more clock pulses will elapse before the teleprinter will be in a position to demand further attention. It has been shown that it is better and more economical to give input/output and similar devices, the highest priority, and to keep arithmetic and similar orders waiting while they are dealt with. Thus a teleprinter, or a filled line in a compiler system, is given the power to interrupt, with the high priority, taking precedence over any other order not actually in progress. In Supervisor for instance a register is maintained, in which each di position signifies a peripheral or similar device; when one calls for attention the digit is set, Supervisor scans this register before accepting any other program instruction, and deals with it first. Stretch uses a similar procedure.

12.12 Further complications

In the original concept of Stretch the look-ahead facility was arranged to look ahead up both branches, when a branch instruction was set. It is possible for two or more branch instructions to follow each other, and it was found that this system was not practicable without the system getting stuck, in unfavourable circumstances. Accordingly, it was decided to restrict the look-ahead to the operations which would be appropriate for *branch fails*, that is, in which no branch takes place, and the program follows its normal sequence. In the event of the branch succeeding, the look-ahead activity which will already have been initiated, must be cancelled. This entails the clearing of the operand fetch registers, and the unmodifying of any instructions which have been brought in, before returning them to their place. This is a most intricate piece of housekeeping; we easily see why it was impracticable to allow look-ahead up both branches.

The design of the Stretch order-code, and the facilities provided, were based on the philosophy that such a powerful machine was only likely to be used by highly skilled programmers, who would be happy to accept a complicated system of programming in exchange for a very great range of facilities. Atlas, on the other hand can be worked easily and economically through autocode and program languages, and the operator's skill has little to do with its operation. Paradoxically, both these design philosophies go to make the control system very elaborate and complicated. Both systems have very complete sets of overflow and underflow indications, for instance, connected with the arithmetic; indications are given of zero register contents, and of the sign of the zeros and infinities, that is, in which direction positive or negative, the overflow or underflow went. The provision of facilities of this kind, in a multi-programmed, high-speed, system provides many interesting exercises for ingenuity and skill for the logic designer.

12.13 Computer time

final and very necessary complication of multi-programmed machines that of recording the time spent on each program, so that in commercial applications it can be fairly charged; in scientific applications it is sometimes necessary to assess costs, also; but, apart from costing, it is only possible to run a computing system efficiently if actual program time consumption is determinable. Thus in Supervisor and similar systems, as well as all the other various duties it must perform, the control unit logs the time used up by each program – we should not forget that these machines work in nanoseconds, doing millions of processes in an hour; timing alone would provide enough work for a small fast computer.

12.14 Multi-processing

We have mentioned multi-programming and concurrency; a further complication of modern large computing systems comes from the trend towards multi-processing. We have considered concurrency between arithmetic and input/output operations, operand fetching, and the like: in some systems today units such as the central processor itself are duplicated and work concurrently.

Multi-processor systems can take several forms: the simplest form is that in which a store is shared by several processors; each demands access to the store on an 'as and when' basis, and if necessary has to wait its turn. Another interesting configuration (Gamma 60) is organised so that various processing units act independently – logical processors, *multiply-divide* and *add-compare* units can all be operated concurrently. The ultimate in complexity is arrived at when a system is multi-programmed and a multi-processor. In this case the central control unit executive programme has to determine object program priorities, assemble data in the right processors, and progress it through and, afterwards, reassemble the object programs in their correct sequence. This sequence requirement demand that the executive or control program has control, to some extent, of priorities, since it must ensure that orders in a particular programme are maintained in sequence: in mathematical and scientific programmes particularly, data is generated in early parts of the program for use in the later parts. It is feasible in some data processing work to allow whole blocks to be run out of sequence, since they may be self-contained and independent of each other; they may be progressed as convenience dictates, and then sorted into order later.

There are two schools of thought about the trend of computer development: one school tends towards larger, more complex and sophisticated systems, while the other is in favour of many more smaller, self-contained systems. Almost certainly, the demand will be for both. Small systems can for modest financial outlay, and are easy to maintain and operate: some users like the system to be entirely at their own disposal. Nowadays mass memory storage is becoming more economic on a cost per bit basis and small systems can have quite large storage capacity.

The very large system is likely to be more efficient: the maximum advantage can be made of multi-programming and multi-processing; very large stores, indeed, become practicable. Multi-programming allows data-link operation, that is, remote control from several places, of the same system. Multi-processing adds reliability to a system in that facilities are duplicated, and failures may, therefore, slow the system but need not stop it. Proponents of the large systems also make the point that, as a result of the size and complexity, more effort must be spent in preparing maintenance and diagnostic techniques, and this greater effort is economic in view of the system cost and capability; because of this, the large system should be more reliable.

Certainly the concept of multi-processing does embody a form of redundancy, but not wastefully; this would seem to add to its promise of reliability.

Doubtless, the proponents of large and small systems will argue their cases for a long time to come; the competition between the two methods should improve the performance of both.

12.15 Conclusion

We have briefly surveyed some of the characteristics of the most advanced computing systems; our first reaction, quite naturally, is to boggle at the size and complexity of machines like Atlas and Stretch, and to wonder at the ingenuity of the men who design them. In future there will be many of us engaged in work on systems of this sort; it is well to get them into perspective, therefore. In the first place they are not one man's brain-child, but the product of the ingenuity of many individuals and teams. Each big computing system can be broken down into a number of smaller ones, and each smaller one into its own organs and sub-units. Each small unit will normally be the work of a team of specialists; the smallest units demand electronics experts; logic designers form parts of teams at different levels. The team that coordinates the whole enterprise is primarily concerned with organisation. In this way the problem can be broken down into conveniently sized projects; we must realise this, while we are learning about computers, because this is the way we need also to organise our study. Naturally each of us will develop a special interest in one aspect or another;

however much we do specialise, it is most important that we try to maintain an overall grasp of the whole subject, or philosophy, of automatic computation.

Suggestions for further reading

Automatic Digital Calculators by A.D. and K.H.V.Booth.
  Butterworth, 1956. Chapter 5 is of interest here.
Planning a Computer System – Project Stretch by W.Bucholz.
  McGraw-Hill, 1962. Chapters 10–13, pp. 133–201 are of note.
*Preliminary Discussion of the Logical Design of an Electronic
  Computing Instrument* by A.W.Burks, H.H.Goldstine and J.Von
  Neumann. Institute of Advanced Studies, Princeton, N.J., U.S.A.
  Reprinted in *Datamation*, Sept. 1962, p. 24.
Generalised Multi-processing and Multi-programming Systems
  by A.J.Critchlow. A.F.I.P.S. Conf. Proc. 1963, **24**, p. 107.
The Atlas Supervisor by T. Kilburn, R.B.Payne and D.J.Howarth
  A.F.I.P.S. publication, Computers – Key to Systems Control,
  Macmillan, 1962, pp. 279–94.

13 Mixed analogue and digital systems

Although analogue and digital systems have grown up separately, they are both parts of the same philosophy, of automatic computation. Much work has been done to make devices for converting digital data to analogue, and analogue data to digital; we shall study some of the methods of doing this later in this chapter. Primarily these devices are used to give more adaptable input/output systems to both kinds of computer; there have been some experiments, also, in which digital and analogue computers have been directly coupled through the medium of analogue-digital converters.

In the past the suitability of problems for automatic computation has usually been judged on the basis of whether they are suitable for treatment on one type of system or the other. Study is in progress, and there is much speculation, on whether there is an important range of problems that require a mixture of the two systems for their solution, and when, and to what extent, mixed systems are necessary or desirable. There are two main categories of these systems: the first is best referred to, at this stage, as mixed and left at that; the second can be more closely defined as hybrid. A mixed system is one in which at some, or several stages, data is converted from analogue to digital, or vice-versa. The system may consist of a digital computer with analogue peripheral equipment, or an analogue computer with digital accessories; or it may be that two or more computers of different types are interconnected. To qualify for the more specific definition of hybrid computer, a system should contain within its own organs both analogue and digital techniques. Like all classifications of this kind, it is difficult to separate them with the definiteness of a Venn diagram; we shall study some illustrative examples of mixed and hybrid operation, and these will help us to establish the division between the two.

13.1 Digital control of analogue computers

An analogue computer very often provides the best method of simulation of a process or of a dynamic system's behaviour. A typical problem using such a model is the study of optimum control-parameter settings; on simple systems, this is commonly solved by the operator varying the parameters, in turn, until the desired degree of optimisation is achieved. The basic mechanism of this method is to vary a control parameter value: the magnitude and direction of the output change is observed and compared with the input variation; as a result of the logical comparison of the two values, a further change is made in the control parameter, and the process is repeated, until no further improvement in the system output can be obtained. We should note that there are two logical decision processes here: the first is the logical comparison of the input variation and the output result; the second is the comparison of each output result, to determine when the improvement ceases. The criterion for this last decision can take, in general, one of three forms:

(*a*) the system output reaches or passes the desired value;
(*b*) the improvement tends to a horizontal asymptote and the output stays at, or approaching, a final value;
(*c*) the sign of the improvement changes, and the system output begins to deteriorate.

Some analogue computer systems have built-in logic elements, such as signum relays, to make these decisions automatically, and in this case, such a system might validly be called hybrid. If the magnitude comparisons were in digital form, then the definition could be even more validly applied.

The examination and optimisation of a large and complicated system having many variable parameters is extremely tedious; one method of attacking the problem is to program a digital computer to direct the changes, and make the comparisons and decisions. It can be made to vary all the parameters in turn, in different order, compare the relative effectiveness of each parameter and find an overall optimum output value, together with a set of optimum parameter settings. This would not be a hybrid system, since the digital computer would be operating in its own mode as would the analogue part, as though each were acting separately under normal program control. We should call this a mixed system; the digital computer is merely doing what the human operator would do – we do not call an analogue computer hybrid when it is being operated by a human. The analogue computer supplies problem data to the digital computer; the source of problem data does not qualify a digital computer.

13.2 An analogue computer controlling a digital computer

Sometimes the role of the computers in the example above is reversed: some non-linear functions, particularly delays, are difficult to simulate by analogue techniques. A digital computer may be programmed to be the slave of an analogue system, to generate functions of this kind: the system is again a mixed system, since the computer is merely being used as an on-line function generator, but is not integral with the analogue machine. However, we could justly style an analogue computer hybrid if it had its own built-in digital function generators, and delay units.

13.3 Hybrid systems and hybrid computers

Digital computers are often set the task of on-line control of real systems, in the same way that they control or perform operations on simulated systems. Typical of such applications are the control of power station operations, such as running up turbines and load-sharing, or driving radio telescopes, such as Goonhilly and Jodrell Bank, or controlling large processing systems, like refineries. It may well be that there are analogue computing elements fully integrated in these systems, such as analogue data feedback devices, and the like. In this case the *system* would be hybrid, but the computer would not. True hybrid computers are at this time fairly rare, though considerable work is being done on applying hybrid techniques to analogue computers. Digital integrators, multipliers and summers are possibilities in analogue machines, as are logical control circuits. In general, these items are more expensive than their analogue counterparts but may be demanded when especially high precision or stability is required. Digital integrators might be included as function units in digital computers; though this would hardly make them hybrid. It does not seem that any great degree of hybridisation is likely in the digital computer field.

13.4 Analogue-digital conversion techniques

At first consideration it would seem simple to categorise these into analogue-to-digital, or digital-to-analogue; in practice, the distinction is not very satisfactory since both basic techniques can be used in devices to do either task. Fig. 13.1 shows two arrangements of a *digitizer*, that is, a device for translating a voltage into a binary number representation.

Fig. 13.1(*b*) shows the same type of digitizer as in (*a*) but connected in a

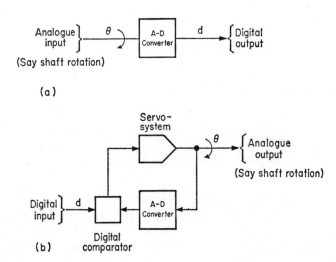

Fig. 13.1

feedback circuit so that the overall conversion is that of a binary number to a shaft rotation, that is, digital-to-analogue. In general, each converter type can have its role reversed by use of feedback. The choice of technique for use in any system depends on circumstances. We shall first consider the elements and techniques in their direct application, that is, without feedback.

13.5 Conversion of digital representation to voltage

The basic requirement of devices for this purpose is to produce, at the output, a voltage proportional to the value of a binary number offered to the input. The input to the device may be serial or parallel and may be continuous or shifted-in in a cyclic manner, depending on the source of the binary input. There must be a register to hold the binary number while it is being converted: generally, this is part of the converter and we shall consider that the input is, in fact, such a register, and not concern ourselves here, with the details of how the binary input is got into the register.

The most direct approach to meeting the basic requirement comes from considering the structure of binary numbers: consider, for example, a four bit register, capable of holding the binary combinations representing the decimal integers 0 to 15. The most significant digit position is 2^3, and, set it represents the number eight. If we scale directly in volts, the setting

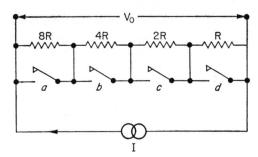

Fig. 13.2 Weighted resistor. Digital to analogue conversion

of this digit demands a contribution of 8V to the output voltage; the setting of the next bit demands an addition of 4V to this, and so on. Application of Ohm's Law leads us to consider a network as shown in Fig. 13.2.

The chain of resistors a, b, c, d, have binary weighted values corresponding to the register digit significance. The register digit positions are arranged to control the shorting relays; if a constant current is applied through the network it is evident that the voltage, V, will be proportional to the sum of the resistor values not shorted out by the relay contacts. We arrange that the relay coils are energised by the register settings so that the contacts are open when a one is set, and closed otherwise. With this arrangement we can, in principle, perform the required conversion.

A similar effect can be obtained by arranging a series of current sources as in Fig. 13.3. In this case each branch contributes a current, and the current values are weighted to represent the binary numbers. The currents are summed at e and the output voltage developed across the resistor **R**.

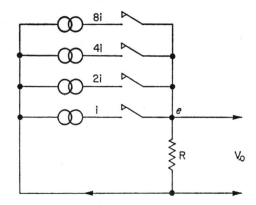

Fig. 13.3

Implementation of the circuits we have considered, as they stand, is not very easy. In the first case, a constant current source must be provided which will have to maintain a constant value even with a short circuit across its output, as when the zero volt output condition is required. For accuracy, the switches need to be perfect, that is, to have zero resistance when closed, and infinite resistance when open. The resistors have to be of computing accuracy and stability. If the device is to operate rapidly, for instance, to convert the output from a digital computer, the switches will have to operate very rapidly, also. Relays are comparatively slow switches, in this context; transistors are fast, but are far from being perfect switches, having neither infinite resistance when cut-off, nor zero resistance when cut-on. We can make as near an approach to a constant current source as accuracy demands, but the nearer we get to it, the more the complexity and cost.

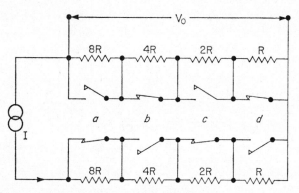

Fig. 13.4 Compensated weighted resistor method

The stringency of the demand for the constant current source can be much reduced by the arrangement shown in Fig. 13.4. As each of the resisters in the upper chain is switched out, the corresponding resistor in the lower, or 'ballast', chain is switched in; the current generator is thus presented with a virtually constant value of resistance. If both sets of resistors are of computing accuracy, the cost of the system is high due to the extra provision of high quality components; normally the ballast resistor chain is made up of standard, good quality resisters, and in this case there will be small variations of the voltage across the terminals of the constant current generator. It is not difficult to make such generators if they are required to cope with only minor changes of voltage.

Relays with two or more sets of contacts are readily available, and thi arrangement is suited to relay implementation: it, is not so suited to implementation using transistors. In the first place, each switch needs to have two separate transistors which must be switched simultaneously; more important is the fact that each switching stage operates under different voltage conditions. If the overall voltage range is to be 100V, for example, then the most significant digit switch must operate over this range, while the least significant digit switch has to be switched completely in the range of a volt, or fraction of a volt. As was mentioned in the discussion, earlier, on chopper techniques, the relay has the great merit that its control circuit and contact circuits are physically separate.

The very high output impedance of a transistor in the common base configuration makes it a good approximation to a constant current generator: this leads to its use in the second type of circuit we considered. Weighted resistors are used to control the emitter current of a transistor in each branch of the circuit; the collector currents are not very susceptible to the voltage variation at the summing point. It is good practice to use a transistor, also, as the summing point: the collector current is then passed through the output resister and the output voltage developed across it. Since this is also virtually a constant current device, this permits the output resistor value to be varied, for calibration or scaling purposes, without materially affecting the current values in the branches. This method of operation has the considerable advantage that the branch transistors are all operated in the same voltage range. If the required voltage range is fairly high, say 100V, as is commonly the case in analogue computer work, transistors need to be suitably chosen for high voltage working, but there are plenty available today with an adequate voltage capability. Transistors are not perfect switches and the circuit designer must cope with the problems of leakage current and drift. Several good circuits of this kind have been evolved, however, giving four-figure accuracy or better, that is, a precision of better than one part in a thousand, over ranges of 100V or more. Due to its reliance on transistors, this conversion technique is generally faster in operation than the series resistor method, which is nearly always implemented with relays.

The idea of weighted current summation leads naturally to considering the possibility of the virtual earth technique which is so effective in analogue computer summation. Fig. 13.5 shows a virtual earth amplifier system arranged for digital-to-analogue conversion.

It is immediately apparent that this system has much to commend it. In the first place, no constant current generators are needed: a computing datum voltage can be used to supply each branch of the circuit, and the

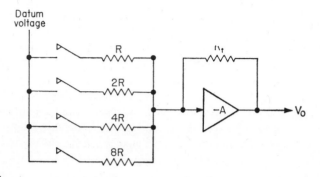

Fig. 13.5

current is regulated by weighted resistors, once again. The virtual earth point, if we use a high gain amplifier, will have a very small range of voltage excursions permitting the resistor controlled branch currents to be maintained with a high degree of accuracy. The feedback resistor R_f can be made to give whatever output voltage scale that is required. If used in connection with an analogue computing system, the reversing amplifier can be of the same type as used in the remainder of the system and the overall accuracy of the converter can be the same as for the system as a whole. Normally high gain d.c. amplifiers have a rather poor frequency response and this factor will need to be considered, since the cycle frequency of the digital input will, in general, be much higher than the normal operating frequencies of the analogue computer system.

We must realise that the raw output of systems such as we have discussed is not continuous: each binary combination will remain set up for a clock-pulse time, or a cycle time, and will then change suddenly to its new value. The output voltage will therefore change in steps and may not be suitable for direct input to a device such as an analogue computer. To achieve a continuous output, or an approximation to it, the voltage output will need to be smoothed or filtered. If the converter system operates rapidly, with a switching rate much above the frequency response capability of the analogue device into which it is connected, the smoothing problem may be fairly easily solved, for instance, by a simple R–C network.

If the switching cycle frequency is within the frequency range of the analogue device, the step changes will generate noise and the smoothing problem becomes complicated. Work is being carried out on the development of devices which give out segmental approximations rather than step changes. Consider Fig. 13.6(*a*) which shows a step-changing waveform;

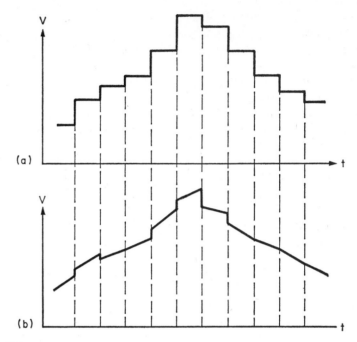

Fig. 13.6

if the rate of change of output is measured and averaged over several steps, this can be used to control an integrating circuit which transforms each level to a ramp, giving a straight line segmental approximation somewhat of the form of Fig. 13.6(*b*); more sophisticated circuits using the second and higher derivatives, give even better approximations, but, necessarily, with increased complexity and cost. This technique is used in the production of digital waveform generators and low frequency oscillators; these have the possible advantage over their conventional tuned-circuit and R–C counterparts, of very high frequency stability and precise control over wave shape and distortion.

There are many variations of the techniques described; the reader requiring to study them in more detail is referred to the references at the end of this chapter. Broadly, the engineering problems of accurate digital-to-analogue conversion, are the same as those of analogue computation. For instance, the problems of amplifier drift are common to both, and where the highest possible drift stabilisation must be achieved, the same methods can be used. Likewise the computing resistors used must be chosen using the same criteria; if we consider the weighted resistors, either in chain form, or as current controllers, we see that the largest must be held to the same absolute accuracy as the smallest, and this imposes the practical limit to the precision obtainable. For instance, suppose we work to a precision of twelve bits, the largest resistor will need to be 4 096 times the value of the smallest. If the smallest is 10 ohms say, with an accuracy of ± 10 per cent, that is, ± 1 ohm, then the absolute accuracy must be to within ± 1 ohm also. The largest resistor, in this case, will have a value of 40 960 ohms, with an accuracy of ± 1 ohm, that is a tolerance limitation of $\pm \cdot 0025$ per cent. Most converters are in BCD form rather than pure binary; few systems have been made to work to better than twelve bit precision, that is, three decimal places, or a precision of one part in one thousand. For high precision data logging, or measuring devices, this may be a severe limitation, but for analogue computer work it is usually more than adequate.

13.6 Analogue to digital conversion

This is, in principle, the reverse process to that which we have been studying in the previous section; the implementation is very different, since we have no suitable voltage-to-voltage converters that work in this direction. For voltage-to-voltage conversion we normally use a feedback application of a digital-to-analogue converter, or use an electro-mechanical converter, servo-controlled by the voltage to be converted. These electro-mechanical converters are called digitizers; there are two principal varieties, the coded plate type, and the magnetic.

13.6.1 The coded plate digitizer

This device works on a principle analogous to a paper tape reader: Fig. 13.7 shows a simple binary pattern such as might form part of a coded plate. As the plate, and pattern, is moved longitudinally in the axis Y–Y, a row of sensors on the line X–X detects the pattern. Thus, for each longitudinal division there is a binary combination which can be picked off by the sensors. Commonly the plate is made of glass and the pattern is photo-deposited on it: the pattern is sensed, in this case, using a light and an array of photo-cells, or photo-transistors, similar to the optical arrangement of a tape reader. Another method is to make the marks of conducting material, and the spaces of an insulator, and to use brush contacts for the sensors; by careful engineering this technique can achieve a high degree

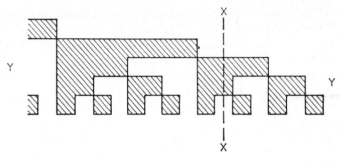

Fig. 13.7

of precision, say, one hundred divisions to the inch. The optical system is usually limited in this respect by the physical size of the photo sensors, though high precision is possible by using lenses and a focussing system. The linear coded plate is less common than the coded disc, that is, a circular plate with the binary-coded pattern round the periphery. The converter, in this form, is called a shaft rotation digitizer; it has the advantages of compactness and that two or more discs can be used together in a coarse-fine system. Linear movements are converted to shaft rotations through a rack and pinion system. For voltage-to-voltage conversions the disc is more convenient, also, since it can be attached directly to a position-servo output shaft, for instance, the shaft of a servo-multiplier. Plate 6 shows a high precision shaft rotation digitizer, in exploded form. The contact brushes are carried, in four banks of four, on an insulated plate; when the unit is assembled they bear lightly on the sixteen digit tracks on the coded plate. Examination of the picture will show that the inner track is a complete ring, whereas all the other tracks are divided into segments; it will also be seen that all the metallized segments form part of a continuous surface. This allows the metallic pattern to be deposited onto the surface of the supporting disc or plate by a photo-etch method similar to the formation of a printed circuit. The inner ring forms a common return for all the sensor circuits. When any brush sensor element is on the metallic surface, continuity is established through it to the inner brush. This particular digitizer has therefore, fifteen sensor circuits, giving a possibility of fifteen bits precision for a single shaft rotation.

The simple pattern arrangement of Fig. 13.7 is in the form of a binary count. Normally, coded plates are not coded in this way but in what are called Gray codes, or other special purpose codes. The reason for this is to avoid ambiguous and false read-outs when the sensors are passing over division boundaries. Consider the case, for instance, with the pattern of Fig. 13.7, when the sensors move from binary seven to binary eight; it is virtually impossible for the contacts all to change over exactly simultaneously, and thus, during the transition any number may be read out, between zero and eight. Gray, and similar codes are arranged so that, at each transition, only one track or digit changes at a time, and the read-out is unambiguously either one code combination or its neighbour. This technique solves the problem of ambiguity, but adds the complication that in most applications, a decoding device must be arranged to convert the Gray code combinations into BCD, or pure binary. When it is necessary for a true count binary code to be used, a further artifice can be arranged: the least significant digit track is duplicated but positioned half a division out of phase with the rest of the tracks. The sensor connected to this track prevents any change of read-out on the remaining tracks until all the sensors have crossed from one pattern to the next. The topic of Gray codes, and the avoidance of ambiguous read-outs from coded discs and digitizers, is quite a large one and rather too specialised for detailed treatment in this work; we shall instead pass on to the magnetic digitizer.

13.6.2 The magnetic digitizer

The magnetic system is very neat, and robust, but it is difficult to make it as precise as the coded plate; it can be made more precise by using coarse-fine techniques. The principle can be studied by reference to Fig. 13.8. The general arrangement is shown in Fig. 13.8(a), while (b) shows the end view of a considerably simplified armature, similar to that of an electric machine; for simplicity, the armature shown has only eight slots. In the slots are three layers of coils. The inner layer pitch is four slots, the intermediate is two, the outer is one, arranged as in the diagram. Each layer of coils is brought out to a slip ring. The field system is arranged as in Fig. 13.8(a), so that the field path is through one segment of the armature at any time; an alternating current is passed through the field windings. The alternating flux through a segment induces an output voltage in each coil wrapping the segment, and this voltage appears on the appropriate slip ring. Each of the eight segment positions produces a binary combination of outputs at the slip rings, and these can be rectified and used as signal voltages. Typically these devices are made with a precision of 256 divisions per revolution, that is, eight binary digits precision. The designer is faced with the same problem of the mid-value as with the coded disc, and it may be tackled in a similar way.

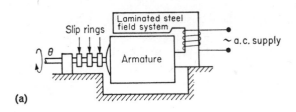

(a)

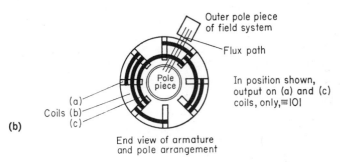

(b)

End view of armature
and pole arrangement

Fig. 13.8

13.7 Digital voltmeters

There are two main reasons why we should include these in our studies;
the first is that they are typical of analogue-to-digital converters; the second
reason is important from the point of view of analogue computer construction. Many modern analogue computers, such as described in Chapter 3,
have a built-in digital voltmeter for potentiometer setting and checking.
Using the weighted resistor method, we do not need a servo-motor to
perform the nulling process as we have seen it in Fig. 13.1; instead, the
digital voltmeter has a built-in program, which causes it to switch in
each resistor in turn starting with the largest and a comparator tests which
voltage is the larger, V_o or V_i (the measured voltage). If V_o is larger, the
resistor is switched out again; if smaller, it is left in; the process is repeated
for each resistor weight, down to that of the least significant resistor. For
a sixteen digit system, this means sixteen simple logical processes and it
can be accomplished in a small fraction of a second. The switched pattern
can be indicated as a decimal display derived from a BCD arrangement.
We see immediately, that this is a null method; if the comparator is sensitive, and if the resistor chain is highly accurate and well compensated, the
accuracy of the whole system can depend on it. Potentiometer setting is

very quick and easy, since the adjustment is made, or the potentiometer set to the desired value, while watching the display. Likewise, potentiometer values and voltages can be read off directly. The normal arrangement is to have a push-button selection system which selects the potentiometer or monitor point according to a code. The code number is displayed alongside the voltage, to avoid selection error. An added advantage of this arrangement is that the digital output can very easily be fed to a printer; any value that needs to be recorded can be printed out by the operator pressing a button; the record shows the value of the voltage and the monitor point identity code. In addition to its facility and speed, this method of potentiometer setting obviates any requirement for highly linear, calibrated potentiometers, other than in the voltmeter.

It was mentioned earlier that the absolute accuracy of the largest resistor in the weighted resistor chain, must be of the same order as for the smallest. If we consider the sequentially switched system as used in digital voltmeters, it is easy to see that if the largest resistor tolerance is as big as the absolute value of the smallest resistor then there may be an ambiguity and the selector logic may be caused to hunt, or make a wrong decision in the setting of the least significant values.

Another technique that is often used in digital voltmeters, is analogous to that used in the variable mark-space ratio multiplier. An integrater is used to generate a linear sawtooth voltage waveform. At the instant that the sawtooth sets out from zero, a counter is started, counting timing pulses. The sawtooth voltage is compared with the measured voltage by a sensitive comparator; when they become equal, the comparator stops the count, and the counter output is displayed to represent the measured voltage, to a suitable scale. The accuracy of this system depends on the accuracy and stability of the integrator and timing pulse generator. The sawtooth may be generated by integrating the timing pulse train, which gives some advantages, but in this case the amplitude and duration of the timing pulses require to be accurately controlled. In general, for compurable accuracy and speed of operation, both systems are of the same order of complexity and cost. Both these systems are feedback or servo-systems, and both are used for analogue-digital conversion in other applications as well as in digital voltmeters. Whereas, in the analogue computer arrangement, the value may be printed out at the operator's wish, or automatically, so the output can as easily be transmitted to a computer register, or into a memory store, under computer control.

13.8 Moiré fringe technique

Today considerable progress is being made in the field of machine tool operation, and similar control functions, directly under digital computer control. We should look briefly into the technique of using moiré fringes, derived from a diffraction grating, as a very precise method of analogue to digital conversion. The details of the technique for generating moiré fringes by the movement of diffraction gratings will be found in works on physical optics; it suffices, here, for us to know that, by such an arrangement, the lateral movement of one grating past another generates, in an optical system a series of black and white 'stripes', which traverse the viewing system as the gratings move. It can be arranged that hundreds of stripes traverse the viewing system, corresponding to a lateral movement of one grating relative to the other, of a millimetre or less. Counting the stripes, or fringes, can thus be used as a very highly accurate measure of linear displacement, and is used in high precision measurement and control. If we arrange to count the fringes by a photo-electric device and register the count on a reversible counter, the count registered, at any instant, will correspond very accurately indeed to the position of the grating, relative to the datum established at the zero setting of the counter. We have, then, an analogue-to-digital converter.

This technique, though simple in principle, requires very careful instrumentation; the problem of establishing the datum is often a difficult one, in practical applications; likewise the control of the direction of the count may require an exercise in sequential logic. The technique is now well established and has been described in the literature on measurement and machine-tool control.

13.9 Digital differential analysers

A number of analogue computers, of the differential analyser type, have been built using entirely digital techniques: these are, of course, not hybrid. They depend for their operation on the process of digital integration, which works on a quite simple principle. The basis of the integrater is a digital adder, and a register. The variable to be integrated is sampled and the resulting digitized, or quantized, value is fed to the adder, and added into the register which maintains the accumulated total. The device can be made to work in either polarity by using an adder/subtracter. The quantization may be performed at regular intervals, in which case the increment is variable, or it may be time divided so that varying numbers of equally sized increments may be added in in each time period. In the latter case, instead of an adder, a counter may be used to register the accumulated value. The digital system has several advantages. First, the precision of the computation is easy to define, due to its digital form. Secondly, if high speed logic is used, and a store is included, one integrater can be made to do the work of several; the variables are sampled in turn, and their accumulated totals drawn from store, incremented, and returned to store again. Thirdly the digital analyser, by its form, lends itself to programmed control in the same way as a digital computer – we should note, that this kind of system is, in fact, a rather simple special purpose digital computer. A fourth advantage is stability.

Digital differential analysers are used when it is necessary to work with very great precision or accuracy; they also show considerable promise, in the time-shared form, as highly compact analysers for use in aircraft and similar instrumentation.

Suggestions for further reading

Digital Techniques by D.W.Davies. Blackie, 1963. For a brief further treatment of analogue-digital converters pp. 7–25 are recommended.
Electronic Digital Integrating Computers by F.V.Mayorov, edited by Yaohan Chu. Iliffe, 1964. This book covers the topic of digital differential analysers very thoroughly.
Hybrid computers are still somewhat of a new topic. The interested reader should look out for articles and papers on the subject in conference proceedings, such as those of the A.F.I.P.S.

14 Engineering considerations of digital computers

We should, by now, have formed a good idea of the functional aspects of computers, of the parts that go to make them, and what they do. We need to study some of the problems in the realisation of a complete system.

14.1 Reliability

In any computing device, achieving the necessary accuracy is a first consideration: in a static sense, the accuracy of a digital computer depends on its precision. When we humans do sums, we use the term, very often, in another sense. We work 'accurately' if we do not make mistakes; an aspect of computer reliability is analogous to our accuracy; it must not make mistakes. The precision of a computer is provided by its logic provision; its accuracy depends on engineering, the design, manufacture, and use, of reliable components, and the combination of these components to give a quite remarkable order of reliability.

It is an interesting reflection that by the early 1920s there were, at our disposal, all the necessary ingredients of digital computing systems – gates, relays, flip-flops, and magnetic storage techniques. Babbage had outlined a system which would function, and had proved some of it with hardware, half a century before. A facile explanation of why there were no great efforts to build digital computers prior to 1940 is that none were demanded and nobody thought of it. This would imply a lack of enterprise and forethought among scientists and engineers, which is quite incompatible with their efforts in other directions during this time. The lack of progress in the field of digital computation can, much more reasonably, be attributed to the fact that engineers could already see the complexity of the problem, and could see no way of surmounting the difficulties of achieving enough reliability of operation to make such an enterprise worthwhile; the computer-minded were forced to bide their time until device technology was sufficiently advanced.

It is worthwhile to look a little more deeply into what is entailed by 'reliability', leading to accurate computing. In one of the pioneer machines, Booth's APE(X)C, there were 200 double valves, amounting to about 400 logic elements; the machine had a clock rate of 50 kc/s. Very roughly, we could assume half the logic elements to be in use at any time; this gives some 200 × 50 000 switching operations per second, as a rough approximation. In ten minutes – a short program for a slow machine – the operations amounted to six thousand million. The important point is that not one of these six thousand million operations could fail if the computation was to be accurate – or even successful. On APE(X)C it was not easy to get ten minutes successful operation; much adjustment was necessary before each run: although the logic of APE(X)C was most elegant, it lacked engineering design, and, to make it do productive work, a great deal of engineering effort was required.

14.2 Worst case failures

The kind of failure that bedevilled the operations of APE(X)C and similar prototype computers could mainly be categorised under the heading of 'worst case' failure. These failures arise when components are operated close to their limits of operation and have little margin of safety: circumstances arise where several components in this state operate together and in worst case combination, one or more fails to operate, giving a momentary failure. Even with highly reliable components the probability of such failures is apt to be high in thousands of millions of operations. The particular point of failure in these circumstances is hard to find, and fault finding is very time-consuming; to avoid it we must see that every component operates with a high safety margin – high enough to ensure that it never fails due to worst case circumstances. This is not only a matter of components; the design engineer must ensure that all pulses are kept within limits of permitted amplitude, duration, and delay, and must make provision for them to be reshaped, or regenerated, whenever required.

14.3 Stability

Electrical components can be qualified in terms of their stability, that is, the constancy of their characteristics over a period of use. Some components are inherently stable, but some, valves in particular, have characteristics which change radically in quite short periods of operation, particularly in switching applications; they have lifetimes which vary very markedly between individuals, even of the same batch. A typical valve lifetime, in the period immediately prior to the introduction of transistors, was 1 500 hours. This was an average figure: some valves perished on switching on, some after minutes, and some lasted many thousands of hours. A further problem with valves is that their characteristics do not change uniformly; some improve, for some time, with running; some are constant and then fail suddenly; while some deteriorate slowly and continuously over a long lifetime. A medium sized computer of that period would contain about 3 000 valves. With an average lifetime of 1 500 hours, the average time of operation between failures could be anticipated to be about half an hour, but this was not enough to allow a payroll or atomic physics calculation to be attempted with any hope of success. The solution to this problem lay in the technique of preventive maintenance.

14.4 Preventive maintenance

This is a highly skilled engineering technique, and very important in the scheme of things in the world today. The reliability of airways, telecommunications, power distribution, and many complex services of the same kind, depends upon it. Maintenance engineering has, hitherto, received little credit in scientific and engineering circles; it has deserved much.

The idea of preventive maintenance, is to prevent faults from occurring. Failures of components and sub-units must occur; thus, to achieve the object, the component must be removed and replaced before failure. At first sight this technique seems to call for the gift of prophecy, possessed by few. The ungifted have to find other ways; the first of these is to make an accurate assessment of the life of each component, and replace it before its lifetime expires. This assessment may be the result of experience or laboratory trial, and produces a statistical average lifetime figure, and failure probability figures. For some components, having consistent behaviour, this is quite a satisfactory method; for components such as valves, it is inadequate, due to the statistical spread of values about the average.

A better method of assessment is to determine the causes of failure. This is best done prior to manufacture, and then the causes can sometimes be eliminated. Good design of the component's environment, and the careful use of it, may also help. When this cannot be, or has not been done, the maintenance engineer uses the information available to him in assessing the components useful lifetime. Ideally each component should be replaced just before it would have failed; if a large safety margin has to be applied this becomes uneconomical in components and labour: if the safety margin is insufficient, faults occur in operation, and the system is inefficient for this reason. Thus, where components are in use for which accurate lifetime assessments cannot be made, other methods must be used. It is a strange paradox, that semiconductor devices have a very long average lifetime, and the causes of their failure are not easy to assess; due to their long lifetime, compared with our experience in their use, it is also difficult to predict it, and so they pose problems somewhat similar to valves, though, mercifully not so frequently.

14.5 Cyclic replacement and testing

A methodical, though laborious, system of preventive maintenance, is to test and log the characteristics of each component or sub-unit at regular intervals. The test figures show how the characteristics vary with time; if they show marked fluctuations, or if they approach preassigned limits, the component or sub-unit is rejected. Testing *in situ* is not always easy or convenient, and so, for this method to work satisfactorily, each component or sub-unit is replaced, periodically, by another tested unit. The item removed is then tested, and if still satisfactory, is reinserted after the next test period. This method entails a large amount of additional equipment, both in the form of spare parts, and of test apparatus. It was much used in the days of large valve computers, and the form of construction of present day computers, using 'plug-in' sub-units, owes much to the original maintenance requirements of valve machines.

Even using cyclic test and replacement, unless the replacement rate is laboriously high, the operating safety margin of each component has to be large, and this is uneconomical. As units deteriorate towards limits, worst case failures are still likely. It is advantageous to spot these before they actually occur in operation and a powerful technique has been evolved for doing this.

14.6 Margin testing

It seems a valid assumption that if a component or unit is about to fail through deterioration or similar cause, in normal use, then if subjected to abnormal use, it will fail immediately. This is the basic assumption for the technique known as margin testing. Artificial, abnormal, constraints are imposed on the whole system; its parts and components on the verge of failure are caused to fail forthwith. The applied constraints take the form of raising and lowering voltage levels, (power supply and reference lines) outside their normal operating tolerances, or injecting noise into the system by applying alternating voltages on the d.c. supplies, or sometimes by varying the clock frequency. These constraints are applied separately or altogether, by fixed or varying amounts. The computer is run on tes programs, at each stage, and as faults occur they are cleared by the maintenance engineer. Such tests require to be well thought out and strictly controlled; the system must not suffer lasting damage from margin tests. The success of the system depends, to a great extent, on the skill of the maintenance engineer, in finding the faults as they occur and rectifying them. A large computer is very complicated and it calls for considerable skill and a highly logical mind to find faults quickly. There is a simple, but inescapable logic, here; the valve computer mentioned earlier would be expected to fault about every thirty minutes. To put up the reliability, so that eight hours work could reasonably be expected, relying on margin tests alone, would entail the maintenance team inducing and finding an average of sixteen faults in each daily maintenance period. The very much higher reliability of semiconductors has made larger and more complicated systems feasible; none the less, maintenance engineers have to be possessed of much skill and perseverence. One of the best ways to gain practical knowledge of computing systems is to work on maintenance, or commissioning, for a period.

14.7 Testing by program

For large and complicated systems, testing can only be done quickly and exhaustively by a test program run on the machine; on small and medium-sized systems, too, it is a highly desirable method. Test programs may be divided into two categories: proving programs, and diagnostic programs. Programs of the first category are designed to prove that the system is functioning correctly; those of the second are to find the faults, or to indicate their whereabouts to the engineer, when they have occurred.

Proving programs can be quite simple, if they are designed merely to run through the machine's functions, to give conviction to the operator and engineer that all is well. At the end of commissioning, after major faults, or overhauls, and during major maintenance activities, a much fuller type of proving program is required. Faults can occur in a computer that are not immediately detected, if the part that fails is not used in the program under treatment; for example, a fault may occur in a store location that is not used. An accumulation of faults is much more baffling to the maintenance engineer, than faults occurring one at a time. A full proving program should test each and every facility of the machine, every store location, and every likely combination of functions and store transfers. On a large machine this entails a very long and complicated process; it also entails the shifting and testing of all stored program data, and is simplified if the machine is emptied as much as possible. This may be done by transferring all the stored data onto one tape machine in the backing store, for instance, while the rest of the machine is spring cleaned. A necessary test in programs of this sort is to test all lockouts, and overflow and similar alarm systems. Such a program requires considerable programming skill if it is to be thorough and not occupy more machine time than is necessary.

Diagnostic programs are designed to assist the engineer in fault finding. They are usually written with one type of fault or one function or location in view. When a failure occurs during normal operation, or in a proving program, the engineer or programmer can generally assess what kind of failure has occurred. The diagnostic programs are then selected that deal with this. Some computers have had developed for them very sophisticated diagnostic programs that are capable of locating logical faults precisely, giving the engineer enough information to go straight to the faulty component and replace it. In general, this is an ideal that has yet to be achieved. The writing of diagnostic programs requires both programming and engineering skill of high order; usually it is a team enterprise.

14.8 The engineering construction of digital computers

Although computers are very complicated and often very large, the constructional designer has his problem simplified somewhat by the fact that the logic, meaning the electronic circuitry, is compounded of great numbers of the same types of element; we have seen that all the logic functions can be accomplished using AND, OR, and NOT gates, or even using NAND or NOR elements exclusively. In a very large computer system there are about 100 000 logic elements, and, of these, the large majority will be of one or two types. Practically every design has been started with the laudable intention of using a very small number of standard element types; in course of development, however, problems crop up and have to be solved with extempore solutions, and more and more specials become included. This standardisation, and the requirements for quick replacement when faults occur, has led to a constructional arrangement that is, at this time, universal in the digital computer industry, and has become used in the construction of much other electronic equipment, also.

The basic elements, sometimes a single gate, though more often a small group of gates, are made up on small chassis; these are usually flat 'cards' of paxolin or similar hard insulating material. Commonly the cards are printed circuits, and one edge of the card is printed to form a plug, having contacts which are usually gold-plated on one or both sides. Components are mounted on the cards and soldered into place and are usually self supporting, with the exception of transistors. These are usually mounted in small metal clips that also act as heat sinks and prevent them from being displaced in the course of handling. The whole card, with components, is called a plate. If it is rigid enough, the end remote from the plug is shaped to form a handle, by which it is carried, or pushed into place in its rack. To give greater strength the card is often fitted into a frame which reinforces it, and the handle is attached to, or is part of, the frame. In the method of construction favoured by English Electric-Leo, the handles are plastic and have a series of small pilot lamps in them that indicate the state of the circuits on the card. A photograph of a typical computer plate is shown on Plate 7, while an assembly of racks filled with sub-units is shown in Plate 8. The racks are made up of a thin metal frame with guides, top and bottom, for the edges of the plates, which can be slid in or withdrawn easily. The back of the rack carries the multiway sockets into which fit the plate plugs. The terminals of the sockets provide a wiring field for the connections between the plates; this section of the system is referred to as the back-wiring. Finally, the racks are assembled one above another in frames, and the frames are enclosed in cabinets. This form of construction allows for the plates to be inspected, or changed, from the front of each cabinet, while access to the back-wiring is by a door on the rear of the cabinet. Plates 9 and 10 show examples of this method of construction. This form of building is called modular and has some obvious advantages. In the first place, it gives the maximum ease of access for checking, fault finding, and maintenance. Secondly it facilitates production. The large majority of the plates are standard and required in large numbers; they are small and not complicated. They are particularly suited for the techniques of mass production; they require little skill in the assembly stage and the work is highly repetitive and, because of their plug-in construction, they are suited for automatic testing. The back-wiring is not so simple, but can also be highly rationalised. Generally each rack is back-wired on the bench, as far as possible; this is not highly skilled, and it is also fairly repetitive. The wiring is done 'point to point' according to a preset schedule. When the racks have been fitted into the frames, further back-wiring is done, between the racks. Major assemblies, consisting of several frames are sometimes made up as one piece, and then the back-wiring may run point to point between the frames more or less directly. Every effort is made to restrict wiring between frames to a minimum; where frames and cabinets have to be separable for reasons of portability, or through space limitations, interframe wiring is carried through ducts, or shielded flexible cables.

Some manufacturers have now developed highly automated back-wiring techniques, based on the wrapped-joint. Fig. 14.1 is a diagram of one of these joints. The terminal on which the wire is wrapped is square or rectangular. The wire is wound on to the terminal and is tensioned largely by

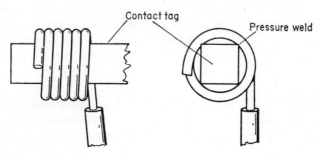

Fig. 14.1 Wrapped joint

its own stiffness as the wrapping tool bends it on. The points of contact at the corners of the terminal develop a very high contact pressure between the wire and the terminal, and each penetrates the other to some extent. So high is the pressure that pressure-welding takes place and the joint forms a perfect electrical connection, more reliable and durable than the conventional soldered joint.

Wrapped joints can be made by hand, using a simple tool, but they lend themselves especially to automated wiring. In this technique the automatic wiring tool is clamped to the back of the frame and exactly located. Each point-to-point connection is made by the machine, acting on instructions from a punched card. This method is fast and reliable, and once the capital cost of the machinery has been met, very economical. We should see, in this, the next step in the process of computer-building automation: the punched cards directing the wiring operation are generated by a computer which is programmed to work out the connections required between the plates, and between the racks. I.B.M. in particular have developed this manufacturing technique very highly.

It would be a surprising thing if we found anything in engineering that did not also have drawbacks and disadvantages; the principal disadvantage of the present method of computer construction is the length of the point-to-point connections. The capacitance of a wire in the back-wiring of a computer is estimated to be about 6–10 picofarads per foot, to ground.

The accumulated capacitance of the wiring of a whole system is most difficult to estimate; certainly it calls for a very conservative estimate of the maximum operating speed of a design, however promising it looks on paper. The great computers have an operating speed of the order of 10 Mc/s; most large machines operate with clock rates of 1 to 2 Mc/s. A few feet of wire, in these circumstances, can cause an appreciable delay to a pulse passing down it, and its capacitance and inductance, can cause severe pulse deterioration. The new generation of computers, now well on in development, are designed to operate at clock rates of 100 Mc/s or so. A very different form of construction is going to be needed for these machines, with coaxial or parallel strip lines being used for the point-to-point connections, and this entails matching at each termination. The present-day designer has the problem of arranging his machine in a much more compact form than the plate and rack construction; he has a good deal of food for thought, and must resort to the techniques which telecommunication engineers have exploited hitherto.

14.9 Power considerations

The power requirements of a computer form an interesting problem in themselves. A medium-sized computer may well contain many thousand logic units; for every milliamp consumed by a logic element, a thousand such elements demand an ampere. It is easy to see that even a medium-sized machine requires tens or hundreds of amps on its main power supply lines. Stretch is quoted as having nearly 170 000 transistors, which consume twenty-one kilowatts. These are distributed over about 23 000 plates. These figures are quoted here, not to impress, but to help us envisage the designer's problems. In the first place a very large amount of a.c. power must be rectified, smoothed, and stabilised for supply to the computer elements, and to provide reference voltages. Secondly all this power is dissipated as heat within the computer, in addition to the heat generated in the rectification and stabilisation. This must be extracted from the system, if the component temperatures are to remain in their working range. Naturally this entails fans, and air conditioning, and this again absorbs power.

Not so obvious is the fact that all the supply current must return through the circuit ground connection, and there must be no appreciable voltage gradient between parts of this.

The problem of the ground connection is met, in Stretch, by using a copper sheet as a ground plane, which covers the whole of the back panel, beneath the back-wiring. This has the added advantage of providing a very comprehensive electrostatic screening for the system, reducing noise pick-up generally. Smaller installations do not require such an elaborate arrangement, but massive earth connections need to be provided. In this respect, a computer installation is very like a telephone exchange and has many of the same problems; readers who have had to deal with telecommunication systems will find themselves on familiar ground.

The sensible approach to the power supply problem is to use a modular method: each frame can be fitted to provide its own d.c. supplies, having its own rectification and smoothing circuits. The stabilisers are arranged to use a common reference line. This avoids the transmission of large direct currents over long distances, and makes the rectifier and stabiliser units small enough to be easily maintainable and replaceable; it entails, too, that the cabinet ventilation has to cope with the heat dissipation of the power units. The smoothing and stabilisation of computer supplies has to be very good indeed if we are to have reliable operation. It is of considerable advantage if the a.c. supplies to the cabinets do not come from the normal fifty or sixty cycle supply. It is often economical to supply the computer installation with a motor-generator set, driven from the a.c. mains, but generating power for distribution within the machine at a higher frequency, say 400 cycles. This permits the smoothing component values to be reduced greatly and still achieve the same smoothing, or conversely, the same values to give a much better degree of smoothing. For the frequency quoted, of 400 cycles, a smoothing network to achieve a necessary degree of smoothing could be made with reactances one eighth the value of those required at fifty cycles. Three-phase operation also helps in this respect.

A major problem that occurs in high speed operation, in which pulse switching-times are necessarily very short, is that of switching transients being generated in the power supply lines, as noise. In a synchronous system many circuits will switch simultaneously; if each switching causes a change of current demand, a large current pulse will occur in the supply line. Now, for high frequency operation, the supply line is likely to be a parallel strip arrangement, approximating to a transmission line; for good regulation, the source impedance of the stabiliser must be very low, of the order of a tenth of an ohm or less, which amounts to a short circuited termination to the transmission line. The current pulse which is passed down the line is likely to be reflected, and not absorbed by the stabiliser and, on reflection, it may trigger other circuits; this is especially the case if any circuits are in a state of transient instability due to their own switching at the instant of onset of the noise pulse. Considerable thought has been given to this particular problem, but it has, so far, proved intransigent.

The computers in the 100 Mc/s and over class seem likely to use other than square pulses. For instance the Elliott development, using tunnel diode logic uses a three-phase sinusoidal supply which acts as a three-phase clock wave.

It is obvious that the power problems, like every other part of a computer's development, should be borne in mind by the whole design team from the outset of the design. The circuit designer can do much to aid the power supply designer; he must use no more current than is absolutely necessary, in the logic elements. If possible, the elements should have a steady current consumption under all conditions; 'current steering' type elements are desirable for this reason as well as on account of their inherent speed. Finally, the circuit designer should ensure that his elements and circuits make as uncritical demands as possible on the power supplies. A great saving can be made if supply stabilisation is allowed to have a fairly wide tolerance. It is the constraints of this kind, on the work of the computer circuit designer, that make such demands on his skill; they also make this work a highly beneficial exercise for the engineer who is developing his skill.

Finally, a word on redundancy. Some designers are happy in the knowledge that there is a small percentage of redundancy, even 5 to 10 per cent. It bears thinking about as to how much saving, in power supplies alone, might be achieved if redundancy is eliminated by careful checking in the design stage.

14.10 Commissioning

This is the process of finally assembling all the piece parts of a computer system, putting them together, making them work, and proving that the system is up to specification. It is probably the best training process for the student computer engineer, since it entails a thorough examination of every part and function of the system. Development engineers tend to grow more and more specialised as their experience grows. Good development and design entails that the team leaders, at least, have a good grasp of all the system's functions; commissioning experience is invaluable.

Once a system has been designed, it is first built in prototype form; it is commissioned in this form, largely, by the development team since, at this stage, there is often a good deal of redesign or modification called for. The production commissioning teams commence work when the first production models appear; usually large computers are to some extent tailor-made to suit the user; that is they need to have various numbers of tape units, and different arrangements of peripherals for different customers; this entails a good deal of variety in the life of the commissioning teams. Until production has settled down and a number of machines of the same kind have been built, commissioning has to be a most painstaking business. The very great complexity of a computing system means that, even if inspection of the piece parts at all stages is most carefully carried out, there are likely to be malfunctions when they are all joined together. The commissioning team, therefore, work to a carefully thought-out plan, starting with the empty frames; they first check each plate and all the power supplies thoroughly, and then build up the machine functionally, plate by plate, checking each operation as they go. In a synchronous machine, this process usually starts with the *clock* generation and distribution. Until the control unit is built, it is not possible to work the parts of the computer automatically; much thought must, therefore, be given to how to make each part operate, as it is installed, and usually a lot of extemporisation is called for. When the whole system has been assembled and persuaded to work, it must go through a rigorous testing period. There will normally be available test programs and service programs written for use with the machine. The commissioning engineer must satisfy himself that the system is completely reliable; if adequate test programs do not exist he must devise them. Such tests must include the working of every function, and part, in conjunction with every other; transfers of data must be made correctly from every store position and area to every other. What is most important is that the tests should not be run once, but many times, without fault.

This description makes commissioning sound a leisurely procedure; even in the best regulated enterprises, computers seem to arrive in the commissioning bays behind schedule; they are always wanted, also, for urgent delivery. This offers to the commissioning engineer a challenge to have the machine working before the delivery dead-line date. Like most other engineering systems, the final performance of a computer depends greatly on the thoroughness and skill used in its final assembly. Though more and more of the construction of computers can be entrusted to automated machinery, the commissioning engineer will have a valuable and highly skilled role for some time to come.

14.11 Engineering aspects of logic circuit design

The electronics of a digital computer can be divided into two principal categories: the logic and the circuitry involved with storage, peripherals and the like. The logic is essentially that part of the electronics which is the analogue of binary mathematics and Boolean algebra – in fact, the part of the computation process that does not need, necessarily, to be electronic; this is the part which interests us most in the study of automatic computation. Electronics which is part of the storage systems, for instance, can most easily be categorised as device electronics, consisting of the design of amplifiers, pulse generators and other useful and vital components, but which is embodied in studies of electronic devices, generally.

The electronics of logic has a characteristic structure – a very great number of fairly simple, identical switching circuits, interconnected in a great variety of combinations; it is in many ways analogous to that of modern telephony apparatus, such as exchanges and the like.

In the construction of a special purpose circuit for a device, such as a magnetic tape-reader amplifier, the prime requirements of design are functional excellence and economy in manufacture. The device is not generally required in very large quantities, and it has its own power supplies. Its operating parameters are fixed by its designer: external constraints on the design are almost entirely confined to its performance specification – speed, input signals, and the required quality of its output. Logic circuits are rather different.

The typical logic circuit, which is to form a computing element, regarded functionally, on the basis of input and output, is a rather trivial piece of design; for instance, we can design and build a two-input AND gate using two diodes and a resistor, in a few minutes. The requirements, when we wish to use the circuit in thousands, in the context of computer logic, are not simple, and the problem is no longer a trivial one. We should spend a little while thinking about some aspects of this problem. Let us enumerate the requirements.

(1) Function: naturally the first design requirement is that it performs its defined function, in terms of input and output.

(2) Reliability: as we have already considered, an hour's computing at, say, 10 Mc/s demands that the element fulfils its function many millions of times without failure – without any failure at all, even for a nanosecond or so.

(3) Interchangeability: the element must be capable of use in any part of the logic system where its function is required, and in conjunction with all other elements, in any permitted configuration.

(4) Stability: the element must operate correctly in any permitted ambient condition for a long time, and it must continue to do so after

large numbers of changes in ambient conditions within the permitted range.

(5) Economy: the element must be as economically constructed as possible from the point of view of components and assembly. Every additional half-penny on the cost of a specified component will be paid for several thousand times over.

(6) System tolerance: the element must be able to be used without throwing unnecessarily heavy demands on the specification of other system parameters. A too closely specified tolerance on a supply voltage will make the supply problem more exacting, and consequently, costly.

(7) System demand: the element must demand as little power as possible: many thousand of elements, each drawing an unnecessary milliamp will cause a power supply requirement for many additional amperes: this will entail many watts, or kilowatts of waste, as well as increased cooling problems.

(8) Noise susceptibility: the element should be resistant to interference from extraneous noise sources. An element that is too critical in operation will, when used in thousands, cause a considerable problem in noise suppression to the system designer.

(9) Noise generation: the element must be designed to prevent its operation from adversely affecting other system parts.

(10) Accessibility: the design of the element should permit as much access as possible for the maintenance engineer – if it is to be reparable. If it is to be considered as an expendable unit, then it must be easy to test and replace. Visible fault indication may be provided: it is a matter of balancing the cost of the hardware provision against the cost of down-time saved by quick fault finding.

This formidable list of requirements should indicate why the design ceases to be a trivial one. Let us now examine some of the requirements in further detail: the first two, we have already discussed: the third, that of interchangeability, merits some more consideration, and is closely involved with economy. We should note that the requirements detailed are often conflicting, and those of economy militate against the others in every case.

14.12 Component tolerances

Every component has a specified nominal value, and a specified tolerance, that is, a permitted range over which its actual value may vary from its nominal one. In the manufacture of a resistor, for instance, the chemical composition of the resistive material affects the final value, as do the linear dimensions, and the various processes used in the manufacture. Every effort is made to control each factor within fine limits, but there must be variations; the closer the control, the higher the cost. In the cheapest manufacturing techniques, a final value for a batch is arrived at: when the batch is completed it is tested, and those that fit into the band of tolerances for which the batch was intended, are accepted. The remainder are included in other ranges, into which they do fit. We should note that the standard range of 20 per cent components provide a niche for every possible value that is produced. These are naturally the cheapest. As we demand a closer specification, so we must pay more, due to the more careful control of manufacture, and the higher precision in the grading. Transistors have several parameters which can vary, and on which limits require to be specified. The tighter the limits, and the higher the performance, the greater the price. If we consider the transistor/resistor logic element, this consists only of resistors and transistors: the function of the element is between two definite limits; the branching factor, in and out, depends on the gain, β. To get the maximum branching factor demands close specification of all circuit parameters, the input and output resistors, β and I_{co}. A compromise must be worked out, between the cost of the element, the branching factor, and the number of elements required in a particular configuration. If we have a small branching factor, we can use inferior components, of wider tolerance, but we may need more elements, or more levels, to achieve a logic function, such as an adder. It is for the engineer to work out the best compromise.

One of the requirements of the logic element is that it will work in any permitted configuration of elements: this must include the worst case, that is, the condition when all element performance tolerances have the worst effect, in combination. We might infer from this that a similar criterion should be used when we consider the tolerances on the values of the components of the logic elements themselves; but, this is not necessarily so. There are two schools of thought about the tolerancing of components of logic elements. One school uses the worst case criterion and every component is specified sufficiently closely to ensure that in their worst combination, the element still meets the functional specification. The other view is that the statistical probability can be accurately calculated, of the worst case occurring during manufacture; the number of elements which will fail to meet the specification is caculable, and the tolerances of components adjusted so that the failure rate is just acceptable. Since every element must be rigourously tested, anyway, the rejects are discovered and thrown out. It is found that the cost of the rejects can be amply compensated by the reduced cost of the components. Naturally this system can only apply when the elements are of the expendable type – a component replacement cannot be made in case of failure. This idea should be easily comprehensible even with a limited knowledge of probability statistics; a worst case failure requires that a certain combination of highest and lowest tolerances occur, in a combination of several components, and this particular combination should be rare; furthermore, some cases are also likely to occur in which a bad component is counter-balanced by a specially good one. We must remember, though, that each element, when assembled, that is, passed for use, must be within the worst case specification limits for the whole system.

In view of these considerations we can see that logic element design is itself a highly specialised technique; there are many organisations today that specialise in logic element manufacture. The elements are used in computers and other digital devices, which makes for overall economy.

In some cases computer manufacturers do design their own elements, particularly when a new range of machines is envisaged or when the computer under design is to be based on a new logic technique. Often, when the design work is completed, final development and manufacture are passed over to another manufacturer who specialises in logic elements and similar small assemblies, since the specialist is likely to achieve greater economy in the quantity production process.

The worst case conditions must, of course, include the possible, or permitted, variations of operating conditions such as power supply levels and ambient temperature.

14.13 Noise considerations

Since computers work with fairly large signal voltages, and in pulsed mode, with good safety margins, we might think that noise would be a minor, or even negligible, problem. The exceedingly high accuracy or reliability that is required, however, does cause the exclusion of noise to be an important consideration. We should remember that, although logic circuits have a comparatively small terminal gain, that is, gain between actual input and output, in order to get high switching speeds, the circuits have a very high gain under switching conditions: in these conditions, they are susceptible to noise and are capable of amplifying noise impulses into full-sized digits. The faults which ensue are particularly hard to trace since they are rarely repeatable. The elimination of noise in computer systems is often called 'sanitation', rather aptly. The designer must be careful, throughout the design, that he suppresses or eliminates any noise pulses which may be generated within the system: typical sources of such pulses are relays controlling supervisory lamps, or fans, and similar ancillaries. Tape punches, printers and readers, and all electro-mechanical equipments attached to the system are potent noise generators if not carefully suppressed. The major problem, thereafter, is isolating the system from external noise sources. In office buildings, the typical environment of data processors, there are automatic lifts, electric typewriters and fluorescent lights. In scientific institutions and industrial enterprises there are machines, often, that have remarkable powers of generating noise'impulses in mains supply lines, and in the earthing connections. Mains supplies to computers, generally, are fitted with filters to prevent noise impulses reaching the machine; large systems usually have a motor-generator set of their own, and this provides a useful noise filter.

Finally, on the subject of noise, we should consider the possibility of random noise pulses being generated during the period of switching the system on and off. Circuits such as core-store pulse-amplifiers are apt to be unstable during the switching off period particularly, that is, while supply voltages are falling to zero at different rates. Spurious pulses at these times can cause erasure of stored information, or writing in otherwise locked-out areas.

The whole problem of noise gets increasingly acute as we design for speed; typically, low level logic makes for speed, – but it also makes for a lower S/N ratio relative to a particular noise source. High speed switching circuits are both highly susceptible to noise and excellent producers of it.

15 Future trends

The discussion of future trends of a fast-moving technique such as computation must always smack of prophecy. The best we can hope to do is to make a well-informed extrapolation, based on existing progress, and existing needs – for engineering is aimed always at meeting needs; good, foresighted engineering aims to meet future needs.

Certain future needs can be fairly well forecast: the computers of tomorrow will be faster, smaller, cheaper than they are now. They need to be more easy to operate and instruct. They will need to have very large stores, indeed, for many applications – translation of written language is an urgent problem that is being tackled; the translation of spoken language is a future need. As computers become better known to people in business and industry, and become increasingly trusted, they will be much more in demand; there will be scope for them in on-line control of processes and manufacture, in the control of transport and traffic, in booking agencies and libraries. Simple machines will be required by ordinary people to do sums for them; they may be used in time to control the kitchen stove. Let us hope they will not also be occupying the nursery.

We should be able to prophesy that there will always be a demand for very large versatile machines which will be used by research establishments, and large data processing machines for use in business centres. These will be in the direct line of descent from Atlas and Stretch, and the Leos and Orions of today. They will presumably be much on the same lines, but with faster and more comprehensive logic, larger and faster memories, and in the case of the data processors, considerably improved input/output and data handling equipment.

The probable range of special purpose machines is more difficult to predict. Certainly there will be a range of airborne machines for aircraft and satellite control and navigation. These will have to use the techniques which give compactness and light weight: if they are to achieve this, it would seem probable that they will need to be versatile also, doing several different tasks on a time-sharing basis.

The computer for process control may well be analogue or digital, mixed or hybrid. The trend seems to be towards the special purpose machine with the built-in program: this may either be read into memory during manufacture, in the way that a general purpose machine accepts programs, or may be built of hardware, like the fixed store used in some machines – the electronic analogue of a patch-board.

The possibilities for small computers are too difficult to assess. As the techniques get cheaper they will spread to all kinds of application. We can better survey the probabilities of the future machines in light of the developments now being pursued. Some of these show early promise; many more appear to demand a great deal of work to be done on them before they are likely to yield much.

15.1 Micro-miniaturised elements

A technique that is showing very much promise today is that of depositing molecular thickness films of metals and semi-conductors on glass or other suitable substrates. Very briefly, the method of manufacture is this: the substrate is carefully cleaned and placed in a vacuum chamber. A perforated mask is applied to the substrate, sometimes in the form of a closely fitted plate, or sometimes by applying a coating of protective material by a photographic process and etching away apertures in the mask. The chamber is evacuated and the material to be deposited is vaporised electrically, sometimes by a tungsten filament, close to the masked substrate: the vapour condenses over the mask and through apertures in it, on to the substrate, in a thin film of even and controllable thickness; removal of the mask leaves the film on the substrate in the required pattern. Several masks may be applied in turn, and different materials vaporised giving an overall pattern of different materials. Using photo-etch techniques to make the masks allows them to be made very precisely and also of very small dimensions. Fig. 15.1. shows simple shapes of deposited material films to serve as passive circuit elements.

The upper figure shows a resistor, made of a thin film of high resistance metal, such as nichrome: the thinness of the film, its composition, and the length and width of the conducting path, control the resistance. Sometimes several extra turns are added, each with a terminal point so that the value can be trimmed by selecting the best termination, or shorting out a length. The capacitor is more complicated since it requires three layers to be laid down; the first and third are conducting metal, while the middle is on insulating film. This can be put on as metallic silicon, and the surface is then oxidised to give a thin film of insulation. The possibility of achieving worthwhile values of capacitance may not be apparent until we recall that the capacitance of a parallel plate capacitor is inversely proportional to the

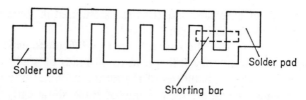

Fig. 15.1 (a) Nichrome deposited resistor

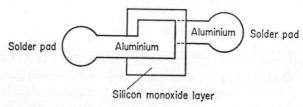

(b) Form of deposited capacitor

plate separation. The insulating film is of molecular thickness, and quite large values of capacitance can be achieved, with plates of minute size.

Transistors and diodes for use with these circuits are fabricated from tiny chips of silicon and these are connected to the circuits by wires of the order of 0·001 inch thick. In the early stages of the development of this method of circuit construction it was not cheap, and there was a very high failure rate; the chances of making a successful complex circuit with several superimposed layers were not high. The problems that had to be overcome were mostly the result of trace impurities in the deposited materials, which caused them to fall away from the substrate, or each other, often many weeks after the process seemed to have been achieved satisfactorily. Now a great deal of useful work has been done, by engineers, chemists, physicists and metallurgists in collaboration, and many of the difficulties have been overcome. The process, when applied to mass production, turns out to be very much cheaper than was originally hoped. Multi-layer circuits can be made with a low reject rate, and out of hundreds of circuits, deposited on a ceramic plate of a few square inches area, a trifling percentage fail.

An advancement on this technique is known as *monolithic integrated circuit fabrication*. In this technique a single crystal of silicon is grown, about nine inches long and one inch in diameter, and usually doped with *p*-type impurity. The crystal is examined by an X-ray diffraction technique to establish the exact orientation of the crystal structure, and is then cut into thin, coin-like wafers using a diamond-tipped saw. The wafers are ground and lapped to the required thickness and surface polish, and then chemically etched to clean them and render the surface suitable for the next process, that of *epitaxial deposition*. In this process the wafer becomes the substrate and a layer of *n*-type impurity is deposited on one surface; this deposit is direct from the gas phase, that is the *n*-type silicon and doping material are deposited from gas direct on to the surface by suitable conditions of temperature and pressure. The layer of *n*-type material forms part of the lattice structure of the substrate when grown this way. The layer thickness commonly used is about twenty-five microns.

The wafers are then coated with a photo-resist material which has the property of being fairly soluble to etching fluids unless subjected to ultra-violet light. The coated wafers are then 'masked' by glass slides and subjected to ultra-violet light, after this they are dipped in an etching fluid which dissolves away the photo-resist, which has been screened from the light by the glass mask, leaving the silicon exposed where required. It is now possible to diffuse in *p*-type or *n*-type impurities through the apertures in the photo-resist, normally directly from gas, and at high temperature. This masking, etching, and diffusion cycle can be performed several times to build up transistors and passive elements – mainly capacitors – and to make isolating barriers between them. Finally, resistors and aluminium conductor strips are vapour deposited on to the wafer, and to these are welded the fine wires which lead out of the circuit. Normally many integrated circuits are made on one wafer and it is then cut into sections; as the technique has progressed, these integrated circuits have been possible in greater complexity so that already complete multi-stage shift registers for example have been fabricated as one integrated 'monolith'. After the final treatments the wafer pieces are encapsulated and the leads attached. Plates 11 and 12 shows a chip and its mounting.

Already there are some very small but complex computers manufactured by these techniques. A good deal of logic and storage could be made on a few square inches of substrate, and the whole encapsulated. There then remains the problem of input/output, which does not show the same signs of rapid development.

15.2 Cryogenics

This is the physicists' name for the study of very low temperature phenomena; the temperatures of interest are within a few degrees of absolute zero, that is, $-273°$ C. It has been shown that certain metals not only show a continuous decrease in resistance as their temperature is lowered, but within a few degrees of absolute zero, their resistance becomes zero. This means that they can pass current without any voltage drop, or power dissipation. If a ring of lead, for instance, can have a current induced into it while below a certain absolute temperature, the current then flows round the ring indefinitely so long as the temperature is not raised above the limiting value. This state of zero resistance is called *super-conductivity* and is being closely investigated by the physicists.

The term 'cryotron' was coined by Buck, of the U.S.A., for an ingenious logic element he evolved using super-conductivity. His element consisted of an inch of thin tantalum wire, which he called the gate. Round this was wound a coil of thinner, insulated niobium wire, called the control winding. Tantalum becomes super-conductive at $4·4°$ K; at $4·2°$ K, a small magnetic field applied to it causes it to have a resistance. Fig. 15.2 shows a simple logic element made of cryotrons:

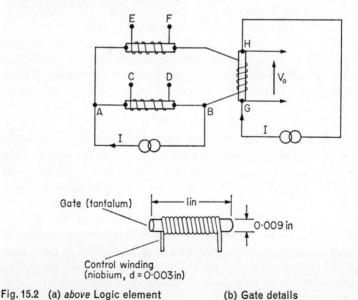

Fig. 15.2   (a) *above* Logic element   (b) Gate details

The two cryotron gates, with control windings CD and EF, provide alternative paths for the current through terminals A and B, provided from a constant current generator. G and H likewise have a constant current supply. Now, either EF or CD is energised with a small current which causes one gate, or the other, to become resistive. When this happens all the current through AB flows through the gate which is super-conductive. If EF is allowed to remain super-conductive, then the monitor gate GH is made resistive by its control winding and a voltage can be detected across G and H. But if EF is made resistive while CD is not energised, then all current passes through that branch and no voltage appears across G and H. We can visualise the action of cryotrons as logic circuits most easily by considering them as normally-closed relays: when their control windings are energised they become resistive; since the alternative path has zero resistance this means that the resistive path passes no current. Two or more cryotrons, in series, equate to a NOR gate; the parallel connection gives a NAND. The circuitry is complicated by the necessity of providing always an alternative, complementary path.

These units can have current and power gain, and switch quite quickly. Work is now in progress on cryotrons of a different form as shown in Fig. 15.3.

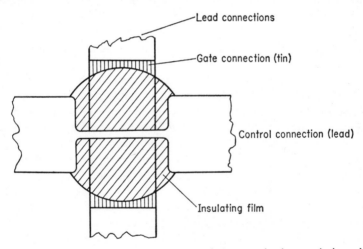

Fig. 15.3 Tin cryotron. Films deposited on insulation over lead ground plane. Lead is superconductive in all conditions at operating temperature.

The very low temperature is achieved by immersing the whole system in liquid helium, which is now fairly plentiful and reasonably cheap. A working system will need to be very compact, or miniaturised, but this is the trend anyway. Since the whole system will be super-conductive or nearly so, power consumption will be trifling, and the economy from this may be expected to offset the helium and pumping costs.

15.3 Multi-megacycle logic

The faster a computer works, the more work it can perform in a given time, and this makes it a more economical proposition. There are, also, many problems in atomic physics and like subjects, which cannot be solved in a reasonable time by computers working at speeds customary today. For these reasons, designers are continually working to increase computer operating speed; by speed here, we mean the raw speed of the machine, the speed that depends on the switching time of the electronics.

When transistors were first introduced into computer logic circuits, the main limitations on operating speed were due to the fairly long switching times of the transistors themselves. These were due to hole storage effects and internal capacitance in the transistors, and effects due to the bulk of the semiconductor material. Advances in device technology have been rapid; transistors can be obtained now at reasonable prices, which can be switched in very few nanoseconds. The ingenuity of logic circuit engineers, up till recently, has mainly been devoted to making switching time as small as possible; the interconnections between logic elements were kept reasonably short, as a matter of good practice, but posed no particularly difficult problems. Now the switching devices have become so inherently fast, it is not difficult to make logic elements that switch in nanoseconds; the logic circuit designer has now to direct his attention particularly to the interconnections between elements – and units and sub-units. With pulses of nanosecond duration, a short length of wire a few inches long becomes a transmission line, having all the interesting behaviour that has, in the past, been a preoccupation of telecommunication engineers. At each end, the wire has to be terminated with its correct characteristic impedance, or else reflections will take place; these can cause spurious pulses, delays, and poor energy transfer into the driven element with resultant loss of stage gain, and restriction of branching capabilities.

Naturally, the characteristic impedance of a wire is dependent on its capacitance to ground, and its inductance. The capacitance, in particular, can vary between quite wide limits for open wiring, in typical point-to-point wiring configurations, and this makes it impracticable for use at high switching speeds. The solution to this problem seems to lie in the use of a ground plane of copper sheet on which logic elements are mounted, and joined together by strip lines, of copper foil, spaced from the ground plane by a layer of insulation of fixed thickness. Printed circuitry can be made, to conform to this specification. This gives connections which have a fairly constant value of characteristic impedance, and permits the necessary matching. For typical construction technique now in use, connecting lines have a characteristic impedance of about 150 ohms; logic elements are designed to have input and output impedance close to this value, so that reflections are reduced to a minimum, and all the transmitted energy is absorbed at the receiving termination. Transistor/resistor logic elements lend themselves particularly to this technique and it seems probable that, at pulse rates of 200 Mc/s, or so, they will be extensively used. We should remember, with this in prospect, the difficulties in the design of these logic elements, discussed in Chapter 8. Other probabilities, arising from these considerations, are the extensive use of delay lines as stores and registers, in the form of coaxial cables, and of the delay method of pulse regeneration mentioned in Chapter 12, section 12.5.

Tunnel diodes have an inherent fast-switching behaviour between stable states, and have naturally aroused much interest as switching elements for logic circuits. They have the difficulty that they are two-terminal networks and require considerable ingenuity in the design of functional logic units. Elliott Automation, of England, have made a successful experimental computer using tunnel diodes, which operates satisfactorily at 50 Mc/s; efforts are in progress to improve the speed to 200 Mc/s. This experimental computer has thrown up some interesting problems, most of which have been solved, and the development has led to valuable gains in technique and experience. Interconnections in this computer are by strip lines and the lines are tapered for impedance matching. The logic is controlled in synchronous mode by a three-phase, sinusoidal, clock. The logic circuits are on printed-circuit laminae, and these are stacked and fixed together to make a laminated block, with connections plated through from lamina to lamina.

This three dimensional logic technique seems a likely trend for the future, but it has a serious snag: once it is assembled, it is a permanent assembly, allowing no adjustment or alteration within it. Each block of a few inches square contains many logic elements, and costs several hundred pounds, at this stage of the development. It must be correct in every detail on assembly for the cost of a reject is prohibitive; this entails most careful checking beforehand, much of it requiring a computer to analyse all possible paths and functions.

15.4 Design automation

Design by automatic methods is a subject of very present interest in many branches of engineering. Computer design, in particular, seems to lend itself to the idea of automated design, and we have the enlivening prospect of computers designing more computers. Some progress has already been made, but the problems are difficult and there is a long way to go before computers become self-regenerating.

The design of printed circuit plates and automatic back-wiring have been mentioned earlier. The design of the logic itself, by computer, is proving to be a formidable problem. Some of the rising generation of very fast computers seem likely to use a majority form of transistor/resistor logic: this form has as yet no simple technique of algebraic minimisation, and before it can be easily programmed a good deal of rationalisation must be achieved. Due to the work already done on the design of printed circuits by computer, this problem might well appear near to solution: the added requirement that, at very high speeds, all delays must be equalised, calls for a design technique which makes all path lengths equal, and this adds another dimension to the problem, and puts a valid solution to it once more into the future.

15.5 Conclusion

For the engineer looking for a career with an 'open end', computers should provide ample scope for many years to come. Automation, which must spread, and spread rapidly, in all kinds of human endeavour, is based on automatic computers. In their design, development, operation, maintenance and manufacture, there is room for every kind and level of talent. If the author's experience is anything to go by, workers in this field will never have a dull moment.

Suggestions for further reading

A fruitful source of further study in the field of future trends is the American twice-annual Joint Computer Conference, under the auspices of A.F.I.P.S. Likewise the conference reports of the I.E.E. and I.R.E. Computer Group meetings and discussions will be found valuable.

Plate 1   Patch-panel

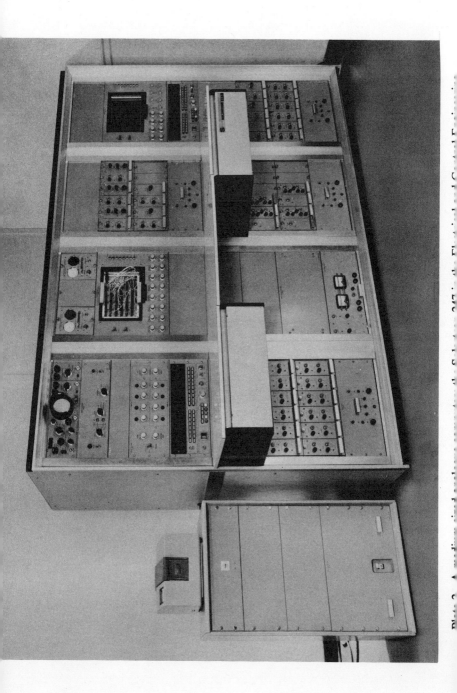

Plate 2. A medium-sized analogue computer: the Solartron 247 in the Electrical and Control Engineering...

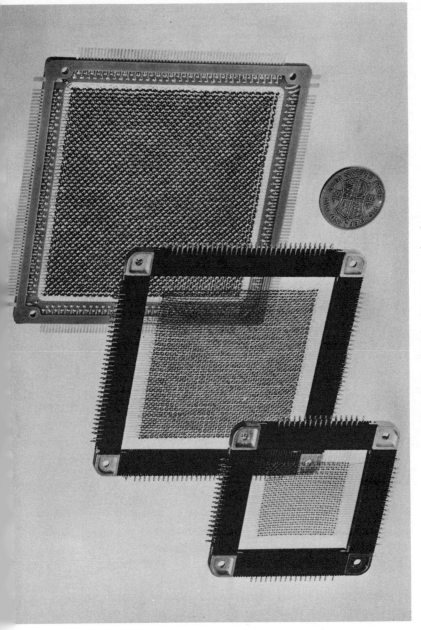

Plate 3   Typical ferrite core matrix planes

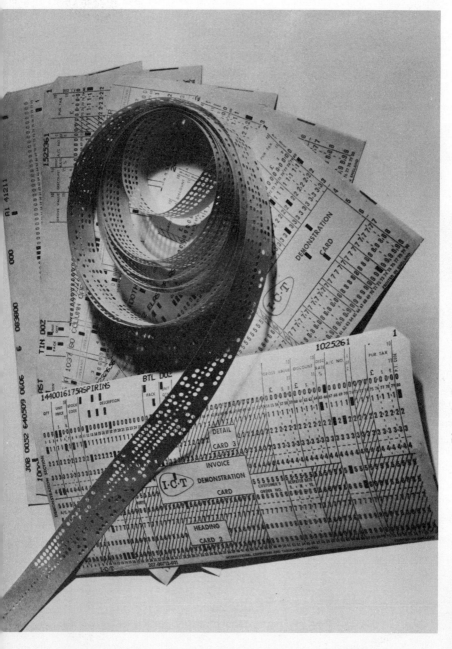

Plate 4   Data: punched cards and paper tape

Plate 5 Mechanical line printer; the upper photograph shows the print matrix.

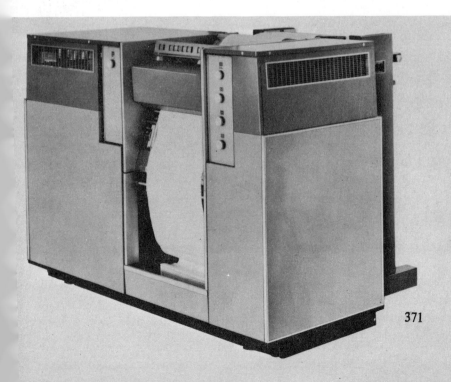

Plate 6   Digitizer

Plate 7   Testing a logic circuit on the first Leo 326 computer

Plate 8   Replacing a plug-in package in one of the electronic racks of a Leo III offic
data processing system

Plate 9   Rear view of a 503 computer, showing 'back-wiring'

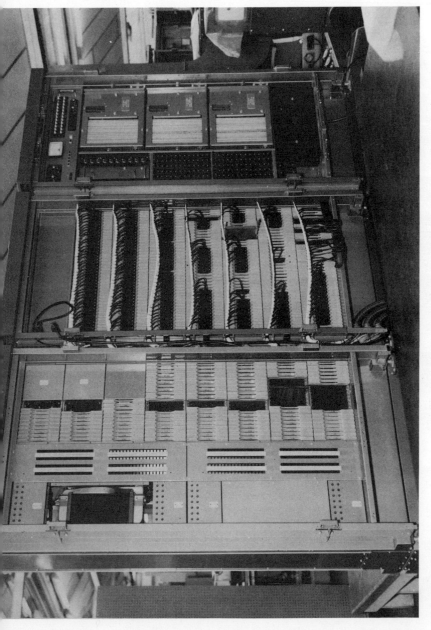

Plate 10   Front view of the 503 computer

376

Plate 11   Micrologic chip, 30 thou. square

Plate 12 Mirologic chip mounted on **TO-5** header showing interconnecting wires from chip to outer lead pins

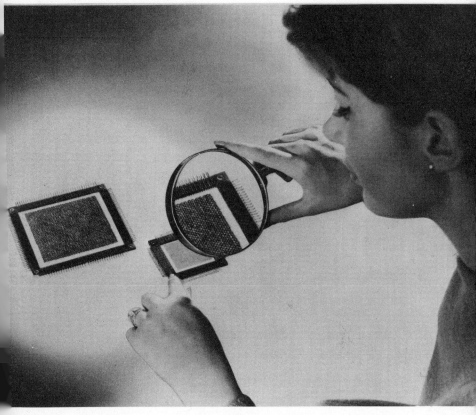

Plate 13   A matrix plane containing 4096 cores of 0·05 inch diameter compared with a similar plane using the new 0·02 inch diameter cores

Index

DATE DUE

GAYLORD

PRINTED IN U.S.A.